SCHOLASTIC

LITERACY PLACE®

Acknowledgments and credits appear on pages 690–695, which constitutes an extension of this copyright page.

ISBN 0-439-06153-9

TABLE OF CONTENTS

Making a DIFFERENCE

THEME
Each of us is inspired by the lives of others.

UNIT 1

TABLE OF CONTENTS

It's a Mystery

THEME
We can solve mysteries using reason, logic, and intuition.

UNIT 2

TABLE OF CONTENTS

Voyagers

THEME
We depend on a network of people when we explore.

UNIT 3

TABLE OF CONTENTS

IN THE SPOTLIGHT

THEME
We use our
creativity to reach
an audience.

UNIT 4

TABLE OF CONTENTS

AMERICA'S JOURNAL

THEME
Considering different points of view gives us a fuller understanding of history.

UNIT 5

TABLE OF CONTENTS

CITYSCAPES

THEME

Cities depend on the strengths and skills of the people who live and work there.

UNIT 6

Making a DIFFERENCE

Making a DIFFERENCE

THEME
Each of us is inspired by the lives of others.

UNIT 1

Welcome to

LITERACY PLACE

Concert Hall

Each of us is inspired by the lives of others.

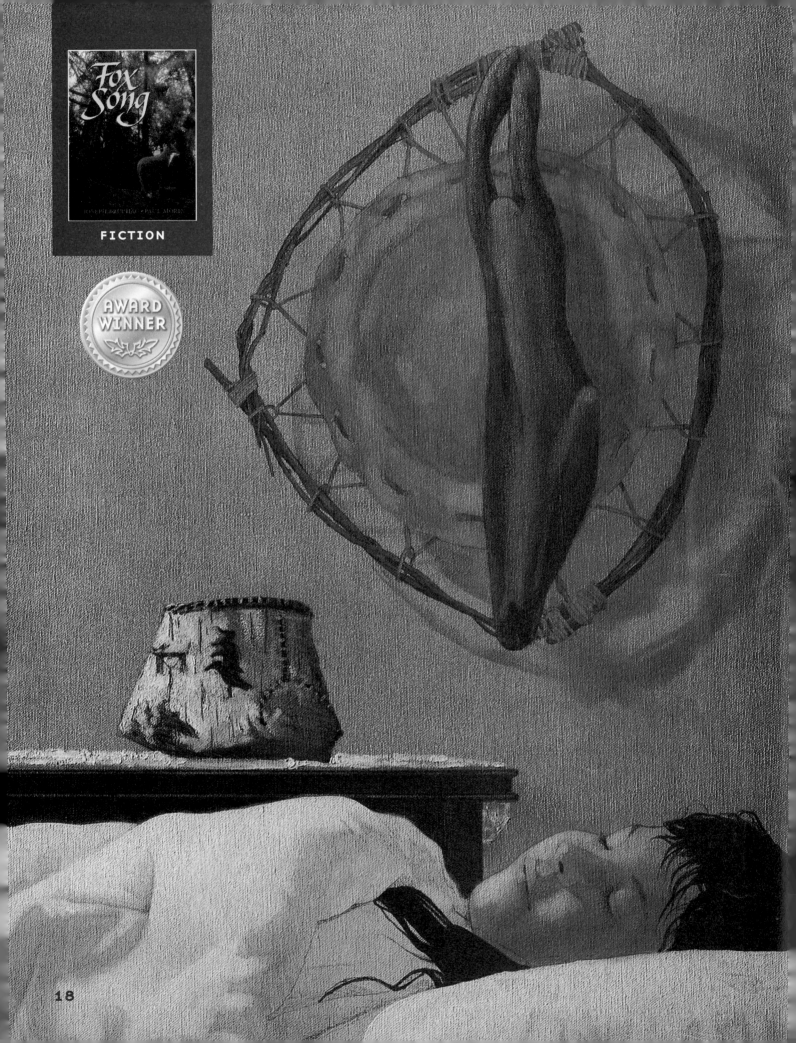

Fox Song

By Joseph Bruchac

Illustrated by Paul Morin

The sun came slanting in through the window at the foot of Jamie's bed. She felt it on her face, but she didn't want to open her eyes. She knew what she would have to remember when she opened her eyes. She felt so alone. Perhaps now if she kept her eyes closed, she might be able to find her way back into the dream where Grama Bowman was with her.

There were so many things that she and Grama Bowman did together. It had been that way ever since Jamie could remember. Grama Bowman was actually her great-grandmother. She was Abenaki Indian and the mother of Jamie's mother's mother, and she was over ninety years old when she came to live with them in their house on the Winooski River, with the maple woods up the hill behind them. Such a long time ago, Jamie thought, six whole years. Most of my life. But not long enough. She kept her eyes closed, hearing Grama Bowman's voice telling her stories, seeing pictures in her mind of the things Grama Bowman and she loved to do together.

She saw them walking up Fox Hill in the heat of summer toward the slopes where the blackberries grew wild. Together they would pick out the berries that were, as Grama put it, "Just a little too ripe for us to take back, so we have to eat them here." Those berries were always the sweetest ones. Jamie remembered Grama explaining to her how their old people always cared for *alniminal*, the wild berries.

"They took care of them for hundreds of years before your father's people came here from France," Grama said. "Your father's people were good people. They learned from us that you have to burn off the dead bushes each year so that the new ones will be green and strong." Grama Bowman smiled. "His people were quick to learn, and we were ready to teach them. I think that is why we have kept on marrying them all these years." Jamie nodded and smiled, even though she was not quite sure what the joke was. She knew it was one of those things that Grama Bowman told her to hold on to and remember because the knowing of it would come to her when she was a little older.

The sun's warmth was even stronger on her face now. Jamie heard her mother come into the room and stand by the bed. Her shadow was cool across Jamie's face, but Jamie lay still, knowing her mother would not bother her. Her mother's soft steps went out of the room. Jamie looked for another memory and found them walking along the river until they came to the grove of birch trees. It was spring and the trees were green with buds.

Grama Bowman put her hand on the trunk of one of the trees. "You see this mark here?" she said, pointing to the shape on the bark that looked almost like a bird. "We Abenaki say this is the mark of Badogi, the Thunder. The lightning is his arrow and he shoots it during the storms. But he doesn't want to hurt our people and so he marked these trees. Lightning never strikes these birch trees, so if you have to be near any tree in a storm, better to be near a young birch tree."

Jamie looked up and nodded. "I understand, Grama."

Grama Bowman took some tobacco from her pouch and placed it near the base of the tree. "Brother, we are going to take some of your clothing," she said to the tree. "We thank you for this piece of your blanket." Grama Bowman smiled at Jamie. "You know, that is our Indian name for the birch. We call it *maskwa*, blanket tree." She took her knife and made a cut straight down the bark.

"We don't take too much so the tree won't die, Grama?"

"That is the way, Granddaughter, our old Indian way. Be careful what we take and only take what we need. Now," she said, "you help me pull. We must go this way, to the left. The same direction the sun goes around the sky."

The basket they had made that day, using spruce roots to sew it together after folding it and making holes with Grama Bowman's bone awl, was sitting on Jamie's table near her bed. She opened her eyes for a moment to look at it, and she could still see the patterns on the basket that her grandmother had made. The shapes of birds and ferns and animals. And her grandmother's bone awl was in that basket now. She hadn't understood why Grama Bowman had given it to her from her bag when she last saw her. Now she knew. She closed her eyes again, looking for her grandmother's face.

Grama Bowman's feet crunched through the snow in her white snow boots as they started on the trail to the maple grove up Fox Hill. Those boots were so big that the first time Jamie put them on—when she was a little girl—she couldn't move in them without falling. Grama Bowman always pretended that she couldn't remember which pair was hers and which was Jamie's. She would sit and struggle to put on Jamie's little galoshes while Jamie would stand in Grama's, giggling and saying, "Grama, I really think that these may be yours!" Finally they would have their galoshes on and they would finish the tea that Jamie's mother always insisted they drink before going out to check on the trees.

"Warm inside, warm outside," Jamie's mother said.

"You see, Granddaughter," Grama Bowman said, "that is the way the circle of life goes. You take care of your children when they are little ones and when you get old your children will take care of you. And they will tell you what to do, too!" The way she said it made everyone smile. Grama Bowman had a way of pursing up her face that would make her look like a little girl.

Then they went out into the late winter snow and up the trail toward the maple grove. All along the way Grama would point things out, the way the ice had formed on the twigs, the places where deer had browsed on the trees, the tracks of the animals. She loved to tell Jamie the stories those tracks told her. Listening to Grama's words, Jamie could see the animals as if they were still there.

"Old Owl, Kokohas, he dove down right there for Madegwas, the Rabbit," Grama said. "You see his wing marks on the snow? But Rabbit, he was too quick."

As they walked along, there was one set of tracks that Grama Bowman especially loved to see. "Look," she would say, "those are the prints of my best friend, Wokwses, the Fox. She is a clever one. I know her tracks well. Now she is out looking for her old man. She wants to have some little ones for the spring. Sometime," Grama Bowman said, "when you are out here and I am not with you, you keep your eyes open. You might see her and when you do, you will think of me."

Jamie nodded but she wasn't sure that she understood. She couldn't imagine being in the woods without Grama by her side.

It was another quarter of a mile beyond that clearing where they saw the tracks of the fox that they came to the line of trees that Jamie's father tapped for maple syrup. He would be along later in the morning with his tractor to collect the sap, but Grama always insisted that it was important for the two of them to come out whenever they could, just to make sure things were going right.

"We have to taste this sap and see that it is good," Grama Bowman said. She unhooked one of the buckets and tilted it so that Jamie could drink. There was nothing as light and subtly sweet as that taste.

Jamie opened her eyes and blinked away the tears. She closed her eyes again, afraid that she would no longer be able to see her grandmother in her memory.

But instead she found herself walking beside her along the hillslope. It was autumn, the leaves blowing in the wind, and it was very early in the morning. The sun was just coming up.

"My old Indian people," Grama Bowman said, "told me that the leaves love to dance. But they can only do their best dancing when they are ready to give themselves to the wind. That is when they are old, but they are the most beautiful then. They put on their best colors and then they dance."

A leaf came drifting past them and it brushed Jamie's face. It spiraled in the wind, went up and down, and then it touched the earth.

"When I see the leaves," Grama Bowman said, "I see my old people and remember they are still with me. We say that those who have gone are no further away from us than the leaves that have fallen."

The sun was a red arc lifting over the ridge and Grama reached out for Jamie's hand. "I brought you here to teach you a song. I forgot to teach it to my own daughter. But I know that you'll remember this song. It is a welcoming song and it says hello to the new day. It says hello to every new person you meet and it welcomes them. When you sing it, you will not be alone."

Grama Bowman began to tap her open palm on her leg as they sat there in the fallen leaves, facing the east. In a clear high voice she sang:

Hey, kwah nu deh
Hey, kwah nu deh, kwah nu deh
Hey, kwah nu deh
Hey, kwah nu deh, kwah nu deh
Hey, hey, kwah nu deh

She sang it twice and the second time she sang it, Jamie sang with her. By the time they finished, the sun was up and its warmth was on their faces.

Jamie opened her eyes and sat up. She felt the sun on her face and she got out of bed. She hadn't taken her clothes off from the night before, and her mother had come in and covered her as she lay on the bed. She went out of her room, past her grandmother's empty room. She went downstairs and walked through the kitchen. Her mother and father were there, but they said nothing to her. She loved them for that understanding. She took her light jacket from its peg near the back door and went outside.

As soon as she reached the path she began to run, her feet scattering the leaves that gleamed yellow and red in the October morning light. When she reached the slope that looked over their house toward the east, she leaned back against the same tree where Grama Bowman used to sit, and faced the sun. She took four deep breaths and the racing of her heart slowed. Then, still facing the sun, she began to sing:

Hey, kwah nu deh
Hey, kwah nu deh, kwah nu deh

Something moved at the edge of her vision and she turned her head slowly. A meadowlark came flying out of the bushes at the edge of the clearing. Then, a few steps behind it, a small dog came walking out. It stood perfectly still. Jamie saw it wasn't a dog at all, it was a fox. It was as if it was waiting for something. Jamie began to sing again:

Hey, kwah nu deh
Hey, kwah nu deh, kwah nu deh
Hey, kwah nu deh

The fox yawned and sat down on its haunches. The sunlight was bright on its coat and its eyes glistened. Jamie continued the song:

Hey, kwah nu deh
Hey, kwah nu deh, kwah nu deh
Hey, kwah nu deh
Hey, kwah nu deh, kwah nu deh
Hey, hey, kwah nu deh

Jamie finished the song and looked away from the fox. She closed her eyes, feeling the warmth of the sun, which touched her face and touched the earth. When she opened her eyes again, the fox was gone. Had it really been there? She didn't know, but as she rose and went back down the hill, she knew that she would never be alone.

MENTOR

Joseph Shabalala

Musician

Joseph Shabalala inspires his fellow singers.

Led by Joseph Shabalala, the singing group Ladysmith Black Mambazo performed on Broadway, toured the world, and won a Grammy Award. But singing is not all fun and games for Shabalala—it has a much deeper meaning. Joseph Shabalala's goal is to pass on his country's culture and traditions through his songs.

PROFILE

Name: Joseph Shabalala

Job: leader of Ladysmith Black Mambazo, a South African singing group

Favorite things to sing about: hope and peace

Career highlights: singing with Paul Simon, winning a Grammy Award, appearing on *Sesame Street*

Favorite thing to do when not singing: spending time with his nine children and his grandchildren

MORE ABOUT
Joseph Shabalala

Find out how this musician is inspired by his ancestors.

Returning to Roots

Ladysmith Black Mambazo is an *a cappella* singing group. They sing without instrumental accompaniment. The ten members of the group sing together in such perfect harmony that their voices become the instruments.

Joseph Shabalala was inspired by the work of a great Zulu tribal leader, Shaka Zulu. "Ladysmith Black Mambazo's music originated from Zulu songs and dances," Joseph Shabalala explains. "Shaka Zulu was a great warrior, but he was also an incredible dancer," he says. Shabalala and his group use a lot of traditional Zulu dance steps when they perform.

As leader of the group, it is Joseph Shabalala's mission to preserve his cultural heritage. "It's time to follow the footsteps of our ancestors," he says. "That's the only way to know ourselves."

Passing on the Music

How does Joseph Shabalala create his songs? "Sometimes I dream a song at night," he says. "Sometimes it's only the harmony. Sometimes I dream only the words." But whatever part Shabalala dreams, it's hard work putting the whole song together. It is important to him that his songs have meaning. Two themes that run through many of Shabalala's songs are hope and peace. "My music is about peace. It is about forgiving each other," he explains.

Shabalala hopes that his music will inspire others to remember their roots. "I want to give the message," he says, "to be proud of who you are."

After Shabalala composes a song, he teaches it to his sons. "My sons are great singers and dancers," Shabalala says. "They are even better than I am." They are so good, in fact, that three of his sons are members of his group. But Shabalala doesn't just teach his sons how to sing and dance—he teaches them about their culture and the importance of preserving it.

Looking Toward the Future

Joseph Shabalala is also trying to preserve South African traditions for future generations. His goal is to open the Mambazo Academy of South African Music and Culture. Besides teaching basic academics, the school would teach children traditional music, dance, and customs.

Joseph Shabalala's Tips
for Young People of All Cultures

1 Talk to your parents. They may be able to tell you something about your heritage.

2 Write down what you learn. You might want to write a poem, a story, or even a song inspired by your cultural traditions.

3 Share what you've learned. Tell others who you are—and don't forget to listen to them, too!

Think About Reading

Complete the story map by answering the questions.

CHARACTERS

1. Who are the main characters in the story?

SETTING

2. Where does the story begin?

3. Where do the things that Jamie remembers take place?

PROBLEM

4. Why doesn't Jamie want to open her eyes at the beginning of the story?

FLASHBACKS

5. What does Jamie remember about the following?

      a. blackberries
      b. birch trees and baskets
      c. the fox
      d. leaves
      e. sunrise

SOLUTION

6. What does Jamie do to feel better at the end of the story?

Write a Lyric Poem

A lyric poem often expresses strong feelings. Choose a subject from *Fox Song,* such as the wild blackberries, autumn leaves, the birch bark basket, the fox, or maple syrup and write a poem about it. You can make your poem rhyme or not. The important thing is that it tells your feelings about the subject. Try to use images that will help the reader see, smell, taste, feel, or hear the subject of the poem.

Literature Circle

Both Joseph Shabalala and Grama Bowman are interested in preserving the culture of their people through song. Talk about why music is a good way for people to express and preserve their heritage. What are some other ways people can pass along their cultural traditions? List your ideas on a concept web. Then share what you've learned from your own ancestors about your heritage.

AUTHOR
Joseph Bruchac

Joseph Bruchac's work as a writer and storyteller has allowed him to travel all over the United States, to live in Africa, and to meet interesting people wherever he goes. When he was small, Bruchac's Abenaki grandfather taught him how to walk quietly in the woods and how to fish. His grandmother encouraged his love of reading. *Fox Song* was inspired by his own family's stories and his feelings about how important a grandparent can be in a young person's life.

MORE BOOKS BY
Joseph Bruchac

- *The Arrow over the Door*
- *A Boy Called Slow: The True Story of Sitting Bull*
- *Children of the Longhouse*

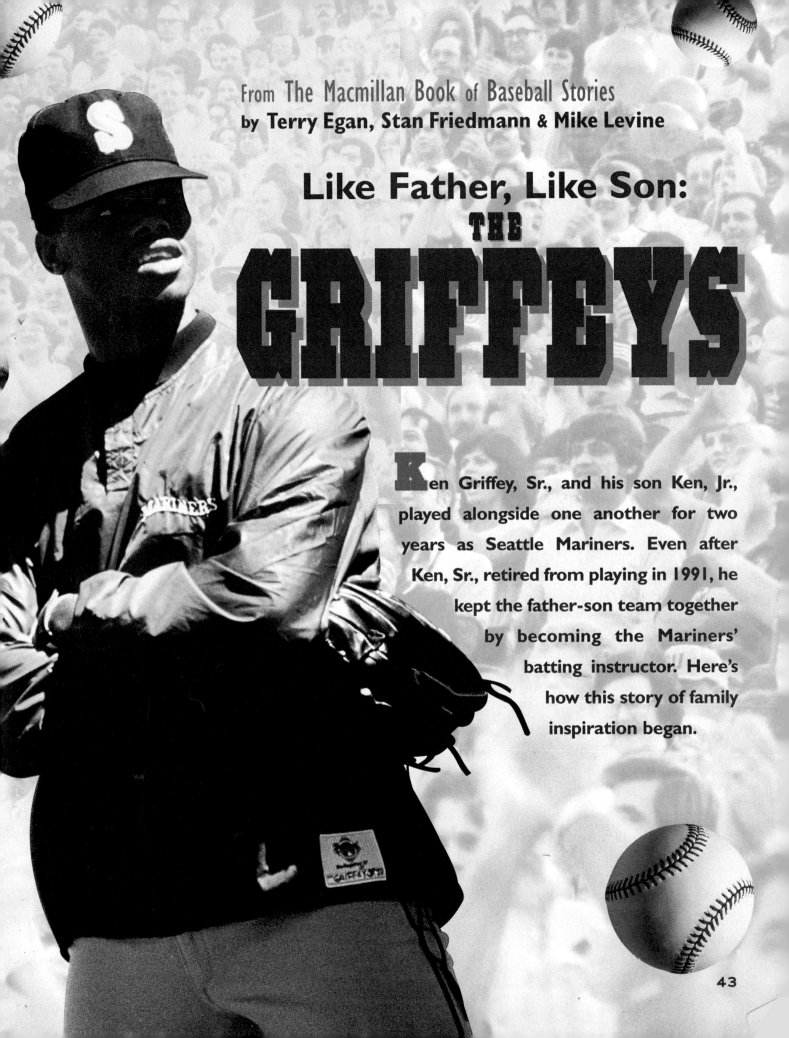

From The Macmillan Book of Baseball Stories
by **Terry Egan, Stan Friedmann & Mike Levine**

Like Father, Like Son:
THE GRIFFEYS

Ken Griffey, Sr., and his son Ken, Jr., played alongside one another for two years as Seattle Mariners. Even after Ken, Sr., retired from playing in 1991, he kept the father-son team together by becoming the Mariners' batting instructor. Here's how this story of family inspiration began.

On a chilly April morning in 1976, seven-year-old Ken Griffey, Jr., was playing catch with his dad.

"Hey, Pops, throw me some more grounders," said young Ken.

His dad, All Star outfielder for the world champion Cincinnati Reds, fired a hard bouncer to the boy's left. The boy lunged with his outstretched glove and snared it.

For millions of kids, the first day of a new baseball season is magical. Families everywhere rediscover the simple joy of playing catch, as generations share this springtime celebration on playing fields across America.

"Hey, that's not a bad catch, son," said Ken senior.

The boy couldn't hide his proud smile. "C'mon, Dad, throw me another."

The next grounder hit a pebble and took a bad bounce. Junior bobbled it once, picked it up, and dropped it again. He grabbed it once more but as he was about to throw, the ball slipped out of his hand and rolled down his arm.

Ken Griffey, Sr.

"Bet you can't do that again," joked his father.

They both nearly fell down laughing on the new grass. Dad had always told his boy that the best thing about playing baseball was having fun.

After a few more throws, Junior's mom, Birdie, called out into the backyard, "Time for breakfast, fellas." Father and son rushed inside, sweaty and dirty, still laughing about the muffed grounder. Dad and Birdie cooked up some eggs and toast for Junior and his little brother, Craig.

"Dad, can we go to the ballpark with you today?" asked Ken junior.

"If it's okay with Mom," said his father.

Mrs. Griffey smiled and said, "Well, I guess we could find our way out there."

Junior loved going out to Riverfront Stadium, where the Reds played. He'd watch the big crowd file in and listen to the vendors yelling, "Get your scorecard!" and smell the hot dogs sizzling on the

grill. He'd pound his glove hoping a foul ball would come his way.

This day, his dad invited him out to the field where the players were warming up. Again father and son played catch. Dad threw some grounders and the boy gobbled up nearly every one. Ken senior introduced his son to some of his Reds teammates—catcher Johnny Bench, first baseman Tony Perez, second baseman Joe Morgan.

"Hey, son," asked Perez, "you wanna be a ballplayer one day like your dad?"

Junior blushed. "Only if that's what he wants," said his father.

Many seasons passed. Father and son kept playing the game they loved. Dad continued to be a major league star. He traveled from town to town far away from home. Ken junior didn't get to play catch with his dad as much as he wanted. He missed him.

The boy rode his dirt bike and went skateboarding. To his mother's horror, he liked collecting worms and leaving them in his pockets. What he loved most, though, was playing baseball. He would throw

the ball around with his younger brother, Craig. He played ball with Pete Rose's son, Pete junior, and with Tony Perez's kids, Victor and Eduardo. Ken's mom took him to play in the Little League games. He wished his father could watch him play, especially when he had a great game.

"Dad, guess what?" he shouted to his father over the phone. "I had three hits today."

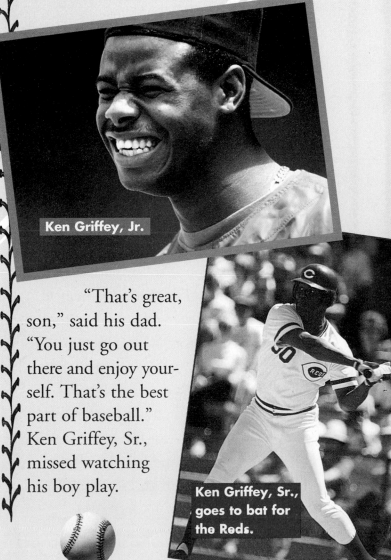

Ken Griffey, Jr.

"That's great, son," said his dad. "You just go out there and enjoy yourself. That's the best part of baseball." Ken Griffey, Sr., missed watching his boy play.

Ken Griffey, Sr., goes to bat for the Reds.

Ken Griffey, Jr.,
at the plate

The more baseball Ken junior played, the better he became. His left arm uncorked powerful throws. Soon he was belting baseballs over fences on high school fields. His brother, Craig, and his mom always came to watch him play. One day men with clipboards came to watch young Ken and take notes. They were major league scouts.

At the age of seventeen, Ken Griffey, Jr., signed with the Seattle Mariners. He went to play on the Mariners' Bellingham, Washington, farm team. He was away from home for the first time and he was a little scared. He missed his

Father and son

46

family. He just wanted to be in the backyard having a catch with his dad.

For the first time in his life, Ken junior stopped having fun playing baseball. He fell into a horrible slump, batting only .230. Everyone was on his case, even his dad. He felt like his father was looking at him as a ball player and not as a son. Finally, his mom came to visit. His dad, playing in Cincinnati, called again. He had thought it over.

"Son, I know what it's like being homesick. I miss you and mom and Craig a lot. We'll all be together soon. Now, don't worry about a thing. Just go out and enjoy yourself."

Ken took his dad's advice. The next day, the boy's season turned around. He began pounding the ball. By the end of the summer, his batting average zoomed one hundred points.

The next year, Ken Griffey, Jr., still only a teenager, made the big league club. He dazzled fans with his speed, his power, and most of all, his love of the game.

In 1990, young Ken got off to a great start, leading the American League in hitting.

His dad's Cincinnati Reds were on a roll, too. They talked often on the phone, sharing their good news. More than anything, the son wished his father could watch him play.

On April 26 Ken junior was standing in center field in Yankee Stadium. His Mariners were playing the Bronx Bombers. It was the bottom of the fourth. Yankee Jesse Barfield blasted a fastball into left center field, the deepest part of the stadium. Everyone in the ballpark thought it would be a home run.

Ken wouldn't give up. He raced back, legs churning, his eye on the ball. Back, back, back to the warning track. He dug his right cleat halfway up the eight-foot wall. He leaped. As the ball disappeared into the night, Griffey flung his arm over the center field fence.

When he came back down he held his glove high above his head. The ball was tucked safely in his mitt. Without breaking stride, he headed toward the Mariners' dugout, holding the final out of the inning.

At first the Yankee fans were silent in disbelief. Then they rose to their feet, thundering applause upon the young ballplayer from the opposing team. Ken junior broke into a big smile. He waved his glove at a distant figure in the stands. His father waved back.

The elder Griffey had flown to New York on his day off to see his son play. After the game, a mob of reporters gathered around Junior to ask about his spectacular catch. They were hanging on his every word. Here was a young sensation, hitting close to .400, stealing bases, banging home runs.

"What's your secret?" the writers asked Ken Griffey, Jr.

He shrugged his shoulders and said, "I guess I have fun playing baseball."

His father was standing in the locker room watching him. Junior looked up and saw his dad.

"Hey," Dad told his son, "that wasn't a bad…"

Nothing more was said. They stood there for a long moment and smiled at each other. That night they had dinner together. Then Dad had to catch a plane to rejoin the Reds.

"See you soon," said his dad.

Junior continued to star for the Mariners. He talked to his father on the telephone when they could. After one of those conversations, Ken Griffey, Sr., had an idea.

On the last day of August 1990, Ken junior trotted out to center field for the start of a game against the Kansas City Royals. Jogging alongside him was the left fielder. Ken junior felt a tingle of excitement down his back. The new left fielder was none other than his dad.

They were major league teammates. Ken senior had given up his chance to play on a championship team in order to play alongside his son. The crowd at the Seattle Kingdome let out a roar. This was the first time in history that a father and son had played on the same team. The two started warming up, throwing the ball back and forth. It seemed so familiar, yet so new. Ken junior looked up into the stands and saw his mom. The young man was so happy. I feel like crying, the center fielder thought to himself.

In the bottom of the first inning, the Mariners came up to bat. With one out, Ken senior stepped into the batter's box. On deck was Ken junior. A thought crossed his mind: Wouldn't it be great if Dad got on base and I was able to drive him home? He started laughing.

Suddenly Junior piped up, "Come on, Dad!"

Ken senior heard him. He began laughing so hard, he had to step out of the batter's box. He had never heard "Come on, Dad" before in the major leagues. No one had. Even the guys in the dugout were laughing.

Griffey stepped back in to hit, and Kansas City pitcher Storm

Ken Griffey, Jr., keeps his eye on the ball.

Davis threw him a fastball. He punched it past the second baseman for a single.

With his dad on first, Ken junior came up to bat. He lined a single to center, sending Dad to second. The bases were full of Griffeys. They both came around to score that inning as the Mariners breezed to a 5–2 victory.

Microphones and cameras surrounded the Griffeys in the clubhouse. And when later that month father and son hit back-to-back homers, they were the talk of America. The Griffeys were invited to appear on TV shows. President George Bush sent them a telegram of congratulations.

They were grateful for the honors they received and knew that in some way their lives had changed forever. They also realized that what was most important to them hadn't changed at all. Once again, father and son were playing catch, as they have throughout the years on fields across America.

A CLOSER LOOK

The Griffeys are a great father-son team, but how do they stack up as baseball players? The statistics below show each Griffey's performance after five years in the major leagues. How do father and son compare?

KEN GRIFFEY, SR.

Home Runs	37
RBI	273
Hits	783
Runs	456
Extra Base Hits	202
Batting Average	.286

KEN GRIFFEY, JR.

Home Runs	132
RBI	453
Hits	832
Runs	424
Extra Base Hits	317
Batting Average	.303

Stats compiled by Wayne Coffey
Sportswriter, *New York Daily News*

WHO'S ON FIRST?

by **Bud Abbott** and **Lou Costello**
illustrated by Gary Locke

The comedy team Bud Abbott and Lou Costello began making Americans laugh in the 1930s. Their side-splitting routine "Who's on First?"—first performed on the radio in 1936— paved the way for a career in radio, film and TV. In 1956, thanks to "Who's on First?", Abbott & Costello were the first non-baseball players to be inducted into the Baseball Hall of Fame.

COSTELLO: When we get to St. Louis, will you tell me the guys' names on the team so when I go to see them in that St. Louis park I'll be able to know those fellows?

ABBOTT: All right.

COSTELLO: I wanta—I wanta find out the fellows' names.

ABBOTT: Strange as it may seem, they give ball players nowadays very peculiar names.

COSTELLO: Funny names?

ABBOTT: Nicknames. Nicknames.

COSTELLO: Nicknames?

ABBOTT: Oh, yes, yes, yes!

COSTELLO: Funny nicknames?

ABBOTT: Oh, absolutely. Yes. Now, on the St. Louis team we have

Who's on first, What's on second, I Don't Know is on third—

COSTELLO: That's what I want to find out. I want you to tell me the names of the fellows on the St. Louis team.

ABBOTT: I'm telling you. Who's on first, What's on second, I Don't Know is on third.

COSTELLO: You know the fellows' names?

ABBOTT: Yes.

COSTELLO: Well, then who's playing first?

ABBOTT: Yes.

COSTELLO: I mean the fellow's name on first.

ABBOTT: Who.

COSTELLO: The fellow playin' first base for St. Louis.

ABBOTT: Who.

COSTELLO: The guy on first base.

ABBOTT: Who is on first.

COSTELLO: Well, what are you askin' *me* for?

ABBOTT: I'm not asking you—I'm telling you. Who is on first.

COSTELLO: I'm asking you. Who is on first?

ABBOTT: That's the man's name!

COSTELLO: That's whose name?

ABBOTT: Yes.

COSTELLO: Well, go ahead and tell me!

ABBOTT: Who.

COSTELLO: The guy on first.

ABBOTT: Who.

COSTELLO: The first baseman.

ABBOTT: Who is on first.

COSTELLO: Have you got a baseman on first?

ABBOTT: Certainly.

COSTELLO: Then who's playing first?

ABBOTT: Absolutely.

COSTELLO: When you pay off the first baseman every month, who gets the money?

ABBOTT: Every dollar of it. And why not? The man's entitled to it.

COSTELLO: Who is?

ABBOTT: Yes.

COSTELLO: So who gets it?

ABBOTT: Why shouldn't he? Sometimes his wife comes down and collects it.

COSTELLO: Whose wife?

ABBOTT: Yes. After all, the man earns it.

COSTELLO: Who does?

ABBOTT: Absolutely.

COSTELLO: Well, all I'm trying to find out is what's the guy's name on first base.

ABBOTT: Oh, no, no. What is on second base.

COSTELLO: I'm not asking you who's on second.

ABBOTT: Who's on first.

COSTELLO: That's what I'm trying to find out.

ABBOTT: Well, don't change the players around.

COSTELLO: I'm not changing nobody.

ABBOTT: Now, take it easy.

COSTELLO: What's the guy's name on first base?

ABBOTT: What's the guy's name on second base.

COSTELLO: I'm not askin' ya who's on second.

ABBOTT: Who's on first.

COSTELLO: I don't know.

ABBOTT: He's on third. We're not talking about him.

COSTELLO: How could I get on third base?

ABBOTT: You mentioned his name.

COSTELLO: If I mentioned the third baseman's name, who did I say is playing third?

ABBOTT: No, Who's playing first.

COSTELLO: Stay offa first, will ya?

ABBOTT: Well, what do you want me to do?

COSTELLO: Now what's the guy's name on first base?

ABBOTT: What's on second.

COSTELLO: I'm not askin' ya who's on second.

ABBOTT: Who's on first.

COSTELLO: I don't know.

ABBOTT: He's on third.

COSTELLO: There I go back on third again.

ABBOTT: Why?

COSTELLO: I don't know. And I don't care.

ABBOTT: What was that?

COSTELLO: I said, I don't care.

ABBOTT: Oh, that's our shortstop.

THINK ABOUT READING

Write your answers.

1. How did Ken Griffey, Jr., prepare himself for a career in baseball?

2. Why do you think Ken Griffey, Jr., played poorly when he first went to play for the Mariners' farm team?

3. Why do you think Ken Griffey, Sr., left a championship team to play on his son's team? Would you have made the same choice?

4. Even before reading "Like Father, Like Son," you knew how the story was going to end. What did the writers do to keep you interested?

5. Ken Griffey, Sr., and Ken Griffey, Jr., worked as a team. So did Bud Abbott and Lou Costello. In what ways was their use of teamwork different?

WRITE AN INTERVIEW

Imagine that you are a TV talk show host. Choose Ken Griffey, Jr., or Ken Griffey, Sr., to interview. What do you want your guest to talk about? What events in his life do you want to share with your viewers? What questions can you ask? Write a list of interview questions. Then write the answers you think Ken Griffey, Jr., or Ken Griffey, Sr., would give.

LITERATURE CIRCLE

"Like Father, Like Son" and "Who's on First?" are both about baseball, but the two selections are very different. What feelings did you have as you read each story? Make a list of other books and stories about a sport that you've read. Did they inspire you, make you laugh, surprise you, or make you think in new ways? Record your ideas on a chart.

AUTHORS
TERRY EGAN, STAN FRIEDMANN, AND MIKE LEVINE

Sportswriter Terry Egan has written for daily newspapers and an Internet sports magazine. He gets his knowledge of baseball from the many hours he has spent coaching his sons in Little League.

Former slugger Stan Friedmann now directs children's sports and fitness programs and still enjoys a good game of stickball.

As a boy, Mike Levine, an award-winning newspaper columnist and editor, played first base for his hometown Little League team.

MORE BOOKS BY EGAN, FRIEDMANN, AND LEVINE

- *Heroes of the Game: True Baseball Stories*
- *The Good Guys of Baseball: Sixteen True Sports Stories*

How to

Compile a Biographical Sketch

When a person's accomplishments have been truly inspirational, the world should know all about him or her. Compiling a biographical sketch is a good way to share information about an important person.

What is a biographical sketch? A biographical sketch is a way of giving basic information about someone's life. This information includes facts such as where the subject was born and what special talents he or she has.

A photo of the subject adds interest. ●········

Basic information about a person is generally provided. ●·····

A profile highlights the ● ········· characteristics that make a person famous, memorable, inspiring, or unique.

R
O
B
E
R
T

N
E
U
M
A
Y
E
R

AGE: 46 years old

DISABILITY: Paraplegic (17 years disabled). Paraplegia is a paralysis of the lower half of the body, including both legs.

COMPETITIONS: 100's. 9-time NYCM competitor. Achilles member since 1986.

Robert won the NYCM (handicapped runners class) in 1989 and again in 1990. He has acted as a safety and health consultant for the Board of Education, New York Telephone and the Hilton Corporation. Robert has also spoken at over 300 schools.

Achilles
Track
Club

1 Choose a Subject

Think about someone who inspires you. What contributions has that person made to a profession, a sport, a country, or to your life? The person you choose can be a celebrity, your best friend, or a relative. In choosing a person, you might also consider the availability of information about that person. Will you be able to locate enough information?

TOOLS

- paper and pencil
- articles and books
- tape recorder (optional)

Tip What is your favorite thing to do? Do you like to go to the movies, play sports, or draw? Think about doing a sketch of the person who got you interested in this activity, or of a person you've discovered through a favorite activity.

2 Plan Your Sketch

Now decide what sort of details you would like to include in your biographical sketch. The information should be brief and to the point. Choose things to find out about your subject that match that person's job or interests. For example, if you've picked an artist, you might want to describe your subject's work and find out which artists inspire him or her. Make a list of all the things you want to find out.

3 Research Your Subject

If the person you chose is someone you know, you should be able to get all of the information you need by talking to your subject or to someone who knows your subject well. If the person is someone you don't know personally, look for information in magazines and newspapers, as well as in biographies or other books. If you can't find all the information you need in one place, check another source. Don't forget to take notes on your research. If you're conducting an interview with your subject, you might want to tape-record it. Find a photo of your subject to accompany the information you collect.

4 Complete Your Sketch

Use your notes or tape to help you decide which information to include in your sketch. Organize the information under headings like "Job," "Pets," and "Hobbies" and write a short entry for each heading. Try to include some unusual facts or particularly interesting information about your subject. If possible, attach a photo or drawing of the subject to the sketch.

Present your biographical sketch to your classmates. Include a brief oral or written explanation of how your subject inspires you.

If You Are Using a Computer . . .

Draft your biographical sketch, using the Report format. If you like, you can keep track of your sources by using the Bibliography Maker.

THINK

If someone were writing a biographical sketch about you, what kind of information would he or she include?

Joseph Shabalala
Musician
▶

PERSONAL
ANECDOTES

from

Just
Like
Me

Stories and Self-Portraits
by Fourteen Artists

Edited by Harriet Rohmer

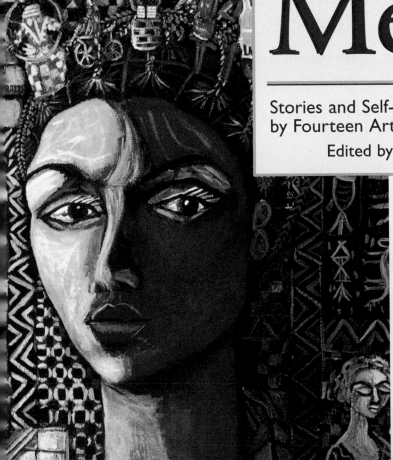

Since I'm a publisher—always dreaming about the next beautiful book to create—I began to imagine a book that could bring artists to a much wider audience. And so I decided to publish a book where the artists I have worked with would make pictures of themselves—and then talk about their self-portraits as a way of inspiring young people to see art from a new perspective, as a way of showing young people that artists come from many different places and work in many different ways.

The result is *Just Like Me*. I hope this book will entertain and amuse you, give you food for thought, and inspire you.

—Harriet Rohmer

Michele Wood

As a child I often imagined myself as Sleeping Beauty, princess of the make-believe African kingdom of Koro. That's how I painted myself here. My hair is plaited in a royal crown of braids, and in my crown are six figures of me as paintbrushes showing different stages of my childhood. I'm playing with a hula hoop, riding a bike, reading storybooks, painting a picture, running track, and learning to sew.

The panels in the quilt show important times in my life. On the left, my mother is holding me as a baby. On the right, Mother and I are sitting on the kitchen floor playing jacks. I was an only child, and my mother would always participate in little games with me.

My character is a strong, fearless woman symbolizing the well-being of my people. I am free of fear, ready to forge ahead, hand in hand with my ancestors.

Michele Wood is a painter, printmaker, and mixed-media artist. She has recently been commissioned to create a mural celebrating Auburn Avenue, the heart of the historic African American community in Atlanta. Her work is shown in galleries in the United States and abroad. She was born in Indianapolis, Indiana, in 1964 and now lives in Atlanta, Georgia.

Carmen Lomas Garza

Most of my paintings are from my recollections of my childhood in south Texas where I was born and raised. My memories of celebrations are very vivid because I usually had a new special outfit sewn by my mother. My favorite was the turquoise cotton organza dress she made for my graduation from elementary school. Every year she sewed new school clothes for all five of us kids, but the funniest were the flannel pajamas in our choice of colors and patterns.

When I was a young girl, I taught myself how to draw clothes for my paper dolls so they could have any dress I wanted—a flamenco dancer's dress or a dress from Mexico called a China Poblana, with lots of shiny sequins. To this day, my favorite thing to paint is clothing.

My mother was the first person I saw paint. She was the one who inspired me to become an artist.

Carmen Lomas Garza is one of the first Mexican American artists to receive national recognition. Her paintings have been shown in galleries and museums throughout the United States. She was born in Kingsville, Texas, in 1948 and now lives in San Francisco, California.

Hideo Yoshida

When I pull back the curtain on my childhood, I see my uncle's pear orchard in the foothills of the Sierras. I'm ten or eleven years old—shirtless with a folded newspaper cap on my head to protect me from the sun. I remember the brilliant blue sky and the high, friendly puffs of clouds.

After I finished my morning task of hammering together 150 to 200 crates which we used to ship our pears to New York, I had the afternoon free. Then my cousin, my brother, and I would run off to go fishing in the streams and deep pools near the orchard.

When I do my work now, I long to feel what I felt then. I want to forget time and care only about what I'm trying to do at the moment. I want to be the way I am in this picture—a kid shirtless in the sun, putting one foot in front of the other, cautiously going forward.

Hideo Yoshida is a painter, printmaker, and mixed-media artist who was recently commissioned to document his family's history as farmers in California's Sacramento Valley. He was born in Sacramento, California, in 1942 and now lives in San Francisco, California.

Daryl Wells

When I was growing up, I didn't understand why the crayon labeled "flesh" in my crayon box wasn't the color of my skin. As a way of proving that my color was also beautiful and real, I went through all my favorite storybooks and colored in the characters with the brown crayon. In this way I was able to relate to them as if they really were part of my world.

As I got older and became more interested in painting, I realized that there is no such thing as a single "flesh" color. Everybody's skin has many colors in it, and the way people look has a lot to do with how they're feeling at the time. I still love painting people, and I guess I'm still "coloring them in." My self-portrait is four different pictures of myself. I look different each time because I worked with four different kinds of artist's colors: oil paints, watercolors, colored pencils, and colored inks with oil pastels.

Daryl Wells was born in Los Angeles, California, in 1969, where she later worked with children creating outdoor murals. She has studied art in Rhode Island and London, England, and has taught art to children and adults of all ages.

Rodolfo Morales

All my life I have painted scenes from my little Mexican town of Ocotlán. When I was a boy, Ocotlán was still feeling the effects of the Mexican Revolution. We were very isolated. The train that stopped in our town twice each day was our only connection with modern life.

I remember that once an airplane passed overhead, surprising the entire town. It was an American who had flown off course and made a forced landing behind the graveyard. He didn't speak Spanish, and only one person spoke English. He caused such a commotion that when he tried to take off, someone threw himself on the plane, not wanting it to leave, and there was almost a huge accident. You see, there weren't any movies, we didn't get any newspapers, and very few people knew that airplanes existed.

That's me on the left looking up at the pilot.

Rodolfo Morales is one of the most important artists in modern Mexico. His painting and collages are shown internationally. He was born in Ocotlán, Mexico, in 1925, lived in Mexico City for many years, and now lives in Ocotlán. (He never had his picture taken as a child. His first photo, shown here, was taken when he was eighteen.)

70

Tomie Arai

New York is a wonderful place to live because there is so much to look at. When I was a little girl, I would spend hours looking out the window of our apartment. I always thought that windows were a place to dream.

As I got older, I could walk for hours around the different neighborhoods of the city, and I started sketching the people I saw. I wanted to be like the painters Diego Rivera and Romare Bearden and the Japanese printmaker, Hokusai, who really looked at the world around them and tried to record the way that people lived.

This is a picture of me looking out the window. Or maybe it is a picture that lets you look into a window at me. I am dreaming that I am a little girl again, surrounded by memories that float across the page like the people who pass me on the crowded streets of the city.

Tomie Arai is a painter, printmaker, and mixed-media artist. She is a recent recipient of a National Endowment for the Arts Visual Arts Fellowship, and her work is in the collection of New York's Museum of Modern Art. Tomie has two children and lives in New York City where she was born in 1949.

Elly Simmons

When I was little, my mother strolled me around museums to see art. The walls of our home were covered with her paintings, with colorful posters of Mexican art, and with prints by Ben Shahn showing people at work. These images stayed with me, shaping who I am.

I paint my love of life! I paint pomegranates, birds, mountains, and people. I paint what gives me joy, or makes me sad or angry. I paint to protest homelessness, war, and injustice, and to celebrate the beauty of a sunflower outside my door.

When my daughter was born, brilliant suns burst into my paintings. Now I gather bright fabrics and photos to piece together a quilt of my Jewish family history. In this painting, my grandmother (as a baby) and my great-grandparents in the pomegranates honor my roots. My parents, in the yellow sun, are my source of life. They gave me love and the encouragement to celebrate life through art!

Elly Simmons is an artist and a community activist. Her paintings, prints, and tapestries are shown internationally. She was born in New York City in 1955, grew up in San Francisco, and now lives in Lagunitas, California.

from Out of the Dust

by
Karen Hesse

Permission to Play

Sometimes,
when Ma is busy in the kitchen,
or scrubbing,
or doing wash,
I can ask her something in such a way
I annoy her just enough to get an answer,
but not so much I get a no.

That's a way I've found of gaining what I want,
by catching Ma off guard,
especially when I'm after permission to play piano.
Right out asking her is no good.
She always gets testy about me playing,
even though she's the one who truly taught me.

Anyway, this time I caught her in the
slow stirring of biscuits,
her mind on other things,
maybe the baby growing inside her, I don't know,
but anyhow,
she was distracted enough,
I was determined enough,
this time I got just what I wanted.
Permission to play at the Palace.

January 1934

On Stage

When I point my fingers at the keys,
                    the music
springs straight out of me.
                    Right hand
playing notes sharp as
                    tongues,
telling stories while the
                    smooth
buttery rhythms back me up
                    on the left.

Folks sway in the
                    Palace aisles
grinning and stomping and
                    out of breath,
and the rest, eyes shining,
                    fingers snapping,
feet tapping. It's the best
                    I've ever felt,
playing hot piano,
                    sizzling with
Mad Dog,
                    swinging with the Black Mesa Boys,
or on my own,
                    crazy,
pestering the keys.
                    That is
heaven.
                    How supremely
heaven
                    playing piano
can be.

January 1934

Think About Reading

Write your answers.

1. Why did Harriet Rohmer decide to publish a book of artists' self-portraits?

2. Why do you think that many of these artists used objects from their childhoods in their self-portraits?

3. If you were going to create a self-portrait, what special objects would you include? Why would you include those objects?

4. Which artist do you find most inspiring? Why?

5. How are the poems in *Out of the Dust* like the portraits of the artists in *Just Like Me*?

Write Catalogue Copy

Choose your favorite self-portrait from *Just Like Me*. Imagine that you are writing the description for a museum catalogue. Tell what is special or unique about the self-portrait, and why you like it. Describe the artist's style and the materials he or she uses. Try to communicate the mood of the portrait.

Literature Circle

There are many varieties of self-portraits. Talk about the different kinds that you have seen or read. Why do you think they are important to people? Why are they interesting to so many readers and viewers? Then discuss which kind of self-portraits you find most interesting and tell why.

PUBLISHER
Harriet Rohmer

In 1975, Harriet Rohmer started a special publishing company, Children's Book Press. Her dream was to create picture books about people from all over the world. She worked with artists from different cultures—the very same artists featured in *Just Like Me*—and produced colorful books in many different languages. The result of everyone's hard work was a group of award-winning books read and loved by young people all over the world.

MORE BOOKS
About Artists

- *Chuck Close: Up Close* by Jan Greenberg and Sandra Jordan

- *Story Painter: The Life of Jacob Lawrence* by John Duggleby

- *Mary Cassatt: Portrait of an American Impressionist* by Thomas Streissguth

From *Number the*

Stars

by **Lois Lowry**

illustrated by **Raul Colon**

The year is 1943. Annemarie
Johansen lives in Denmark with
her father, mother, and her little
sister Kirsti. Annemarie used to
love her home, but now Nazi
soldiers in Denmark are
persecuting the country's Jews—
including Annemarie's best friend,
Ellen Rosen. Now Ellen's life is in
danger, and Annemarie and her
family must act courageously in
order to save their friend.

ALONE IN THE APARTMENT while
Mama was out shopping with
Kirsti, Annemarie and Ellen were
sprawled on the living room floor
playing with paper dolls. They
had cut the dolls from Mama's
magazines, old ones she had saved
from past years. The paper ladies
had old-fashioned hair styles and
clothes, and the girls had given
them names from Mama's very
favorite book. Mama had told
Annemarie and Ellen the entire
story of *Gone With the Wind*, and
the girls thought it much more
interesting and romantic than the
king-and-queen tales that Kirsti loved.

"Come, Melanie," Annemarie said, walking her doll across the edge of the rug. "Let's dress for the ball."

"All right, Scarlett, I'm coming," Ellen replied in a sophisticated voice. She was a talented performer; she often played the leading roles in school dramatics. Games of the imagination were always fun when Ellen played.

The door opened and Kirsti stomped in, her face tear-stained and glowering. Mama followed her with an exasperated look and set a package down on the table.

"I won't!" Kirsti sputtered. "I won't ever, *ever*, wear them! Not if you chain me in a prison and beat me with sticks!"

Annemarie giggled and looked questioningly at her mother. Mrs. Johansen sighed. "I bought Kirsti some new shoes," she explained. "She's outgrown her old ones."

"Goodness, Kirsti," Ellen said, "I wish my mother would get *me* some new shoes. I love new things, and it's so hard to find them in the stores."

"Not if you go to a *fish* store!" Kirsti bellowed. "But most mothers wouldn't make their daughters wear ugly *fish* shoes!"

"Kirsten," Mama said soothingly, "you know it wasn't a fish store. And we were lucky to find shoes at all."

Kirsti sniffed. "Show them," she commanded. "Show Annemarie and Ellen how ugly they are."

Mama opened the package and took out a pair of little girl's shoes. She held them up, and Kirsti looked away in disgust.

"You know there's no leather anymore," Mama explained. "But they've found a way to make shoes out of fish skin. I don't think these are too ugly."

Annemarie and Ellen looked at the fish skin shoes. Annemarie took one in her hand and examined it. It was odd-looking; the fish scales were visible. But it was a shoe, and her sister needed shoes.

"It's not so bad, Kirsti," she said, lying a little.

Ellen turned the other one over in her hand. "You know," she said, "it's only the color that's ugly."

"Green!" Kirsti wailed. "I will never, *ever* wear green shoes!"

"In our apartment," Ellen told her, "my father has a jar of black, black ink. Would you like these shoes better if they were black?"

Kirsti frowned. "Maybe I would," she said, finally.

"Well, then," Ellen told her, "tonight, if your mama doesn't mind, I'll take the shoes home and ask my father to make them black for you, with his ink."

Mama laughed. "I think that would be a fine improvement. What do you think, Kirsti?"

Kirsti pondered. "Could he make them shiny?" she asked. "I want them shiny."

Ellen nodded. "I think he could. I think they'll be quite pretty, black and shiny."

Kirsti nodded. "All right, then," she said. "But you musn't tell anyone that they're *fish*. I don't want anyone to know." She took her new shoes, holding them disdainfully, and put them on a chair.

Then she looked with interest at the paper dolls.

"Can I play, too?" Kirsti asked. "Can I have a doll?" She squatted beside Annemarie and Ellen on the floor.

Sometimes, Annemarie thought, Kirsti was such a pest, always butting in. But the apartment was small. There was no other place for Kirsti to play. And if they told her to go away, Mama would scold.

"Here," Annemarie said, and handed her sister a cut-out little girl doll. "We're playing *Gone With the Wind*. Melanie and Scarlett are going to a ball. You can be Bonnie. She's Scarlett's daughter."

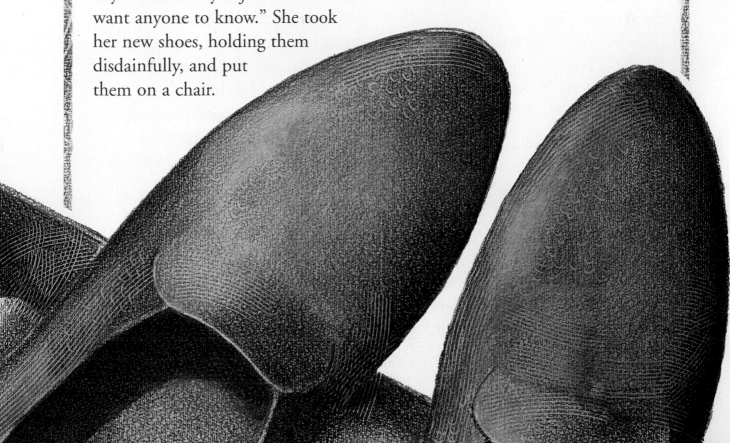

Kirsti danced her doll up and down happily. "I'm going to the ball!" she announced in a high, pretend voice.

Ellen giggled. "A little girl wouldn't go to a ball. Let's make them go someplace else. Let's make them go to Tivoli!"

"Tivoli!" Annemarie began to laugh. "That's in Copenhagen! *Gone With the Wind* is in America!"

"Tivoli, Tivoli, Tivoli," little Kirsti sang, twirling her doll in a circle.

"It doesn't matter, because it's only a game anyway," Ellen pointed out. "Tivoli can be over there, by that chair. 'Come, Scarlett,'" she said, using her doll voice, "'we shall go to Tivoli to dance and watch the fireworks, and maybe there will be some handsome men there! Bring your silly daughter Bonnie, and she can ride on the carousel.'"

Annemarie grinned and walked her Scarlett toward the chair that Ellen had designated as Tivoli. She loved Tivoli Gardens, in the heart of Copenhagen; her parents had taken her there, often, when she was a little girl. She remembered the music and brightly colored lights, the carousel and ice cream and especially the magnificent fireworks in the evenings: the huge colored splashes and bursts of lights in the evening sky.

"I remember the fireworks best of all," she commented to Ellen.

"Me too," Kirsti said. "I remember the fireworks."

"Silly," Annemarie scoffed.

"You never saw the fireworks." Tivoli Gardens was closed now. The German occupation forces had burned part of it, perhaps as a way of punishing the fun-loving Danes for their lighthearted pleasures.

Kirsti drew herself up, her small shoulders stiff. "I did too," she said belligerently. "It was my birthday. I woke up in the night and I could hear the booms. And there were lights in the sky. Mama said it was fireworks for my birthday!"

Then Annemarie remembered. Kirsti's birthday was late in August. And that night, only a month before, she, too, had been awakened and frightened by the sound of explosions. Kirsti was right—the sky in the southeast had been ablaze, and Mama had comforted her by calling it a birthday celebration. "Imagine, such fireworks for a little girl five years old!" Mama had said, sitting on their bed, holding the dark curtain aside to look through the window at the lighted sky.

The next evening's newspaper had told the sad truth. The Danes had destroyed their own naval fleet, blowing up the vessels one by one, as the Germans approached to take over the ships for their own use.

"How sad the king must be," Annemarie had heard Mama say to Papa when they read the news.

"How proud," Papa had replied.

It had made Annemarie feel sad and proud, too, to picture the tall, aging king, perhaps with tears in his blue eyes, as he looked at the remains of his small navy, which now lay submerged and broken in the harbor.

"I don't want to play anymore, Ellen," she said suddenly, and put her doll on the table.

"I have to go home, anyway," Ellen said. "I have to help Mama with the house-cleaning. Thursday is our New Year. Did you know that?"

"Why is it yours?" asked Kirsti. "Isn't it our New Year, too?"

"No. It's the Jewish New Year. That's just for us. But if you want, Kirsti, you can come that night and watch Mama light the candles."

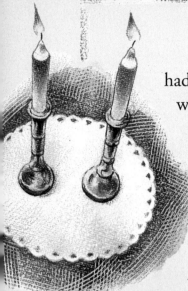

Annemarie and Kirsti had often been invited to watch Mrs. Rosen light the Sabbath candles on Friday evenings. She covered her head with a cloth and said a special prayer in Hebrew as she did so. Annemarie always stood very quietly, awed, to watch; even Kirsti, usually such a chatterbox, was always still at that time. They didn't understand the words or the meaning, but they could feel what a special time it was for the Rosens.

"Yes," Kirsti agreed happily. "I'll come and watch your mama light the candles, and I'll wear my new black shoes."

BUT THIS TIME WAS to be different. Leaving for school on Thursday with her sister, Annemarie saw the Rosens walking to the synagogue early in the morning, dressed in their best clothes. She waved to Ellen, who waved happily back.

"Lucky Ellen," Annemarie said to Kirsti. "She doesn't have to go to school today."

"But she probably has to sit very, very still, like we do in church," Kirsti pointed out. "*That's* no fun."

That afternoon, Mrs. Rosen knocked at their door but didn't come inside. Instead, she spoke for a long time in a hurried, tense voice to Annemarie's mother in the hall. When Mama returned, her face was worried, but her voice was cheerful.

"Girls," she said, "we have a nice surprise. Tonight Ellen will be coming to stay overnight and to be our guest for a few days! It isn't often we have a visitor."

Kirsti clapped her hands in delight.

"But, Mama," Annemarie said, in dismay, "it's their New Year. They were going to have a celebration at home! Ellen told me that her mother managed to get a chicken someplace, and she was going to roast it—their first roast chicken in a year or more!"

"Their plans have changed," Mama said briskly. "Mr. and Mrs. Rosen have been called away to visit some relatives. So Ellen will stay with us. Now, let's get busy and put clean sheets on your bed. Kirsti, you may sleep with Mama and Papa tonight, and we'll let the big girls giggle together by themselves."

89

Kirsti pouted, and it was clear that she was about to argue. "Mama will tell you a special story tonight," her mother said. "One just for you."

"About a king?" Kirsti asked dubiously.

"About a king, if you wish," Mama replied.

"All right, then. But there must be a queen, too," Kirsti said.

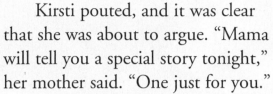

THOUGH MRS. ROSEN had sent her chicken to the Johansens, and Mama made a lovely dinner large enough for second helpings all around, it was not an evening of laughter and talk. Ellen was silent at dinner. She looked frightened. Mama and Papa tried to speak of cheerful things, but it was clear that they were worried, and it made Annemarie worry, too. Only Kirsti was unaware of the quiet tension in the room. Swinging her feet in their newly blackened and shiny shoes, she chattered and giggled during dinner.

"Early bedtime tonight, little one," Mama announced after the dishes were washed. "We need extra time for the long story I promised, about the king and queen." She disappeared with Kirsti into the bedroom.

"What's happening?" Annemarie asked when she and Ellen were alone with Papa in the living room. "Something's wrong. What is it?"

Papa's face was troubled. "I wish that I could protect you children from this knowledge," he said quietly. "Ellen, you already know. Now we must tell Annemarie."

He turned to her and stroked her hair with his gentle hand. "This morning, at the synagogue, the rabbi told his congregation that the Nazis have taken the synagogue lists of all the Jews. Where they live, what their names are. Of course the Rosens were on that list, along with many others."

"Why? Why did they want those names?"

"They plan to arrest all the Danish Jews. They plan to take them away. And we have been told that they may come tonight."

"I don't understand! Take them where?"

Her father shook his head. "We don't know where, and we don't really know why. They call it 'relocation.' We don't even know what that means. We only know that it is wrong, and it is dangerous, and we must help."

Annemarie was stunned. She looked at Ellen and saw that her best friend was crying silently.

"Where are Ellen's parents? We must help them, too!"

"We couldn't take all three of them. If the Germans came to search our apartment, it would be clear that the Rosens were here. One person we can hide. Not three. So Peter has helped Ellen's parents to go elsewhere. We don't know where. Ellen doesn't know either. But they are safe."

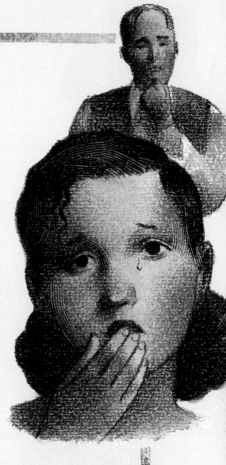

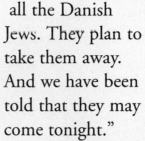

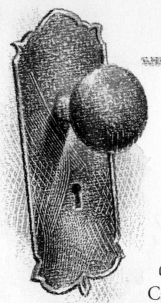

Ellen sobbed aloud, and put her face in her hands. Papa put his arm around her. "They are safe, Ellen. I promise you that. You will see them again quite soon. Can you try hard to believe my promise?"

Ellen hesitated, nodded, and wiped her eyes with her hand.

"But, Papa," Annemarie said, looking around the small apartment, with its few pieces of furniture: the fat stuffed sofa, the table and chairs, the small bookcase against the wall. "You said that we would hide her. How can we do that? Where can she hide?"

Papa smiled. "That part is easy. It will be as your mama said: you two will sleep together in your bed, and you may giggle and talk and tell secrets to each other. And if anyone comes—"

Ellen interrupted him. "Who might come? Will it be soldiers? Like the ones on the corners?" Annemarie remembered how terrified Ellen had looked the day when the soldier had questioned them on the corner.

"I really don't think anyone will. But it never hurts to be prepared. If anyone should come, even soldiers, you two will be sisters. You are together so much, it will be easy for you to pretend that you are sisters."

He rose and walked to the window. He pulled the lace curtain aside and looked down into the street. Outside, it was beginning to grow dark. Soon they would have to draw the black curtains that all Danes had on their windows; the entire city had to be completely darkened at night. In a nearby tree, a bird was singing; otherwise it was quiet. It was the last night of September.

"Go, now, and get into your nightgowns. It will be a long night."

Annemarie and Ellen got to their feet. Papa suddenly crossed the room and put his arms around them both. He kissed the top of each head: Annemarie's blond one, which reached to his shoulder, and Ellen's dark hair, the thick curls braided as always into pigtails.

"Don't be frightened," he said to them softly. "Once I had three daughters. Tonight I am proud to have three daughters again."

"Do you really think anyone will come?" Ellen asked nervously, turning to Annemarie in the bedroom. "Your father doesn't think so."

"Of course not. They're always threatening stuff. They just like to scare people." Annemarie took her nightgown from a hook in the closet.

"Anyway, if they did, it would give me a chance to practice acting. I'd just pretend to be Lise. I wish I were taller, though." Ellen stood on tiptoe, trying to make herself tall. She laughed at herself, and her voice was more relaxed.

"You were great as the Dark Queen in the school play last year," Annemarie told her. "You should be an actress when you grow up."

"My father wants me to be a teacher. He wants *everyone* to be a teacher, like him. But maybe I could convince him that I should go to acting school." Ellen stood on tiptoe again, and made an imperious gesture with her arm. "I am the Dark Queen," she intoned dramatically. "I have come to command the night!"

"You should try saying, 'I am Lise Johansen!'" Annemarie said, grinning. "If you told

the Nazis that you were the Dark Queen, they'd haul you off to a mental institution."

Ellen dropped her actress pose and sat down, with her legs curled under her, on the bed. "They won't really come here, do you think?" she asked again.

Annemarie shook her head. "Not in a million years." She picked up her hairbrush.

The girls found themselves whispering as they got ready for bed. There was no need, really, to whisper; they were, after all, supposed to be normal sisters, and Papa had said they could giggle and talk. The bedroom door was closed.

But the night did seem, somehow, different from a normal night. And so they whispered.

"How did your sister die, Annemarie?" Ellen asked suddenly. "I remember when it happened. And I remember the funeral—it was the only time I have ever been in a Lutheran church. But I never knew just what happened."

"I don't know *exactly*," Annemarie confessed. "She and Peter were out somewhere together, and then there was a telephone call, that there had been an accident. Mama and Papa rushed to the hospital—remember, your mother came and stayed with me and Kirsti? Kirsti was already asleep and she slept right through everything, she was so little then. But I stayed up, and I was with your mother in the living room when my parents came home in the middle of the night. And they told me Lise had died."

"I remember it was raining," Ellen said sadly. "It was still raining the next morning when Mama told me. Mama was crying, and the rain made it seem as if the whole *world* was crying."

Annemarie finished brushing her long hair and handed her hairbrush to her best friend. Ellen undid her braids, lifted her dark hair away from the thin gold chain she wore around her neck—the chain that held the Star of David—and began to brush her thick curls.

"I think it was partly because of the rain. They said she was hit by a car. I suppose the streets were slippery, and it was getting dark, and maybe the driver just couldn't see," Annemarie went on, remembering.

"Papa looked so angry. He made one hand into a fist, and he kept pounding it into the other hand. I remember the noise of it: slam, slam, slam."

Together they got into the wide bed and pulled up the covers. Annemarie blew out the candle and drew the dark curtains aside so that the open window near the bed let in some air. "See that blue trunk in the corner?" she said, pointing through the darkness. "Lots of Lise's things are there. Even her wedding dress. Mama and Papa have never looked at those things, not since the day they packed them away."

Ellen sighed. "She would have looked so beautiful in her wedding dress. She had such a pretty smile. I used to pretend that she was *my* sister, too."

"She would have liked that," Annemarie told her. "She loved you."

"That's the worst thing in the world," Ellen whispered. "To be dead so young. I wouldn't want the Germans to take my family away—to make us live someplace else. But still, it wouldn't be as bad as being dead."

Annemarie leaned over and hugged her. "They won't take you away," she said. "Not your parents,

either. Papa promised that they were safe, and he always keeps his promises. And you are quite safe, here with us."

For a while they continued to murmur in the dark, but the murmurs were interrupted by yawns. Then Ellen's voice stopped, she turned over, and in a minute her breathing was quiet and slow.

Annemarie stared at the window where the sky was outlined and a tree branch moved slightly in the breeze. Everything seemed very familiar, very comforting. Dangers were no more than odd imaginings, like ghost stories that children made up to frighten one another: things that couldn't possibly happen. Annemarie felt completely safe here in her own home, with her parents in the next room and her best friend asleep beside her. She yawned contentedly and closed her eyes.

It was hours later, but still dark, when she was awakened abruptly by the pounding on the apartment door.

ANNEMARIE EASED THE bedroom door open quietly, only a crack, and peeked out. Behind her, Ellen was sitting up, her eyes wide.

She could see Mama and Papa in their nightclothes, moving about. Mama held a lighted candle, but as Annemarie watched, she went to a lamp and switched it on. It was so long a time since they had dared to use the strictly rationed electricity after dark that the light in the room seemed startling to Annemarie, watching through the slightly opened bedroom door. She saw her mother look automatically to the blackout curtains, making sure that they were tightly drawn.

Papa opened the front door to the soldiers.

"This is the Johansen apartment?" A deep voiced asked the question loudly, in the terribly accented Danish.

"Our name is on the door, and I see you have a flashlight," Papa answered. "What do you want? Is something wrong?"

"I understand you are a friend of your neighbors the Rosens, Mrs. Johansen," the soldier said angrily.

"Sophy Rosen is my friend, that is true," Mama said quietly. "Please, could you speak more softly? My children are asleep."

"Then you will be so kind as to tell me where the Rosens are." He made no effort to lower his voice.

"I assume they are at home, sleeping. It is four in the morning, after all," Mama said.

Annemarie heard the soldier stalk across the living room toward the kitchen. From her hiding place in the narrow sliver of an open doorway, she could see the heavy uniformed man, a holstered pistol at his waist, in the entrance to the kitchen, peering in toward the sink.

Another German voice said, "The Rosens' apartment is empty. We are wondering if they might be visiting their good friends the Johansens."

"Well," said Papa, moving slightly so that he was standing in front of Annemarie's bedroom door, and she could see nothing except the dark blur of his back, "as you see, you are mistaken. There is no one here but my family."

"You will not object if we look around." The voice was harsh, and it was not a question.

"It seems we have no choice," Papa replied.

"Please don't wake my children," Mama requested again. "There is no need to frighten little ones."

The heavy, booted feet moved across the floor again and into the other bedroom. A closet door opened and closed with a bang.

Annemarie eased her bedroom door closed silently. She stumbled through the darkness to the bed.

"Ellen," she whispered urgently, "take your necklace off!"

Ellen's hands flew to her neck. Desperately she began trying to unhook the tiny clasp. Outside the bedroom door, the harsh voices and heavy footsteps continued.

"I can't get it open!" Ellen said frantically. "I never take it off—I can't even remember how to open it!"

Annemarie heard a voice just outside the door. "What is here?"

"Shhh," her mother replied. "My daughters' bedroom. They are sound asleep."

"Hold still," Annemarie commanded. "This will hurt." She grabbed the little gold chain, yanked with all her strength, and broke it. As the door opened and light flooded into the bedroom, she crumpled it into her hand and closed her fingers tightly.

Terrified, both girls looked up at the three Nazi officers who entered the room.

One of the men aimed a flashlight around the bedroom. He went to the closet and looked inside. Then with a sweep of his gloved hand he pushed to the floor several coats and a bathrobe that hung from pegs on the wall.

There was nothing else in the room except a chest of drawers, the blue decorated trunk in the corner, and a heap of Kirsti's dolls piled in a small rocking chair. The flashlight beam touched each thing in turn. Angrily the officer turned toward the bed.

"Get up!" he ordered. "Come out here!"

Trembling, the two girls rose from the bed and followed him, brushing past the two remaining officers in the doorway, to the living room.

Annemarie looked around. These three uniformed men were different from the ones on the street corners. The street soldiers were often young, sometimes ill at ease, and Annemarie remembered how the Giraffe had, for a moment, let his harsh pose slip and had smiled at Kirsti.

But these men were older and their faces were set with anger.

Her parents were standing beside each other, their faces tense, but Kirsti was nowhere in sight. Thank goodness that Kirsti slept through almost anything. If they had wakened her, she would be wailing—or worse, she would be

angry, and her fists would fly.

"Your names?" the officer barked.

"Annemarie Johansen. And this is my sister—"

"Quiet! Let her speak for herself. Your name?" He was glaring at Ellen.

Ellen swallowed. "Lise," she said, and cleared her throat. "Lise Johansen."

The officer stared at them grimly.

"Now," Mama said in a strong voice, "you have seen that we are not hiding anything. May my children go back to bed?"

The officer ignored her. Suddenly he grabbed a handful of Ellen's hair. Ellen winced.

He laughed scornfully. "You have a blond child sleeping in the other room. And you have this blond daughter—" He gestured toward Annemarie with his head. "Where did you get the dark-haired one?" He twisted the lock of Ellen's hair. "From a different father? From the milkman?"

Papa stepped forward. "Don't speak to my wife in such a way. Let go of my daughter or I will report you for such treatment."

"Or maybe you got her some-place else?" the officer continued with a sneer. "From the Rosens?"

For a moment no one spoke. Then Annemarie, watching in panic, saw her father move swiftly to the small bookcase and take out a book. She saw that he was holding the family photograph album. Very quickly he searched through its pages, found what he was looking for, and tore out three pictures from three separate pages.

He handed them to the German officer, who released Ellen's hair.

"You will see each of my daughters, each with her name written on the photograph," Papa said.

Annemarie knew instantly which photographs he had chosen. The album had many snapshots—all the poorly focused pictures of school events and birthday parties. But it also contained a portrait, taken by a photographer, of each girl as a tiny infant. Mama had written in her delicate handwriting, the name of each baby daughter across the bottom of those photographs.

She realized too, with an icy feeling, why Papa had torn them from the book. At the bottom of each page, below the photograph itself, was written the date. And the real Lise Johansen had been born twenty-one years earlier.

"Kirsten Elisabeth," the officer read, looking at Kirsti's baby picture. He let the photograph fall to the floor.

"Annemarie," he read next, glanced at her, and dropped the second photograph.

"Lise Margrete," he read finally, and stared at Ellen for a long, unwavering moment. In her mind, Annemarie pictured the photograph that he held: the baby, wide-eyed, propped against a pillow, her tiny hand holding a silver teething ring, her bare feet visible below the hem of an embroidered dress. The wispy curls. Dark.

The officer tore the photograph in half and dropped the pieces on the floor. Then he turned, the heels of his shiny boots grinding into the pictures, and left the apartment. Without a word, the other two officers followed. Papa stepped forward and closed the door behind him.

Annemarie relaxed the clenched fingers of her right hand, which still clutched Ellen's necklace. She looked down, and saw that she had imprint-ed the Star of David into her palm.

RESCUE:
THE DANISH BOAT

Millions of people lost their lives in the Holocaust. Some were lucky enough to be saved—because of the courage of a few people who acted heroically during a time of crisis.

On April 26, 1993, the United States Holocaust Memorial Museum in Washington, D.C., opened so that the stories of the victims wouldn't be forgotten. The poster on the next page, designed by the United States Holocaust Memorial Council, is a testimony to people in Denmark who helped many Jews escape from their country into safety.

The background of the poster is a nautical map showing the Oresund, the body of water between Denmark and Sweden. The boat pictured in the poster is a Danish motorboat built in the 1930s or 1940s. Courageous Danes used these small wooden boats to smuggle nearly 7,000 Danish Jews across the Oresund to safety in Sweden. The black and white photograph at the bottom of the poster shows a small group of Danish citizens making their way across the sea to neighboring Sweden. These men and women probably included members of the Resistance, an underground movement that planned the secret operations to rescue the Jews. Many brave young Resistance leaders sacrificed their own lives to help save their compatriots.

The United States Holocaust Memorial Museum in Washington, D.C.

Right: Poster from the United States Holocaust Memorial Museum

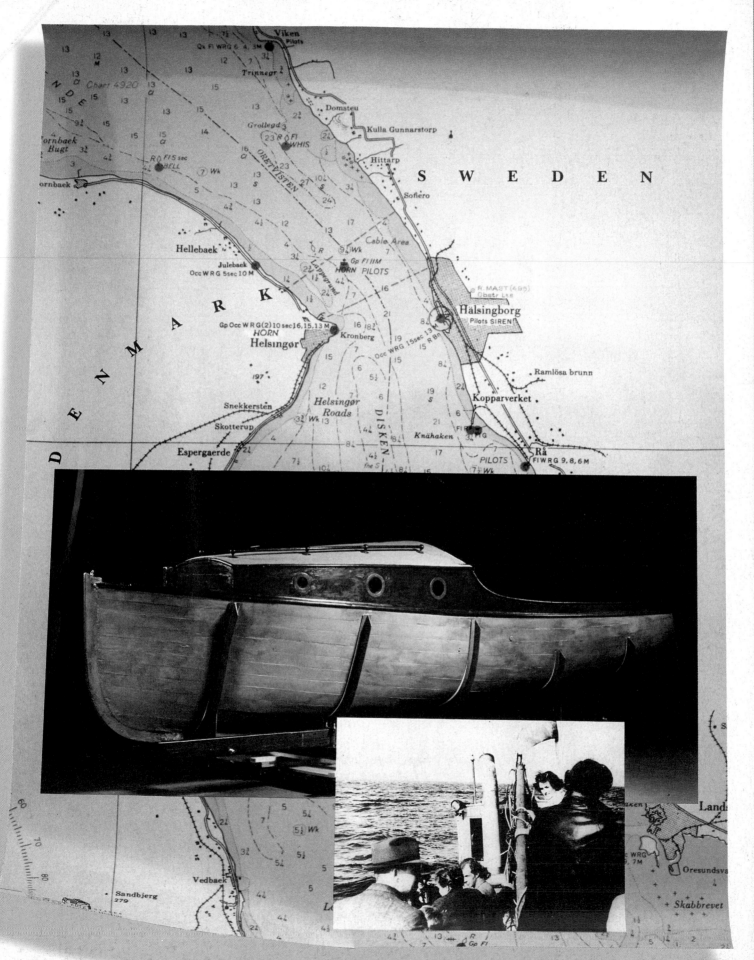

Think About Reading

Answer the questions in the story map.

SETTING

1. Where and when does the story take place?

CHARACTERS

2. Who are the two main characters in the story?

PROBLEM

3. What happens when the soldiers are about to arrest all the Danish Jews?

4. How do the Johansens plan to fool the soldiers about Ellen?

5. What happens to Ellen's necklace with the Star of David on it?

6. What happens when the soldiers are suspicious because Ellen's hair is not blond like the Johansens' other daughters?

SOLUTION

→

→

→

→

RESOLUTION

7. How do the Johansens finally save Ellen?

*W*rite a *B*ook *R*eview

You are the book reviewer for your school newspaper. Write a review for *Number the Stars*. Be sure to include a brief summary and then express your opinions about the story. Did you enjoy it? Why or why not? Would you recommend it to other readers?

*L*iterature *C*ircle

Discuss the characters in *Number the Stars*. Is there any one character that you learn more about that the others? Who is this character and what kind of person is he or she? What words would you use to describe this character? Talk about the ways the author reveals this character to the reader. Record your ideas on a character web.

AUTHOR
*L*ois *L*owry

During World War II, Lois Lowry spent her early childhood away from danger in Pennsylvania. Years later, she got the idea for *Number the Stars* from her friend Annelise Platt who described what it was like in Denmark during the war. By combining some of Annelise's experiences with historical facts, Lowry created her first Newbery Medal winner. She says, "Walking through a scary place is easier if you know that someone else has walked there once and survived."

MORE BOOKS BY
*L*ois *L*owry

- *The Giver*
- *Anastasia Krupnik*
- *All About Sam*

PROJECT

How to

Write a Tribute

Demonstrate your appreciation of someone who inspires you!

Inspirations can come from many sources. The accomplishments of friends and family members can be inspirational, as can the achievements of famous people. One way to show respect for someone who has inspired you is to write a tribute to that person. A tribute contains biographical facts, stories, and personal feelings about the subject, as well as things the person has said. Tributes come in many forms. Some common ones are poems, songs, and speeches.

Jane Goodall

Brainstorm

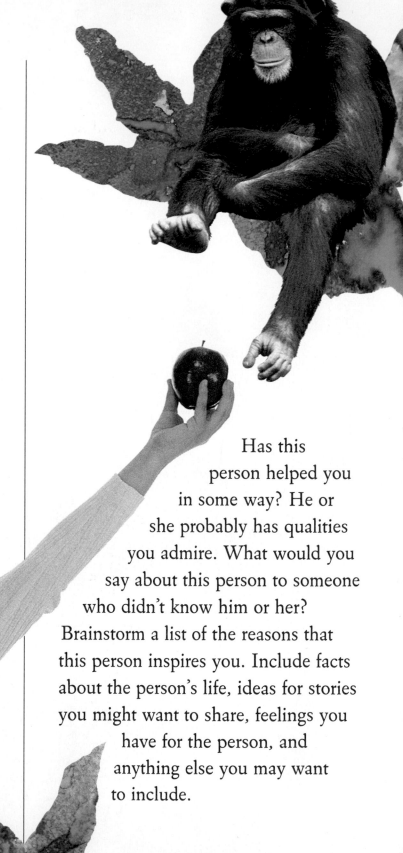

Choose a subject for your tribute. The subject can be a friend or relative, or someone else whom you know well. You could also write a tribute to a celebrity or some other inspiring individual whom you don't know personally.

Before you begin to write, you have to think about what you'd like to say about your subject.

TOOLS

- paper and pencil
- research materials

Has this person helped you in some way? He or she probably has qualities you admire. What would you say about this person to someone who didn't know him or her? Brainstorm a list of the reasons that this person inspires you. Include facts about the person's life, ideas for stories you might want to share, feelings you have for the person, and anything else you may want to include.

2 Choose a Format

After you have decided what you want to say about your subject, you'll need to choose a style for your tribute. The style of your tribute should reflect those things that make your subject special. For example, if you are paying tribute to a musician, you may want to write a song.

Select the format that works best for you. You can create your own, or choose one from the following:

- a poem
- music video
- a play
- a speech
- a collage

Research Your Subject

Before you begin writing your tribute, you'll need some basic information about your subject, such as where and when the person was born, and what he or she does for a living. If you chose the same person you used for your biographical sketch, then you probably already have a lot of this information.

You will also want to personalize your tribute. In addition to sharing your own feelings, comments, and stories about the subject, you may want to collect those of other people.

If your subject is a celebrity, you may need to get your information from books, magazines, newspapers, or videos. Try to find out how your subject became the type of person who inspires you.

Tip Include unique items, such as lyrics from your subject's favorite song or pictures of his or her birthplace or current home, to make your tribute more interesting.

How Am I Doing?

Before you put your tribute together, take a minute to ask yourself these questions:

- Did I find enough information about my subject?

- Did I think about how this person has made a difference in my life?

- Did I gather a good mix of facts and feelings for the tribute?

4 Write Your Tribute

How will you present all the information you've gathered? That will depend on the format you've chosen. If you are writing a poem, for example, you might want to think about how many stanzas it should have and whether it will rhyme. If you are giving a speech, you might want to select a funny quote or an amusing story for your introduction. Remember that you do not have to use all of your information—include whatever is most interesting and important.

If You Are Using a Computer ...

Create your tribute in the Newsletter format on your computer. Write a headline telling just how special your subject is. Use clip art to illustrate the tribute.

5 Present Your Tribute

The format you have chosen will also influence the type of presentation you make. If you wrote a song, for instance, you will probably want to perform it. If you wrote a poem, you might want to make a collage and put your poem in the center. You and your classmates might want to organize a "Tribute Ceremony," and take turns presenting your tributes. If possible, arrange for some of the honorees to attend!

CONGRATULATIONS

An important part of knowing yourself is getting to know the people who are important to you. Maybe you will inspire someone yourself!

Joseph Shabalala
Musician ▶

It's a Mystery

THEME

We can solve
mysteries using
reason, logic,
and intuition.

UNIT 2

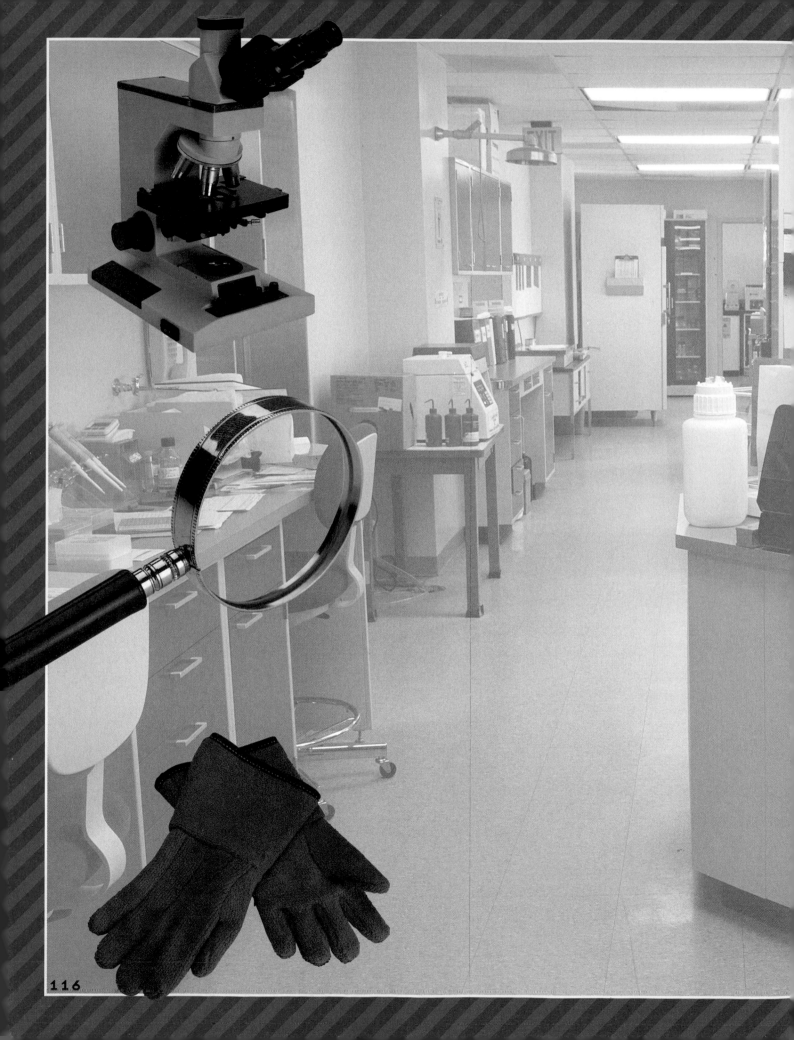

Welcome to
LITERACY
PLACE

Detective Headquarters

We can solve mysteries using reason, logic, and intuition.

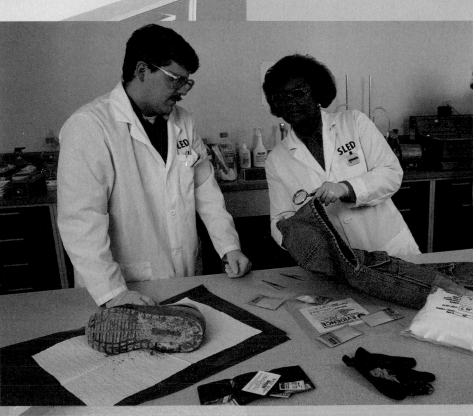

PLAY

THE REDHEADED LEAGUE

adapted from the story by
Sir Arthur Conan Doyle

illustrated by
Tim Jessell

CHARACTERS

Sherlock Holmes
the famous English detective

Dr. John Watson
his friend and assistant

Jabez Wilson
owner of a pawnshop

Vincent Spaulding
a clerk in the pawnshop

Duncan Ross
a member of the Redheaded
League

Peter Jones
a Scotland Yard detective

Reginald Merryweather
a bank president

John Clay
a criminal whose identity
will be revealed later

*I*f it's a mystery, Sherlock Holmes will solve it. People come from near and far to seek the world-famous detective's help, but he only takes on unusual cases that truly interest him. When Mr. Jabez Wilson— a London pawnbroker— appears at 221B Baker Street and tells a curious tale about a lost job, Sherlock Holmes can't resist the challenge. He must solve the perplexing puzzle!

✦ Scene One ✦

It is a Saturday morning in the summer of 1890 in London, England. Dr. Watson enters Sherlock Holmes's sitting room. Holmes is there talking with a man who has bright red hair.

HOLMES: Watson, you could not have come at a better time.

WATSON: You seem to be busy. I can wait outside.

HOLMES: Not at all. *(He turns to the man with the red hair.)* Dr. Watson has helped me in many of my cases, Mr. Wilson. I have no doubt he will be helpful in yours.

WILSON: How do you do?

WATSON: How do you do, sir?

HOLMES: Watson, I know you share my love of the unusual. Mr. Wilson has started to tell me one of the strangest stories I've ever heard. Mr. Wilson, will you be kind enough to begin your story again?

WILSON: Of course.

HOLMES: I am sure, Watson, you can tell that Mr. Wilson has been in China.

WATSON *(puzzled)*: Well . . .

HOLMES: And you can see that he has been doing a lot of writing.

WILSON *(amazed)*: How did you know that?

HOLMES: The cuff on your right sleeve is very shiny. Your left sleeve has a smooth patch at the elbow, where you rest it on a desk. It is clear that you've been writing a lot with your right hand, while leaning on your left elbow.

WILSON: That's true. But how did you know that I've been in China?

HOLMES: There is a tattoo of a fish above your wrist. I've made a study of tattoos. Only in China are the fish scales colored pink, as they are in your tattoo.

WILSON *(laughing)*: I thought at first you had done something very clever. But I see now that it was really very simple.

HOLMES: Perhaps, Watson, I should not give away my ways of drawing conclusions. I might lose my reputation as a genius. Now, Mr. Wilson, will you read us the newspaper ad that led to your adventure?

WILSON *(reading a newspaper ad aloud)*: "There is a position open in the Redheaded League. According to the will of the late Elmer Hopkins, of the U.S.A., a League member will be paid a high salary for doing easy work. Redheaded men over the age of 21 may apply. See Duncan Ross at 7 Pope's Court, Monday at 11:00 AM."

WATSON: What on earth does this mean?

HOLMES: Please note the paper and the date, Watson.

WATSON *(looking at the ad)*: It is from *The Morning Chronicle,* April 27, 1890. That was two months ago.

HOLMES: Now, Mr. Wilson, tell us your story.

WILSON: I own a pawnshop on Coburg Square. It's a small business, and I don't make much money. In fact, I pay my assistant only half the usual salary. He was willing to take the job in order to learn the business.

HOLMES: What's this young fellow's name?

WILSON: His name is Vincent Spaulding, and he isn't very young. He does his job well, but he has one fault. He spends too much time on his hobby, photography. He always seems to be down in the cellar, developing his pictures.

WATSON: He doesn't sound very helpful.

WILSON: Oh, but he is. It was Spaulding who showed me this newspaper ad two months ago . . . .

✦ Scene Two ✦

The scene is Wilson's pawnshop, two months earlier. Spaulding enters.

SPAULDING: Mr. Wilson, I wish I had red hair.

WILSON: Why?

SPAULDING: There's another opening in the Redheaded League.

WILSON: What is that?

SPAULDING: Haven't you ever heard of it? Why, you could apply for the job, with hair that color. You get paid well for doing very little work. You could handle that job—and still run this shop.

WILSON: I certainly could use the money. Tell me about this Redheaded League.

SPAULDING: It was started by an American millionaire who was a

bit odd. He was redheaded. When he died, he left his fortune to help redheaded men live an easy life.

WILSON: I'm sure that thousands of men will apply for the job opening.

SPAULDING: No. You have to live in London. Elmer Hopkins lived in London for a while, and he wanted to do something good for the city. Also your hair cannot be light red or dark red. It must be as bright red as yours.

WILSON: Spaulding, let's close up the shop for an hour or so. We're going to visit the office of the Redheaded League.

✦ Scene Three ✦

Wilson and Spaulding join a line of redheaded men outside a small office. The line moves forward as the men ahead of them enter the office, one by one, then quickly come out again.

WILSON: Did all these men see the ad?

SPAULDING: Oh, yes. The League is very well known.

WILSON: I don't have a chance of getting the job.

SPAULDING: You do, sir. There aren't many men here with hair as bright as yours.

Now they are at the open door of the office. Duncan Ross, a man with bright red hair, is sitting at a desk. Another redheaded man is standing before him.

ROSS *(to the redheaded man)*: I'm sorry, sir. Your hair is a bit too orange for us. *(The man leaves.)* Next!

SPAULDING *(leading Wilson forward)*: This is Mr. Jabez Wilson. He is willing to join the League.

ROSS: Well, he has a very fine head of red hair. *(He stands up and walks around Wilson, looking at his head. Suddenly he pulls Wilson's hair.)*

WILSON *(surprised)*: Oww!

ROSS: Good. That hair is real. We have to be careful. We've been tricked twice by wigs and once by boot polish. *(He shouts out the doorway.)* You men may all go home now! The job has been filled! *(He turns to Wilson.)* My name is Duncan Ross. I'm part of the League. When can you start working for us?

WILSON: Well, I have a business of my own already.

SPAULDING: Never mind that, Mr. Wilson. I'll be able to look after the shop.

ROSS: The hours here are from 10:00 in the morning until 2:00 in the afternoon.

WILSON: That's fine. Most of my business takes place late in the afternoon or early in the evening. Spaulding can handle anything that turns up in the morning. What is the work I'm to do?

ROSS: It's very simple, but you must stay in this office the whole time. If you leave, you lose the job. The will of Mr. Hopkins states that very clearly. No excuse will be accepted, not even sickness.

WILSON: What is the work?

ROSS: You copy an encyclopedia. Here is the first volume. *(He hands a volume to Wilson.)* You bring your own ink, pens, and paper. We provide this desk and chair. Can you start tomorrow?

WILSON: Yes.

ROSS: Then let me congratulate you. You are lucky to be a member of the Redheaded League.

◆ Scene Four ◆

The scene is Holmes's sitting room once again. Wilson continues to tell his story to Holmes and Watson.

WILSON: I was sure the whole thing was a prank. I couldn't believe that anyone would pay a high salary for copying an encyclopedia. But I decided to go through with it. To my surprise, everything seemed to be in order.

HOLMES: Were you paid?

WILSON: Yes.

HOLMES: Was Mr. Ross always there?

WILSON: He dropped by the first few days. Then I saw less and less of him. But I never dared to leave the office. I never knew when he might appear. If he found I wasn't there, I would lose the job.

WATSON: How long did this go on?

WILSON: For eight weeks. I wrote about abbots and archery and armor. Then, suddenly, it all came to an end.

HOLMES: To an end?

WILSON: Yes, sir. At 10:00 this morning, I went to the office as usual, but the door was locked. This card was tacked on the door. *(He hands a card to Holmes.)* You can read it for yourself.

HOLMES *(reading aloud)*: "The Redheaded League no longer exists." What did you do after you found this card?

WILSON: I went to the landlord. He said he had never heard of the Redheaded League, nor of Mr. Duncan Ross, but he had rented the office to a redheaded man named Morris. Mr. Morris, he said, moved out yesterday.

HOLMES: Did he give you Mr. Morris's new address?

WILSON: Yes, and I went there. No one there had heard of either William Morris or Duncan Ross.

WATSON: What did you do then?

WILSON: I went back to my shop and talked to Spaulding. He said there was nothing I could do but wait to see if Mr. Ross would write me a letter. But I didn't want to lose a job like that without a struggle. I had heard that you, Mr. Holmes, give advice to poor people who need help. So here I am.

HOLMES: You were wise to come here. I shall be happy to look into your case. This might be more serious than it seems at first sight.

WILSON: Of course it's serious! I've lost a good job. I want to know more about this Redheaded League. Why did they play this prank on me? Or wasn't it a prank?

HOLMES: We shall try to clear up these questions. First, tell me more about Spaulding. How long had he worked for you before he showed you the newspaper ad?

WILSON: About a month.

HOLMES: Before you hired him, did anyone else apply for this job?

WILSON: Yes. There were several people.

HOLMES: Why did you pick Spaulding?

WILSON: He was willing to accept half the usual salary.

HOLMES: What does he look like?

WILSON: He is small and stout, about 30 years old. He has a white mark on his forehead from some acid.

HOLMES: I thought so! Are his ears pierced for earrings?

WILSON: Yes. He said a gypsy pierced them for him when he was a boy.

HOLMES: Does he still work for you?

WILSON: Yes, sir.

HOLMES: That will do for now, Mr. Wilson. I will be happy to give you my opinion in two days.

WILSON: Thank you, Mr. Holmes. Good day, Dr. Watson. *(He leaves.)*

HOLMES: Well, Watson, what do you make of all this?

WATSON: I make nothing of it. It is a mysterious business. What are you going to do about it?

HOLMES: I'm going to sit here and think. Please do not disturb me for an hour. At the end of that time, we shall go to Coburg Square.

✦ Scene Five ✦

An hour later, Holmes and Watson are outside Wilson's pawnshop on Coburg Square. Holmes knocks on the door, and Spaulding opens it.

SPAULDING: May I help you?

HOLMES: Can you tell me how to get to Fleet Street from here?

SPAULDING: Take the third right and the fourth left. *(He goes back into the shop.)*

HOLMES: Watson, Spaulding is the fourth smartest man in London. He is also one of the most daring. I have heard of him before.

WATSON: You seem to think he matters a great deal in this mystery. I supposed you asked for directions so you could get a look at him.

HOLMES: No, not at him. I wanted to see the knees of his trousers.

WATSON: What did you see?

HOLMES: What I expected to see. Now, Watson, we must study the buildings on this street. I wish to remember the order. On the corner is a tobacco shop. Next is a newspaper shop. Then there is Wilson's pawnshop. Next to that is the Coburg branch of the Bank of London. Then there is a restaurant. Finally, there is a tailor's shop.

WATSON: Why is the order of the buildings important?

HOLMES: A serious crime has been planned. I believe we still have time to stop it. I shall need your help tonight.

WATSON: At what time will you need me?

HOLMES: At 10:00 at my place. I warn you, though, there may be some danger.

✦ Scene Six ✦

At 10:00 that night, Watson enters Holmes's sitting room. Holmes is talking with two men.

HOLMES: Ah, Watson, you know Peter Jones of Scotland Yard. Let me introduce you to Reginald Merryweather. He is the president of a branch of the Bank of London.

WATSON: How do you do, sir?

JONES: Well, Watson, your friend Holmes is a wonderful man for starting a chase.

MERRYWEATHER *(frowning)*: I hope that a wild goose is not at the end of it.

JONES: You may trust Mr. Holmes. His ways of solving mysteries are a little unusual. But now and then he does a better job than our police force.

MERRYWEATHER: All right, but I am missing my Saturday-night game. It is the first Saturday night in 27 years that I have not played.

HOLMES: Mr. Merryweather, you will play for higher stakes tonight than you have ever done before. And the game will be more exciting. The prize for you is a huge amount of money. The prize for you, Mr. Jones, is John Clay.

MERRYWEATHER: Who is John Clay?

JONES: He is a murderer, thief, and forger. I would rather arrest him than any other criminal in London. He's the grandson of a duke. His brain is as swift as his fingers. We find signs of his evil work everywhere, but we've never found the man himself. I've been on his track for years.

HOLMES: I hope that I may be able to introduce him to you tonight. Now, Mr. Merryweather, let us go to your bank on Coburg Square.

✦ Scene Seven ✦

The four men are now in the cellar of Mr. Merryweather's bank. Mr. Merryweather is carrying a lantern. The cellar is filled with crates.

HOLMES *(looking at the ceiling)*: It doesn't look as if anyone could break in from above.

MERRYWEATHER: Nor could anyone break in from below. *(He hits the stone floor with his walking stick.)* Why, it sounds hollow!

HOLMES *(taking the lantern from him)*: I must ask you to be more quiet. Please sit on one of those crates and don't interfere. *(He gets down on his knees, and examines the stone floor.)*

WATSON: What are you doing, Holmes?

HOLMES: I am checking these stones. *(He stands up.)* Well, we must wait until Mr. Wilson goes to bed.

JONES: What do you mean?

HOLMES: Mr. Wilson owns the pawnshop next door. He lives above the shop. As soon as he is asleep, John Clay and his men will make their move. Mr. Merryweather can explain why John Clay would be interested in this cellar.

MERRYWEATHER *(whispering)*: It's the shipment of gold from France. We have thousands of pounds' worth of gold here. It's in these crates. Why, the crate I'm on holds a fortune. We heard that an attempt might be made to steal it.

HOLMES: I believe that this will happen soon. Mr. Merryweather, I must cover the lantern.

MERRYWEATHER: Must we sit in the dark?

HOLMES: I'm afraid so. These are daring men. They will harm us if we are not

careful. I shall stand behind this crate. The rest of you hide behind those crates. When I flash the light upon the criminals, close in quickly.

Silence.

MERRYWEATHER: This waiting could drive me mad.

HOLMES: Control yourself, Merryweather. Jones, I hope you did what I asked you to do.

JONES: Yes. Two officers are at the front door of the pawnshop.

HOLMES: Good. That is the only way they could escape.

WATSON *(quietly)*: Look. Some light is shining between the stones on the floor.

HOLMES *(calmly)*: I see it. Be ready.

Suddenly a large stone is pushed up from the floor. Then two men climb up from the hole and into the cellar. One has red hair.

CLAY *(to the redheaded man)*: It's all clear. *(Holmes uncovers the lantern and grabs Clay.)* Jump, Archie!

The redheaded man jumps down through the hole in the floor. Jones grabs at his jacket, but the cloth rips.

HOLMES: It's no use, John Clay.

CLAY: So I see. At least my pal got away.

HOLMES: I'm afraid not. Two officers are waiting for him at the door to the pawnshop.

CLAY: You seem to have handled everything very well. I must compliment you.

HOLMES: And I compliment you. Your redheaded idea was very clever.

JONES: Clay, you and your partner are

coming to the police station. Now, hold out your hands for these. *(He puts handcuffs on Clay.)*

CLAY: Be careful with your filthy hands. You may not be aware that I have royal blood in my veins. Have the goodness to say "please" and "sir" when you speak to me.

JONES: All right. Would you please, sir, march upstairs?

CLAY *(calmly)*: That is better. *(He bows to the others, then walks off with Jones.)*

MERRYWEATHER: Mr. Holmes, I don't know how my bank can repay you.

HOLMES: I have had several scores to settle with Mr. John Clay. I shall expect the bank to pay my expenses in this case. Otherwise, I have already been well paid by having this adventure.

✦ Scene Eight ✦

Later, Holmes and Watson discuss the case in Holmes's sitting room.

WATSON: Why was the ad placed in the newspaper? And why was Mr. Wilson hired to copy an encyclopedia? It was to get him out of the way for four hours every day. Clay dreamed up the idea of the Redheaded League because his partner and Wilson both have bright red hair.

HOLMES: Exactly. Clay, calling himself Vincent Spaulding, got himself hired by Wilson. We heard that he was working for Wilson for half the usual salary. I knew then that he had a strong reason for taking that job.

WATSON: But how could you guess what that was?

HOLMES: According to Wilson, photography was Spaulding's hobby. He spent many hours in the cellar. I figured he was digging a tunnel to another building. So I went to the pawnshop to ask for some directions.

WATSON: You said you wanted to get a look at Spaulding's—I mean Clay's—trousers.

HOLMES: Right. I saw that the knees of his trousers were worn and dirty. That meant hours of digging. But what was he digging for? We saw that the Bank of London is next to Wilson's shop. That was the answer.

WATSON: How could you tell that they would break in tonight?

HOLMES: Well, they closed the Redheaded League office. That was a sign that they no longer needed Mr. Wilson out of the way. In other words, they had finished their tunnel. Saturday would be the best day to steal the gold. The bank would be closed, and they would have two days to escape. The theft would not have been discovered until Monday.

WATSON: You thought it all out perfectly!

HOLMES: Oh, these little problems keep me from being bored. And this case gave me the added satisfaction of seeing John Clay arrested. Perhaps now there will be a little less evil done in London. ◆

FROM

THE MYSTERIES OF
HARRIS BURDICK

BY

CHRIS VAN ALLSBURG

INTRODUCTION

I first saw the drawings in this book a year ago, in the home of a man named Peter Wenders. Though Mr. Wenders is retired now, he once worked for a children's book publisher, choosing the stories and pictures that would be turned into books.

Thirty years ago a man called at Peter Wenders's office, introducing himself as Harris Burdick. Mr. Burdick explained that he had written fourteen stories and had drawn many pictures for each one. He'd brought with him just one drawing from each story, to see if Wenders liked his work.

Peter Wenders was fascinated by the drawings. He told Burdick he would like to read the stories that went with them as soon as possible. The artist agreed to bring the stories the next morning. He left fourteen drawings with Wenders. But he did not return the next day. Or the day after that. Harris Burdick was never heard from again. Over the years, Wenders tried to find out who Burdick was and what had happened to him, but he discovered nothing. To this day Harris Burdick remains a complete mystery.

His disappearance is not the only mystery left behind. What were the stories that went with these drawings? There are some clues. Burdick had written a title and caption for each picture. When I told Peter Wenders how difficult it was to look at the drawings and their captions without imagining a story, he smiled and left the room. He returned with a dust-covered cardboard box. Inside were dozens of stories, all inspired by the Burdick drawings. They'd been written years ago by Wenders's children and their friends.

I spent the rest of my visit reading these stories. They were remarkable, some bizarre, some funny, some downright scary. In the hope that other children will be inspired by them, the Burdick drawings are reproduced here for the first time.

Chris Van Allsburg
Providence, Rhode Island

ANOTHER PLACE, ANOTHER TIME

If there was an answer, he'd find it there.

THE HOUSE ON MAPLE STREET

It was a perfect lift-off.

THINK ABOUT READING

Answer the questions in the story map.

CHARACTERS

1. Who are the four main characters in the story?

SETTING

2. Where and when does the story take place?

MYSTERY

3. What does Mr. Wilson want Sherlock Holmes to investigate?

4. What is the mystery to be solved?

CLUES

5. What does Holmes find out when he

   a. asks what Spaulding looks like?

   b. visits Spaulding at the pawnshop?

   c. studies the buildings on the street of the pawnshop?

SOLUTION

6. Who is John Clay and what was he planning?

7. What was the Redheaded League, and why did it employ Mr. Wilson?

WRITE A NEWSPAPER ARTICLE

Your next assignment as a news reporter on a large London newspaper is to tell the public about Sherlock Holmes's latest adventure. Write a snappy headline and a short newspaper article about the attempted bank robbery and the arrest of John Clay and his partner. Describe the events by answering the questions: *Who? What? When? Where? Why?* and *How?* Be sure to include Sherlock Holmes's part in the capture of the criminals.

LITERATURE CIRCLE

Everybody loves a good mystery—especially Sherlock Holmes. Discuss what kind of person Holmes is and consider how his character traits help him solve the mystery of the Redheaded League? Why is he such a valued detective? How would he use his detective skills to solve one of Harris Burdick's visual mysteries? List your ideas about Sherlock Holmes on a character web.

AUTHOR
Sir Arthur Conan Doyle

Who is Sir Arthur Conan Doyle? Mystery lovers will tell you that he created the world's best-known detective, Sherlock Holmes. Doyle was born in Edinburgh, Scotland in 1859 and lived until 1930. When his practice as a medical doctor failed, he began writing fiction. In 1887 he introduced the character of Holmes in *A Study in Scarlet*. That popular novel about the London crimestopper changed Sir Arthur Conan Doyle's life. He went on to write a total of 56 short stories and three more novels about Sherlock Holmes.

MORE BOOKS BY
Sir Arthur Conan Doyle

- *The Adventures of Sherlock Holmes*
- *The Hound of the Baskervilles*
- *The Return of Sherlock Holmes*

from

The Case
of the
SECRET MESSAGE

BY SID FLEISCHMAN
ILLUSTRATED BY KEN BARR

Vikki was running.

At this hour of the morning the green strip of park along the river had the look of an outdoor gymnasium. Joggers and runners charged along in broken file. Others leaned against tree trunks to stretch and limber up.

Vikki wanted to get in five miles before going to work. She wore running shorts trimmed in orange and a white T-shirt. In black letters across the back it read:

**BLOODHOUND
DETECTIVE AGENCY**

*Whenever there's trouble,
we're there on the double.*

She maintained a steady long-legged stride. At sixteen, she was taller than most of the boys her age. If she had once felt awkward and self-conscious about it, she now dismissed the matter with a snap of her fingers. She couldn't bother her head with things beyond her control. And she now regarded it as childish to base friendships on feet and inches.

Still, she couldn't help noticing that the boys were beginning to catch up fast. Especially Ricardo, who was a year younger and already as tall as she. The third member of the Bloodhound Gang didn't count. Zach was only ten.

She had tried to get them to run with her, but Ricardo preferred to sleep in. And Zach saw no point in running—unless someone was chasing him.

She had covered almost three miles. Squirrels scattered from her path and birds darted through the trees. A familiar voice broke through the sound of her breathing.

"Hey—Bloodhound!"

She saw Ricardo farther along the path. He had set up his tripod and camera mounted with a telephoto lens.

"Has there been an earthquake?" Vikki shouted.

"No, why?"

"I can't think of anything else that would get you out of bed this early."

"Any sacrifice for my art," Ricardo remarked airily. He too was wearing an office T-shirt, a gift from Mr. Bloodhound to the Bloodhound Gang. "I thought Mr. B. would like a picture of his running billboard."

"Well, I'm not going to break stride to pose."

"Who asked you to? I want an action shot. Keep running. I'll focus on your back."

She passed him by. After a moment she heard the faint clicks of the camera.

She was hardly aware of the shabby woman in old shoes with run-down heels on the path ahead. But quite suddenly a man appeared from behind a tree, as if waiting in ambush. He rushed up behind the old woman.

"Hey!" Vikki yelled.

In a flash the man ripped the old lady's handbag from her grasp and took off. The gray-haired woman set up a wail and tried to run after him.

"Stop! Thief!"

The purse snatcher was cutting across the park toward the street and the early morning traffic. The old lady could do little more than hobble along in her run-down heels.

Vikki turned to shout back at Ricardo. "A purse snatcher! Come on!"

In a matter of seconds Vikki caught up with the woman.

"Bloodhound Detective Agency! We'll catch him!"

She raced across the lawn after the thief. Ricardo gathered up the tripod, threw it against his shoulder, and followed. But the camera equipment slowed him down.

The thief darted through the trees, never looking back. All Vikki could see

of him was faded jeans, a faded blue sweatshirt, and a neck as long and as scrawny as a plucked chicken's.

When he reached the street he barely paused for traffic. Vikki hesitated, waving Ricardo on. Then she crossed and poured on a burst of speed.

The thief sprinted along the empty sidewalk. His ears had turned red as tomatoes. A flat-footed running style, Vikki noticed. He was getting winded.

"Purse snatcher! Stop him!" she yelled out.

He turned his head with a look of surprise that he hadn't shaken her.

Ricardo hadn't crossed the street; he had gained some distance by following the edge of the park.

The purse snatcher ducked down a narrow side street lined with parked cars and trash cans. He looked back again. The long-legged girl was gaining on him. His face was flushed. He hesitated—and then tossed the purse into a trash can.

That stopped Vikki.

"Hey, punk!" she shouted. "Ripping off an old lady—that sure took guts!"

The thief, loping away, tossed back a weary frown. Unheard, a camera shutter tripped open and shut. Ricardo had jammed the tripod in the grass and focused down the narrow street. He had caught the purse snatcher on film.

Vikki dug into the trash can and plucked out the old black handbag. She was glad to see the clasp still closed. The sneak thief hadn't had time to paw through it.

Once again Ricardo gathered up the tripod. He crossed the street and met Vikki at the corner.

"I got him," Ricardo said. "Full face shot."

"Terrific," Vikki gasped. For the first time she realized she was out of breath. "Now, where's the old lady?"

"She was somewhere behind me."

They glanced back across the street to the park. The gray-haired woman, wearing steel-rimmed glasses and a long, shapeless old sweater, was waving to them.

Then a dark limousine pulled up beside her. Two men leaped out the doors, grabbed the woman roughly, and pitched her into the car. The doors slammed, the engine revved up, and the limousine sped away.

Vikki's eyebrows took a leap. "Hey!"

"She's being kidnapped!" exclaimed Ricardo.

"Get the license!"

"Got it."

"Me too."

The license plate read: MR. BIG.

The young detectives returned to the upstairs office of the Bloodhound Detective Agency.

Ricardo called the police and reported everything that had just happened.

Vikki opened the black handbag and shook the contents onto the desk. A plain white envelope fell out.

"What else is there?" Ricardo asked.

"That's all there is," Vikki said.

"Just an envelope? There ought to be some identification."

Vikki nodded. "Ought to be, but isn't." She turned the purse inside out. She felt the sides in the event something was concealed in the lining. Nothing.

Ricardo picked up the envelope. "Blank."

"I can see that. And sealed."

Ricardo held the envelope up to the sunlight streaming through the window. "There's something inside. A letter, I guess."

"Think we ought to open it?" Vikki asked.

"It may be addressed to that old lady."

"There's no stamp. So it wouldn't be exactly as if we were opening someone's mail."

"Right," said Ricardo. Carefully he began to peel open the sealed flap.

At that moment the door opened and Zach came gliding in on his skateboard. He saw that Vikki was in shorts. "What happened? Did your pants shrink up?"

"Wise guy," Vikki said with a distracted air. "Zach, get on the radio. See if you can turn up any information on a Mr. Big."

"Mr. Big? What kind of case are we on?"

"Let's just say it looks like a *big* one."

Zach ambled over to the CB radio, snapped it on, and picked up the microphone. "Breaker one-two, breaker one-two . . ." he said.

Ricardo withdrew a folded sheet of white paper from the envelope. He opened it up.

"Blank, Vikki. Both sides."

For a moment their eyes met in baffled wonder. "It doesn't add up," Vikki said finally. "Why would a woman walk around with nothing in her purse but this? A blank sheet of paper sealed up in a blank envelope?"

"It must add up to something," Ricardo answered. "Why would those guys kidnap a shabby old lady?"

Vikki snapped her fingers. "Maybe it wasn't the old lady they were after. Maybe it was this blank piece of paper."

"Secret writing?"

Vikki nodded. "Secret writing. Must be. I'm going to call Mr. Bloodhound. He knows all about that stuff."

While she dialed the phone, Ricardo snapped on the desk lamp and heated the paper against the light bulb.

Zach's voice droned on. "Breaker one-two. Doesn't anyone have their ears on? This is Private Eye."

A voice erupted from the CB radio. "Go ahead, breaker."

"This is Private Eye looking for an I.D. on a Mr. Big. Any info, you guys? Give me a holler."

Vikki turned from the phone. "Thanks, Mr. Bloodhound. Hang on a minute." She caught Ricardo's attention. "He says if the invisible writing was done with lemon juice, heat will bring it out."

"I know that one," Ricardo replied. "But it's not working. Or this blank paper really *is* blank."

Into the phone Vikki said, "It must not be lemon juice, Mr. Bloodhound. Is there anything else we can try?. . . Salt water? I'll call you back if that doesn't work."

She took the sheet of paper from Ricardo and laid it flat on the desk. Then she pulled open a drawer and chose a pencil. She tested the lead for softness.

"That ought to do it," she declared.

"Do what?"

"Mr. Bloodhound says you can write secret messages with strong salt water. The writing appears when you scribble with a soft pencil."

She laid the pencil point almost on its side and began shading in the left side of the sheet with long strokes.

"See anything?" Ricardo muttered.

"Don't get anxious."

"I *am* anxious."

"I sure hope the police find the old lady," said Vikki, scribbling away.

"We reported it right away, didn't we? They ought to be able to trace the license. Unless it's a phony."

"The purse snatcher was no phony."

"I'll develop the film and hand a print over to the cops. That ought to cure him of grabbing purses. I caught him full face with the telephoto lens."

A ghostly image was beginning to form through the pencil strokes on the paper.

"See that?" asked Vikki. She felt a quick surge of excitement. There *was* a message.

"You've hit it. Keep going."

"It looks like the number ten." Vikki had to stop to sharpen the pencil. Then, hurrying, she shaded in the rest of the page. Faintly, the balance of the secret message appeared.

 Vikki and Ricardo gazed at the coded message.

"Can you make any sense out of it?" she murmured.

"Ten . . . S . . . E . . . Ten . . . S . . . E. Beats me. It's going to take time to break the code, Vikki."

"I'll think about it in the shower. I've got to dash home and change. I won't be long."

Vikki returned in less than half an hour, wearing jeans and a pumpkin-colored turtleneck. Zach was still at the CB radio. And Ricardo was studying the message intensely, as if it were a school test.

"I think I've got part of it," he said, looking up. "Ten . . . S . . . E. It could be a direction. Ten southeast."

Zach turned suddenly from the radio.

"Sounds like Tennessee to me."

"What does?" Vikki asked.

"Ten . . . S . . . E. Tenn-ess-ee."

"Hey—I think you've got it!" Ricardo blurted out. "What took you so long? Sure, Tennessee!"

Vikki looked puzzled. "Tennessee Bay? Is there a place like that around here?"

"Never heard of it," said Ricardo.

Vikki crossed to a wooden cabinet and rummaged around. She withdrew a large rolled-up area map and spread it on the floor. "Let's start looking," she said.

Zach began to take quick notes as a fast-talking voice broke in on the CB. Finally Zach said, "Thanks for the comeback, Invisible Man. This is Private Eye wishing good numbers on you."

He leaped up to face Vikki and Ricardo.

"Got it! Guess who Mr. Big is? A big-time smuggler. Yeah, runs a smuggling ring. Dangerous. His real name is Aces."

"Smuggles what?" Vikki asked.

"Jewels. Stolen stuff, I guess."

"Tennessee Bay," Ricardo said. "Do you suppose—"

The phone rang.

Vikki snapped up the receiver. "Bloodhound Detective Agency," she said hastily. "Whenever there's trouble, we're there on the double. Mr. Bloodhound isn't here. Victoria Allen speaking."

She fell silent, listening, then looked darkly at Ricardo and Zach. Finally, taking a deep breath, she muttered, "Yes, sir. We'll expect you, Mr. Aces." She hung up.

Ricardo and Zach gave her wide-eyed looks.

"Mr. Aces?" Ricardo whispered. "Mr. Big in person?"

"He claims to be that old lady's nephew. He's coming right over. For the purse."

"Gulp," Ricardo said.

Vikki shrugged off a sense of impending danger. "Let's roll up the map and duck it out of sight. We'll seal another piece of paper in the envelope."

The Bloodhound Gang went into action. Zach returned the map to the cabinet. Vikki used office paste to reseal the envelope and stuffed it back inside the purse.

"What'll I do with the real message?" Ricardo asked.

"Just hide it!"

There came a knock at the door. The Bloodhound Gang froze, barely exchanging glances.

"Mr. Big . . ." Vikki whispered.

Ricardo swallowed hard. "He sure got here fast." In a slight panic, he looked for a place to hide the exposed message. Then he crushed it into a ball and poked it into the mouth of a skull yellowed with age

that was sitting among the relics of Mr. Bloodhound's cases.

"Come in," Vikki called out.

The door opened.

The shabby gray-haired woman in run-down heels walked in.

"Ah, there you are, my dear," she said, recognizing Vikki. "What a courageous young lady!"

Vikki was caught almost speechless. "But-but . . ."

"I'm Mrs. Frimple," said the old woman, adjusting her steel-rimmed glasses. "And I see you recovered my purse from that scamp."

"But, Mrs. Frimple, you were kidnapped!" Vikki exclaimed.

"Me? My stars, what gave you that idea?"

"But I saw . . ."

"Who'd want to abduct me? No, no, my dear. Mrs. Frimple is just fine—never better."

She smiled, picked up her purse, and returned to the door.

"Thank you, my dears. All of you."

And she was gone.

Ricardo shook his head in stunned bafflement. "Did you just see what I just saw?"

"She's putting us on," said Vikki, after a moment's thought. "Her story's fishy. She escaped. And she came back for the message."

Zach gave a small whistle. "Wait till she discovers you slipped her a blank piece of paper!"

Mr. Big didn't bother to knock.

He filled the doorway, a stout man with pale blue eyes. His double chins had double chins. He was carrying a gold-handled walking stick. Once through the doorway, he was followed by a bodyguard with a squashed nose and hands in leather gloves.

Mr. Big raised the walking stick like an overweight fencer and pointed at Vikki.

"Let's have it," he growled.

"Have what?" Vikki tried to smile. "Do you have an appointment?"

Mr. Big glanced at his bodyguard. "Knuckles, give 'em my card."

"Which one, boss?"

"Pick any one!"

The bodyguard dug through his pockets and came up with an assortment of business cards. He began shuffling through them. "How about Ace Reducing Saloon?"

"That's 'Salon,' stupid."

The bodyguard kept shuffling through the cards. "Ace Exterminating Company, Ace Jewelry Corporation, Ace Model Airplanes . . ."

"Never mind," Vikki remarked. "You must be Mr. Ace."

"Mr. Aces," the heavy man corrected her. "Hand over the purse."

Vikki was doing her best to play it cool. "How is your aunt?"

"All shook up. Can't leave her room. Come on, kid. I'm in a hurry."

"I'm sorry, Mr. Aces. We don't have the purse."

Mr. Big waved his cane in the air. "Don't give me that! Anything happens on the streets and I get the word. Fast. You got the purse."

"*Had* it," Ricardo put in.

"Mrs. Frimple picked it up about ten minutes ago," said Vikki.

Mr. Big's face reddened with anger. He flashed a hard look at Knuckles.

"You told me the old lady was—"

"These punks are lying, boss."

Mr. Big sliced the air with his walking stick. "Then tear this place apart. Find it!"

The cane swept a shelf, accidentally knocking the skull to the floor. A crumpled piece of paper flew out of its mouth. Mr. Big spied it with his sharp little eyes.

"Well, well, what have we here?"

The Bloodhound Gang held its breath.

"Oh, that," said Ricardo an instant later. "Just trash, sir. We use that old skull for a wastebasket." He bent down to retrieve the wad of paper.

But the tip of Mr. Big's walking stick got there first. Using the cane like a golf club, he putted the ball of paper toward his bodyguard's feet.

"Pick it up, Knuckles."

"Right, boss."

"Now hand it to me."

A moment later Mr. Big had opened the crumpled paper. After a quick look, he stuffed the message in his pocket and peeped at the Bloodhound Gang. The cold blink of his eyelids gave Vikki a quick chill.

Knuckles tugged at his leather gloves. "Want me to take care of 'em, boss?"

Mr. Big shook his head. "Naw—just a bunch of numbers. And a bunch of kids. What do they know? Come on."

He led Knuckles to the door. He stopped and turned for a final look at the Bloodhound Gang.

"Forget about all this, understand? Unless you'd like Knuckles here to fit you for new shoes."

"Shoes?" Zach muttered.

"Cement shoes. Courtesy of Ace Cement Company. And a swim in the river. Courtesy of Ace Funeral Homes. Get it?"

"Got it," Vikki muttered. And then she added with a mocking smile, "Have a nice day."

"Have a nice day?" Ricardo groaned. "His idea of a nice day is to visit the morgue."

"Oh, he's a pussycat," Vikki said, turning to the cabinet.

"A pussycat with claws like meat hooks."

Vikki withdrew the map. "Now, where were we?"

"Didn't you hear what he said?" Zach put in. "He said *forget* it."

"We don't take orders from cheap hoodlums."

"How about expensive ones?" Ricardo remarked. "He's got more businesses than the yellow pages."

"Ah, here it is," Vikki exclaimed, her fingertip on the map. "Tennessee Bay. Looks about thirty miles south of here. Now what were the rest of those numbers?"

"Vikki, I think we ought to turn this case over to Mr. Bloodhound," Zach persisted.

Ricardo gave a defiant shrug. "Naw. *We're* detectives, aren't we? Vikki's right. Let's get on with it. A crook is a crook."

"And a code is a code," Vikki said. "We'll call Mr. Bloodhound when we break it."

"Eight," Ricardo said.

"What?" asked Vikki, as if his mind had begun to wander.

"The next line of the message. It started with an eight."

Vikki snapped her fingers. "Of course. Right. Eight twenty-five."

"Sounds like the time," said Ricardo.

Vikki sat at the desk and picked up a pencil. "But it had a slant in the middle. Like this." On a pad she wrote:

8/25

"Got it!" Ricardo exclaimed. "That's the way you write a date."

"Eight twenty-five." Vikki looked up. "Hey—that's today's date. August twenty-fifth."

Ricardo smiled. "That explains it."

"Explains *what*?" asked Zach.

"Why Mrs. Frimple and Mr. Big were in such a hurry to lay their hands on the message. Some crime is going to happen—today."

Vikki gave a quick nod and held the pencil poised over the note pad. She searched her memory for the last set of numbers in the message.

"Got it," she muttered, and jotted down four numbers.

1930

"Nineteen-thirty," Ricardo said, reading the pad upside down. "If that's the year, the crime was committed more than fifty years ago. Doesn't make sense."

Vikki leaned back in the desk chair. "It can't be the year. Let's think it through. If you were planning a crime, and sending a message, what would you write? The place . . ."

"We've got that," said Ricardo.

"The day . . ."

"We've got that."

"The hour . . ."

"That we *don't* have," Ricardo declared.

"Boy, are you guys dumb!" Zach joined in. "That's the way they tell time on ships and stuff."

"What is?" asked Vikki.

"With numbers like nineteen-thirty."

"Great, Zach. But what time does it make?"

Zach began to enjoy being one-up on Vikki and Ricardo. "You don't start over again at noon. One o'clock is thirteen hundred hours. Two o'clock is fourteen hundred hours. And so on."

Ricardo picked up on the system. "Then you subtract twelve noon from nineteen-thirty—"

"And get seven-thirty. Seven-thirty *tonight*."

She grabbed the phone and dialed. After a moment she said, "Hello, Mrs. Bloodhound. We're onto a case that might interest Mr. Bloodhound. What? . . . Oh . . . Well, never mind. We can handle it. No, there's no danger. But we're going to have to raid the office petty-cash box for bus fare."

All eyes were on her as Vikki hung up. She gave Ricardo and Zach an unruffled smile. "Mr. B. had to catch a plane. Looks like we're on our own."

Ricardo winked reassuringly, inflated his cheeks, and mimicked Mr. Big.

"A bunch of kids. What do they know?"

"What we don't know is exactly what's going to happen tonight," said Vikki.

Zach mused aloud. "Ships . . ."

"And smuggling," Ricardo added.

"Must be it," Vikki nodded. "At Tennessee Bay!"

It was late afternoon when the Bloodhound Gang boarded a southbound bus out of the central station.

By then Ricardo had developed the roll of film shot that morning in the park. He had brought along the prints, still slightly damp, and passed them around.

"Check out this shot of the back of your T-shirt."

"Right on. The letters are razor sharp."

"But look, Vikki. You can make out Mrs. Frimple ahead of you on the path. Of course, she's a little out of focus."

Vikki studied the picture carefully. "I'd say she's out of focus in more ways than one. She's not one of your run-of-the-mill little old ladies. Escaped from Mr. Big's goons like a regular Houdini. And then tried to make us believe she'd never been kidnapped at all."

"Yeah, she's mixed up in this caper somehow."

Then Ricardo handed over a close-up of the purse snatcher. "How's that for a mug shot?"

"The police will love it," Vikki replied. "Look at all those gaps between his teeth. Like a picket fence. He's practically behind bars."

"What time is it?" Zach asked.

Vikki glanced at her watch and did a moment's figuring. "Almost sixteen-thirty hours."

"We're going to be awfully early."

"That's the idea," said Vikki. "To get there long before Mr. Big, settle in, and wait."

Ricardo, burdened with his camera bag, nodded. "He's bound to be careful not to be followed. But we'll be way ahead of him."

The city receded block by block, and after a while the bus began working its way through the beach towns. Zach, who had never been this way before, kept shifting his gaze from the side windows to the broader back windows. That way, the sights didn't zip by so quickly.

"Ricardo," Vikki said, "think you'll have enough light to grab pictures of whatever is going to happen?"

"Plenty. If the smugglers are on time. But just in case, I loaded the camera with fast film."

Zach shifted his eyes from the rear window. "You know how in movies someone jumps in a taxi and says 'Follow that car'?"

"Yeah," Ricardo answered with complete disinterest.

"Have you ever heard anyone say 'Follow that bus'?"

"What are you talking about?"

"There's a tan car tailing this bus."

Vikki and Ricardo spun around to peer out through the back window.

"See it?" Zach asked. "Following about a block behind. I think it's been trailing along ever since we left town."

"Looks like two people in the front seat," Vikki said. "Can you make them out? Wish we had binoculars."

"We don't need binoculars." Quickly Ricardo dug the camera out of his bag and set about changing lenses.

"What are you doing?" Vikki asked.

"Putting the telephoto back on. I can zoom them up almost close enough to touch."

He aimed the camera through the window and carefully turned the barrel of the lens. Then he stopped, squinting through the viewer with one eye. He let out a slow whistle.

"Do we know them?" Vikki asked.

"The man at the wheel—never saw him before. But guess who's sitting beside him?"

"Let's skip the guessing games, Ricky," Vikki said. "Who?"

"Yup. There she is, all right. In perfect focus."

"*Who*?"

"Mrs. Frimple."

 Ricardo arched an eyebrow. "How are we going to give her the slip in broad daylight?"

The bus made another stop to let passengers off and on.

"Maybe we can fake her out," Vikki said, rising. "Come on. We'll walk down the aisle as if we were getting off."

The Bloodhound Gang rose, but partway down the aisle Vikki motioned to duck down and keep out of sight. Scurrying like crabs, the three detectives returned to the back-seat area. The other passengers turned their heads, but Vikki couldn't concern herself with their puzzled stares.

The Bloodhound Gang remained slumped out of sight from the rear window through several more stops. At one point the bus driver motioned a car to pass on the narrow road. Vikki dug out her pocket mirror and caught a glimpse of the car.

"Tan car?" Zach asked.

"You guessed it," Vikki answered. "They must be checking the passengers for us as they drive past the bus. Stay down. They'll be turning back if they figure we managed to slip out at an earlier stop."

It was almost half an hour before the bus approached Tennessee Bay. Ricardo rose slowly and risked a backward glance.

"All clear." He smiled. "Vikki, we sure gave them a lot of busywork. Now they're doubling back on our trail."

Vikki replied with a playful smile, "Why, I just feel terrible about it!"

The Bloodhound Gang straightened up. The bus was slowing. A road sign announced:

TENNESSEE BAY CITY
Population 47

"A regular boom town," Ricardo said.

The bus pulled into the city—a gas station, a grocery store, a café, and a shack with a "For Rent" sign in the window.

No one got off the bus—except the Bloodhound Gang.

The bay was a mud flat about a mile across. It had an abandoned look, as if the tide had gone out and forgotten to come back.

The Bloodhound Gang scouted along a dirt road and then cut off into a patch of tall, dry grass to hide. And wait.

Peering through the telephoto lens, Ricardo began studying the mud flat and the ocean beyond.

"What time is it?" Zach asked. "I'm getting hungry."

Vikki checked her watch. "It's . . . seventeen-twenty hours."

"We should have stopped in that café for something to eat," Zach said.

"That's about the first place Mrs. Frimple would ask about us."

Ricardo lowered the camera. "Vikki, I think we're in the wrong place."

"You like the grass over there better?"

"This bay is so shallow, you'd have to dig to find water. Smugglers couldn't even get a rowboat across."

Vikki shook her head. "This has *got* to be the right place."

Twenty minutes later they suddenly heard a rustling in the weeds behind them.

"Looks cozy," came a voice. "Is there room for one more? And anyone hungry?"

The voice was young and joyous. The figure was old and familiar.

"Mrs. Frimple," Vikki gasped.

"Not exactly." The woman set down a wooden box and a grocery bag. Then she whipped off a gray wig and shook out her own honey-colored hair. She pulled off the steel-rimmed glasses and unbuttoned the shabby sweater to reveal a police badge.

"Police Detective Monroe," she declared, and smiled. "How do I look?"

"Fifty years younger," said Vikki.

"How'd you find us?" Zach blurted out.

"My partner and I figured you'd spotted us. So we drove on ahead.

I took the wheel and he got out and caught the bus. He saw you get off here at Tennessee Bay. Once you were out of sight, he left the bus too—and then flagged me down. I'd have been here sooner, but I stopped to have some sandwiches made up. You have your choice of ham and cheese, tuna fish, peanut butter, or egg salad."

"Peanut butter," Zach said quickly, while there was still a choice.

"But why were you shadowing us?" Ricardo exclaimed.

The police officer grinned. "If you were clever enough to switch the message, I figured you'd be clever enough to lead us to the secret location."

"How did you happen to have the message in the first place?" Vikki asked.

"I worked myself into Mr. Big's organization. Undercover. I got lucky and was able to intercept the message. Somehow they got wise and came after me. That's when the creep in the park snatched my purse. But you came along in the nick of time."

"Speaking of the creep," Ricardo said, "here's a picture of him."

Detective Monroe glanced at the photograph and her eyes lit up. "Rembrandt couldn't have done better. Terrific. We'll pick him up right away."

"But why did you come to the office and deny you'd been kid-napped?" Vikki asked.

"For your own good. I thought once I had the message back, you'd be better off out of the case. But when the message you slipped me turned up blank, I knew you'd broken the code. And I practically ran into Mr. Big as I left your building. So I knew you were in danger. It was then my partner and I decided to keep an eye on you."

"How did you escape from his goons?" Zach put in.

Detective Monroe laughed. "Who expects judo chops from a little old lady?"

"Seems like you should have shadowed Mr. Big instead of us," Ricardo said.

"Oh, we've tried that. A man like Mr. Big grows eyes in the back of his head. Every time we put a tail on him, he leads us on a wild-goose chase. But we've got a chance to catch him red-handed this time. My partner is staked out up the road. What time is the boat due?"

"In a couple of hours . . . seven-thirty—I mean, nineteen-thirty hours," Ricardo replied. "But look at that mud. No boat could get through that."

"Just the sort of spot these smugglers always pick out. We've known for some time that Mr. Big's interest in model airplanes is just a front. His Ace Model Airplane shop always has a 'Closed' sign on it." She pointed to the wooden box she'd carried into the grass. "Exactly why I brought that along. Now, let's eat."

The waiting was over.

At 1923 hours a fishing boat nosed into view outside the bay.

"It's dropping anchor," Ricardo said, zooming the camera lens in on it.

"Can you make out its name?" Detective Monroe asked.

Ricardo squinted at the lettering along the bow. He snapped a picture and rewound the camera. *The Flying Ace.*

"Mr. Big has more aces up his sleeve than a cardsharp," said Detective Monroe, opening up the wooden case. "We'd like any film you shoot. It'll look good in court."

She withdrew a set of earphones from her bag. The box she had brought contained a radio receiver and transmitter.

Moments later Zach exclaimed, "Hey—listen!"

A distant whine floated in the air, sounding like an angry hornet approaching from the sea.

It was exactly 1930 hours.

Quickly the whine became a popping roar as it drew nearer.

"It's coming in over the mud flat," Vikki exclaimed. "Over there! I can see it."

"So can I," said Ricardo, trying to focus his camera. "A model airplane . . . with a gas-powered motor."

"And radio-controlled," added Detective Monroe, slipping on the earphones. "Now all I've got to do is find the radio frequency they're using to guide the plane."

"It's landing at the other end of the bay," Zach declared, pointing through the grass.

"Here comes another one!" said Ricardo, panning his camera back toward the fishing boat.

Detective Monroe, rotating the dials on the receiver, broke into a sudden smile. "Got their frequency. Now to beam our own signal."

She set the dials on the transmitter. "Can you see that second plane?"

"I'm right on it," Ricardo answered, peering through the camera.

"Anything happening?"

Ricardo was hardly breathing. Then he said, "It's turning this way. Coming right for us!"

"Terrific." The police officer was smiling. "Now it's following *our* radio signal."

"And coming in for a landing!" Zach added.

The model airplane roared in low over the mud flat and touched down roughly. It bounced along the ground and disappeared into a clump of grass.

The Bloodhound Gang and Detective Monroe left their hiding place and chased down the plane. It seemed to have disappeared. The motor had stalled out.

Zach dove through the grass and reappeared with the model plane in his hand.

"It's a B-52," he said.

"Never mind what it is," Vikki declared. "Is there something in it?"

"There must be," said Detective Monroe. "Smuggled goods launched from the fishing boat out there. I'll radio the Coast Guard as soon as we know what we've got."

"What we've got," said Vikki, discovering a silk pouch taped inside the plane's cargo hatch, "is something very small." She opened the pouch and poured the contents into her hand for all to see. "Diamonds."

A dark limousine came crashing through the weeds and screeched to a halt. The doors flew open, and out jumped Knuckles. He spread his big hands out like claws.

"Don't move!" he commanded.

Then Mr. Big appeared through the cloud of dust raised by the car's sudden stop. He planted his feet far apart and smiled.

"Hijacking model airplanes," he said, "Tsk tsk, tsk."

And Detective Monroe replied,
"Smuggling diamonds. Tsk, tsk, tsk.
Sir, you are under arrest."

Mr. Big laughed. "Says who?"

Another figure took shape through the
dust, a solidly built man who dropped
Knuckles with a karate chop.

"Says me," he said. "Detective
Flint. And now for a little police
jewelry. Hands behind your back,
Mr. Big, unless you want to hear
bird song like your pal Knuckles."

By 1944 hours the two criminals
were fitted out with gleaming police
jewelry—handcuffs.

"Thanks for the assist, Bloodhound
Gang," said Detective Monroe. "Good
work. Super. Terrific. I'd say everything came up... Aces."

MENTOR

Lilly Gallman

INKED PRINT

Forensic Chemist

This chemist uses science to solve crimes.

When investigators are called to the scene of the crime, the search for clues begins right away. But they can't analyze the evidence by themselves. They rely on the help of experts with the scientific knowledge to tell them what each clue means. That's where a forensic chemist like Lilly Gallman comes in. Gallman knows how to turn clues into solutions!

PROFILE

Name: Lilly Gallman

Home: Columbia, South Carolina

Occupation: forensic chemist (a scientist who helps solve crimes)

Education: college degree in biology; special studies in crime detection with the Federal Bureau of Investigation (FBI)

First investigative job: genetic researcher for the University of South Carolina

Favorite TV detective: Columbo

QUESTIONS
for Lilly Gallman

Find out how forensic chemist Lilly Gallman helps take a bite out of crime!

Q How do you get involved with a case?

A When police are called to investigate a crime scene, they'll contact me. Sometimes I get called at four in the morning and don't get home until the next day.

Q What's the first thing you do at a crime scene?

A I examine the area carefully to see if the suspect left any physical evidence. If so, we can use that evidence to link the suspect with the crime.

Q What kinds of things do you look for?

A Footprints, clothing fibers, strands of hair, fingerprints—things like that.

Q What happens then?

A We take the clues back to the lab and analyze them. I send stray hairs and fibers to be analyzed under an electron microscope.

If the police arrest a suspect, I go to the police station. Sometimes I need to interview the suspect about the crime. Sometimes I take the suspect's shoes or clothing. I make plaster casts of the shoes to see if they match footprints left at the crime scene. I find out if fibers from the suspect's clothing match fibers at the crime scene.

Does your job end there?

No. After I'm done examining the clues, I've got to write up a report for the investigating officer on the case. The officer will meet with me to discuss the report, and later on I may be called on to testify in court.

Is your job really like what we see on TV?

Not really. The so-called forensic people on TV often use methods that don't really work. Further, they usually pick up important clues in a matter of seconds. It rarely happens that way. It sometimes takes hours to find good clues at the scene of the crime.

What was the best clue you ever found?

We had a burglar who left his wallet at the scene of the crime. The wallet had his driver's license in it, so we got him immediately. We couldn't ask for a better clue than that!

Lilly Gallman's Tips
for Young Problem Solvers

1 Be a careful observer. Keep an eye out for the unusual.

2 Think logically. Be aware of causes and effects.

3 Be patient. Take the time to thoroughly think through problems and puzzles.

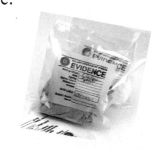

Think About Reading

Answer the questions in the story map.

BEGINNING

1. Why are Vikki and Ricardo worried about the woman whose purse was stolen?

2. What does the Bloodhound Gang find on the paper in the stolen purse, and what does it mean?

3. What does the Bloodhound Gang discover about Mr. Big?

MIDDLE

4. Which two characters come to claim the purse? What happens when each arrives?

5. Where does the Bloodhound Gang go on the bus?

6. What do they discover about the old lady who is following them?

ENDING

7. What does the Bloodhound Gang find in the model airplane that lands near Tennessee Bay?

8. What happens when Mr. Big arrives?

Write a Character Sketch

Mr. Big is on the loose again! As a member of the Bloodhound Gang, your task is to write a description of this criminal that you can send to other detective and police agencies. Include specific details about his appearance and personality that tell about the way he looks, acts, and talks.

Literature Circle

Suppose the Bloodhound Gang and Detective Monroe could meet Lilly Gallman. What do you think they would talk about? What kinds of questions would the Bloodhound Gang ask the forensic chemist? How could she be helpful to them? Which parts of the case of the secret message would Lilly Gallman find interesting? Record your ideas on a chart.

AUTHOR

Sid Fleischman

Sid Fleischman always has a few tricks up his sleeve when he's writing a mystery novel. It makes perfect sense, because he was once a professional magician in a traveling vaudeville show. Many of Fleischman's novels—like Newbery award winner *The Whipping Boy*—contain mysterious twists and turns that keep the reader guessing. Fleischman also likes to write books in a series. He has written five novels about the Bloodhound Gang.

MORE BOOKS BY

Sid Fleischman

- *The Abracadabra Kid: A Writer's Life*

- *By the Great Horn Spoon*

- *Here Comes McBroom!: Three Tall Tales*

How to
Write a Mini-Mystery

Almost everyone loves to solve a mystery, at least when it's contained between the covers of a book. Mystery stories, long or short, allow armchair detectives to match wits with fiction's sharpest sleuths and sneakiest villains.

What is a mini-mystery? A mini-mystery is a mystery story that is just a few short paragraphs or pages long. Like every mystery, it includes a problem or question, clues, and a solution. Unlike most longer mysteries, a mini-mystery is often built around one main clue.

Here's the problem—how to prove that Tilford's scheme is a scam.

This seemingly ordinary statement contains the main clue.

Additional clues are given to wrap up the mystery.

The Case of the Buried Treasure

"From the gleam in your eye, I deduce you are about to get rich quick," said Dr. Haledjian.

"Clever of you, old chap," said Bertie Tilford, a young Englishman with a superiority complex toward work. "If I had a mere ten thousand I should realize a fortune! Have you ten?"

"What's the game now?" demanded Haledjian. "Pieces of eight among the corals? Doubloons from Kidd's chest?"

Bertie opened a sack and triumphantly produced a shining silver candlestick. "Sterling silver," he said. "See what's engraved on the bottom."

Haledjian upended the candlestick and read the name Lady North. "Wasn't that the ship that sank in 1956?"

"The Lady North sank, but not with all hands as is generally believed," replied Bertie. "Four men got away with a fortune in loot before the ship capsized in the storm. They hid their loot in a cave," continued Bertie. "But the storm started an avalanche and sealed off the entrance, burying three of the sailors inside. The fourth, a chap named Pembroot, escaped. Pembroot's been trying to raise ten thousand to buy the land on which the cave is located."

"You put up the money, the cave is opened, and the loot is divided two ways instead of four. Enchanting," said Haledjian. "Only how do you know Pembroot isn't a swindler?"

"Earlier tonight he took me to the cave," said Bertie. "This sack was half buried in the bushes, and I nearly sprained my ankle on it. I took one look and brought the candlestick here nonstop. You've got to agree it's the real thing, old chap."

"It is," admitted Haledjian. "And there's no doubt that Pembroot planted it by the cave for your benefit. How did Haledjian know?

An "expert" or detective, such as Haledjian, is a common character in mini-mysteries.

Here's the solution!

If the silver candlestick had been lying in a sack since 1956, it would have been tarnished, not "shining."

165

1 Brainstorm a Main Clue

In the mini-mystery you just read, the most important clue lies in the description of the candlestick. Before you begin to write your mini-mystery, you should come up with a main clue.

TOOLS

- Paper and pencil
- Art supplies (optional)

Your clue should be a story detail that couldn't really have happened or couldn't really be true, for example, a bogus "cave-painting" that shows people hunting dinosaurs. The painting couldn't be authentic because dinosaurs became extinct before people existed.

2 Create Characters

Now that you've come up with a main clue, you can decide what sort of characters will be involved in your mystery. You'll probably want to create at least two characters. One, like Tilford, will stumble onto or uncover the mystery, and the other, like Haledjian, will solve it. Their identities will probably be related to the main clue. For example, if your clue is about a phony "rare" coin, your characters might be a coin collector or dealer and a quick-thinking expert in rare coins.

Tip Your mystery will be easier to write if you avoid creating too many characters. As your story progresses, write out any characters who are not important to the plot.

3 Outline Your Plot

It's time to incorporate your characters and your clue into a mystery story. Remember that your clue should lead to the solution to a question or problem. For example, perhaps the coin collector from Step 2 wants to buy a rare coin but suspects it's a fake. His or her problem is how to tell whether the coin is authentic. A main clue—some type of information about rare coins—will lead to the answer. Write a plot outline briefly describing the main events of your mini-mystery. In your outline, you should note the following:

- the mystery problem or question
- who encounters the problem/question
- the main clue
- how the main clue is revealed or discovered
- any additional clues
- who solves the mystery

4 Write Your Mini-Mystery

By now, you should be ready to write a mini-mystery! Use your plot outline as a guide. Write up your mystery, filling in all the details that go with each event on the outline. When you're done with your first draft, check your work carefully. Make sure that your mystery "works." Does the solution really solve the mystery? Does the clue really lead to the solution? Make any necessary revisions or corrections. When your work is complete, swap mysteries with a classmate. Try to solve each other's!

If You Are Using a Computer ...

Draft your mini-mystery in the Newsletter format on your computer. Write an intriguing headline to draw your readers into the mystery.

THINK

How can asking the right questions help you become a better problem solver?

Lilly Gallman
Forensic Chemist ▶

FROM
THE
SECRETS
OF
VESUVIUS

By Sara C. Bisel

When Mount Vesuvius erupted almost 2,000 years ago, it poured volcanic ash and boiling mud down upon the Roman town of Herculaneum. By the time the fiery avalanche had cooled, thousands of townspeople and many of the buildings lay preserved beneath sixty-five feet of hardened lava.

For years, archaeologists have been excavating the ruins of Herculaneum in search of artifacts that would tell them more about ancient Roman civilization. Then in 1982 they made a crucial discovery—a group of skeletons was found on a beach at the foot of the town. They quickly called in Dr. Sara Bisel, "The Bone Lady." Dr. Bisel began to examine the skeletons for clues about the lives of the inhabitants of Herculaneum. In this excerpt from her book, her findings bring to life the story of that fateful day in A.D. 79, when Mount Vesuvius stopped history dead in its tracks.

The People on the Beach

Herculaneum, June 1982

It was quiet on Herculaneum's ancient beach. Above my head, drying sheets and underwear fluttered from the apartment balconies that now overlook the ruins.

Today this beach is just a narrow dirt corridor that lies several feet below sea level. But thousands of years ago, the waves of the Mediterranean would have lapped where I now stood, and my ears would have been filled with the gentle sound of the surf, rather than the dull roar of Ercolano's midday traffic.

To one side of me stood the arched entryways of the boat chambers, most of them still plugged by volcanic rock, their secrets locked inside. Only one chamber had been opened so far, and its contents were now hidden behind a padlocked plywood door.

I eyed the wooden door longingly, wishing for a sudden gift of X-ray vision. Dr. Maggi, the keeper of the key, had been called away to a meeting with some government officials, and would not be back until sometime in the afternoon.

"*Dottoressa!*"

Ciro was calling me from farther down the old beach. He was waving me toward a roped-off area surrounding three ordinary-looking piles of dirt.

I have examined thousands of skeletons in my life, but seeing each one for the first time still fills me with a kind of awe. As I walked over to the mound that Ciro was pointing at, I knew I was about to meet my first Herculanean.

It didn't look like much at first—just a heap of dirt with bits of bone poking out. I knelt down and gently scraped earth off the skeleton, exposing it to the light for the first time in two thousand years. Although the skeleton was

badly broken, I had a hunch that it might be female, but I was puzzled by the position of her bones. Her thigh was poking out grotesquely beside a section of skull. It almost looked as if the bones had been carelessly tossed there, they were so broken and tangled.

Then I realized that something dreadful had happened to this woman, and that she had met with a violent death of some kind. Her skull was shattered, her pelvis crushed, and her leg had been thrust up to her neck. Roof tiles were trapped beneath her.

I looked up. Above me was the open terrace where Herculaneans had held sacred ceremonies. Above that was the wall of the town itself, most of the surrounding balustrade now missing.

Had this woman fallen from the wall above? Had some huge force propelled her from the town, perhaps a piece of flying debris, or the blast from the volcano itself, so that she smashed face down onto the ground? What had she been doing on the wall in the first place? Calling down to the people on the beach for help?

Above: The beachfront, the ruins of Herculaneum and Vesuvius as they look today.

I picked up one of the bones and felt its cool smoothness in my hands. Because this was the first Herculanean I got to know, this skeleton was extra special to me. I named her Portia.

By measuring the bones, I could tell that Portia was about 5 feet 1 inch (155 centimeters) tall. She was about forty-eight when she died—an old woman by Roman standards—and had buck teeth.

Later, after a chemical analysis, we learned that Portia also had very high levels of lead in her bones. Lead is a poison, but in Roman times it was a common substance. It was used in makeup, medicines, paint pigment, pottery glazes, and to line drinking cups and plates.

On either side of Portia was a skeleton. One was another female. She lay on her side, almost looking as if she had died in her sleep. As I brushed dirt from her left hand, something shiny caught my eye as it glinted in the sunlight. It was a gold ring.

When we uncovered the rest of the hand, we found a second ring. And in a clump on her hip we found two intricate snakes' head bracelets made of pure gold, a pair of earrings that may have held pearls, and some coins (the cloth purse that had probably once held these valuables had long since rotted away).

We ended up calling her the Ring Lady. She was about forty-five when she died. She was not terribly good-looking; her jaw was large and protruding. There were no cavities in her teeth, but she did have gum disease, which left tiny pits in the bone along her gum line. If she had lived today, her dentist probably would have advised her to floss more often!

Right: I carefully place each bone in a plastic vegetable crate to be transported to my laboratory.

We called this skeleton the Ring Lady because of the two gold rings she wears on her left hand. We also found two bracelets, a pair of earrings and some coins by her side.

In fact, most of the Herculaneans I examined had very good teeth, with only about three cavities each. Today, many of us have about sixteen cavities each, in spite of all our fluoride treatments, regular dental checkups and constant nagging to floss and brush! But the Romans had no sugar in their diet. They used honey, but not much, because it was expensive. Instead, the Herculaneans ate a well-balanced diet, including much seafood, which is rich in fluoride. Not only that, but they had strong jaws from chewing and tearing food without using knives and forks. And they did clean their teeth, scrubbing them with the stringy end of a stick rather than using a brush and toothpaste.

On the other side of Portia we dug up the skeleton we called the Soldier. He was found lying face down, his hands outstretched, his sword still in his belt. We found carpenter's tools with him, which had perhaps been slung over his back. (Roman soldiers often worked on building projects when they were between wars.) He also had a money belt containing three gold coins. He was quite tall for a Roman, about 5 feet 8 inches (173 centimeters).

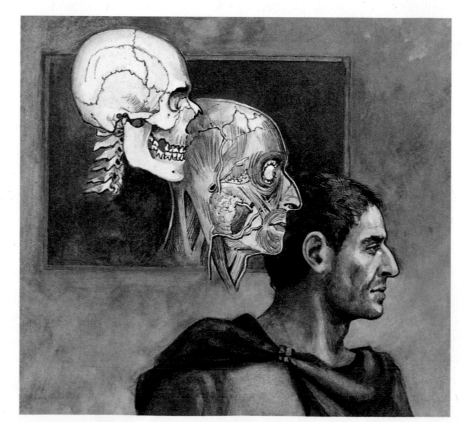

Right: When I examine a skull closely, I can usually tell what kind of features a person had. The soldier's skull, for example, shows that he had a large nose. By "clothing" the skull with muscles and nerves, we can show what the soldier might have looked like.

Left: We found these coins in the soldier's money belt. One of them has the head of the Emperor Nero on it.

When I examined the man's skull, I could see that he was missing six teeth, including three at the front, and that he'd had a huge nose. And when I examined the bone of his left thigh, I could see a lump where a wound had penetrated the bone and caused a blood clot that eventually had hardened. Near the knee, where the muscle would have been attached, the bone was enlarged slightly. This indicated that he would have had well-developed thighs, possibly due to gripping the sides of a horse with the knees while riding (Romans didn't use saddles).

Had the soldier lost those front teeth in a fight, I wondered. Had he been wounded in the leg during the same fight or another one? His life must have been fairly rough and tumble.

While members of the excavation team poured buckets of water on the three skeletons to loosen the debris, I continued to scrape off the dirt and volcanic matter with a trowel. Later, in the laboratory, each bone and tooth would be washed with a soft brush. Then they would be left to dry before being dipped in an acrylic solution to preserve them. Finally, each bone would be measured, then measured again to prevent errors, and the figures would be carefully recorded.

By late afternoon my back and knees were stiff from crouching, and the back of my neck was tight with the beginning of a sunburn.

I stood up and stretched. There was still much to do before the three skeletons would be free of their volcanic straitjackets. I started to think about heading back to the hotel for a shower and bite to eat. But a flurry of activity down the beach caught my eye, and suddenly I no longer felt tired.

To my right, Dr. Maggi stood outside the locked wooden door I had seen earlier. He was unbolting the padlock. When he saw me, he waved. I put down my trowel, wiped my hands on my jeans and hurried over. Inside, I knew, was the only group of Roman skeletons that had ever been found—the twelve people who had huddled in the shelter and died together when the volcanic avalanches poured down the mountainside into the sea.

I could hear an odd echo from inside the chamber as Dr. Maggi clicked the padlock open. Behind me, a number of the crew members had gathered. We were all very quiet.

The plywood door seemed flimsy as Dr. Maggi pulled it open. From inside the chamber came the dank smell of damp earth.

A shiver crept up my neck. We were opening a 2,000-year-old grave. What would we find?

As I entered the cave-like boat chamber, I could barely see, even though the sun flooded through the door. Someone handed me a flashlight, but its light cast green-ish shadows, making it feel even more spooky.

The light played over the back of the shelter, no bigger than a single garage and still crusted over with volcanic rock. I saw an oddly shaped, lumpy mound halfway back. I took several steps into the chamber and pointed the light at the mound.

The narrow beam found a skull, the pale face a grimace of death. As my eyes grew accustomed to the dim light, I soon realized there were bones and skulls everywhere. They were all tangled together—clinging to each other for comfort in their final moments—and it was hard to distinguish one from another. But I knew that twelve skeletons had been found in all—three men, four women and five children. One child had an iron house key near him. Did he think he would be going back home?

I took another step into the cave. At my feet was a skeleton that was almost entirely uncovered. From the pelvis I could see it was a female, a girl, lying face down. Beneath her, we could just see the top of another small skull.

It was a baby.

I knelt down and gently touched the tiny skull. My throat felt tight as I thought about this girl, this baby,

One of our most moving finds was the skeleton of a young slave girl cradling the tiny skull of a baby (*above*). With these two skeletons, the tragedy of that terrible day in A.D. 79 became very real to us.

and what it must have been like for them in this dark cave in the moments before they died.

"*Una madre col suo bambino,*" whispered Ciro behind me.

"I don't think they're a mother and baby," I said. I could see from the pelvis that the girl was not old enough to have had children. I pointed to my own stomach and outlined a beachball tummy with my arms while I shook my head.

"This girl has never given birth."

"*Allora, è la sorella?*"

I frowned, pulled my Italian-English dictionary out of the back pocket of my jeans and flipped through it. I realized Ciro thought these two skeletons belonged to a baby and its older sister.

"We'll see," I murmured. I knew it was important not to jump to conclusions.

You have to question everything about bones, especially ones that have been lying around for two thousand years. I've known cases where people thought bone damage was caused by joint disease, when it was in fact caused by rats gnawing at the dead body.

I struggled to free a bronze cupid pin and two little bells from the baby's bones. Whoever the child was, it had been rich enough to wear expensive ornaments. But I knew it would take many more hours of careful study before we knew the real story behind these two skeletons.

Later, in the laboratory, I gained enough information to put together a more likely background for the skeleton of the young girl.

Unlike the baby, she had not come from a wealthy family. She had been about fourteen, and from the shape of her skull I knew she had probably been pretty. When I examined her teeth I could tell that she had been starved or quite ill for a

WHAT BONES TELL US

The human skeleton contains about two hundred bones. Bones are rigid because they contain calcium — the same substance that is in eggshells and teeth. While you are alive, your bones are alive, too. Blood runs through them, they have their own nerves, and they grow and change shape and absorb chemicals, just like the rest of your body.

Once a body is dead, after the clothes and flesh have rotted away, the hard skeleton still holds many clues as to what the person was like when he or she was alive.

By "reading" and analyzing a skeleton, scientists can discover the person's sex, race and height. We can see approximately how old a person was at death, and approximately how many children a woman had. By looking at the way people's bones and teeth are formed, we can also tell whether they had certain diseases, or whether they had been starved or sick as children. If we grind up a small piece of bone and put it in a chemical solution, we can analyze the solution in a laboratory and find out what minerals have been absorbed by the bone, which can tell us what kind of food the person ate.

Muscles are attached to bones. When muscles are used frequently, they become bigger and pull on the places where they are attached. The bones will change

Who Were the People on the Beach?

The illustration *(above)* shows how the ancient seawall looks today. Altogether, we excavated over one hundred skeletons from the beach and boat chambers.

1. The Ring Lady
2. Portia
3. The Soldier
4. Coin box
5. Chamber with 26 skeletons inside
6. Chamber with 40 skeletons inside, including one of a horse
7. Petronia's chamber, with 12 skeletons inside
8. The boat
9. A slave, perhaps a fisherman

Above: Sometimes it can take as long as four days to glue a skull back together.

Left: Among the ruins archaeologists found these unusual glass beads with tiny faces on them.

181

MYSTERY OF THE CLIFF

An ancient people lived high in the cliffs... then

STEP RIGHT UP
On a wooden ladder Kathrine Warren, 10, of Durango, Colorado, climbs between levels of ancient ruins at Mesa Verde National Park, Colorado.

DWELLERS

disappeared. Or did they?

MYSTERY SURROUNDS the ancestral Pueblo people. It swirls around them like the dry wind of the high country where they lived. Why did they build their homes in the cliffs? Why did they abandon those homes? And who were they, really? Even their name is a mystery. The Navajo called them Anasazi, which means ancient ones. Today Pueblo Indians call them their Pueblo ancestors. No one knows what they called themselves.

A group of these ancient people settled at what is now **Mesa Verde**, in **Colorado**, about A.D. 550. At first they dug pit houses in the mesa, or flattopped hill. Around the year 1200, they began moving off the top of the mesa and into high-altitude dwellings they built of stone and mud under the cliff ledges. No one knows why they made this move. It may have been to cultivate more farmland. Some archaeologists think they moved for protection.

"The cliff dwellings seem safe to me," says Kathrine Warren, 10, of Durango, Colorado. "People could climb up and pull the ladders behind them so their enemies couldn't get to them."

Kathrine visited the ruins of Cliff Palace, one of the cliff dwellings, with Leighana Sisneros and Landon Wigton, both 10 and from Durango. "It would have been neat to be an Anasazi kid," Leighana says. "But," Kathrine observes, "you wouldn't have had things like lightbulbs, and I would have missed reading books." Landon adds, "There weren't any grocery stores." But the ancestral

CLIFF HANGER
Tucked beneath a towering ledge at Mesa Verde, Colorado, are the ruins of 240 ancient rooms at the site called Cliff Palace (above). Cliff dwellings here rise 2,000 feet above the valley floor.

Pueblo people didn't need grocery stores. They grew most of their own food. The men planted corn, squash, and beans on top of the mesa. They conserved water in the dry climate by building dams and reservoirs. The women ground the corn on *metates* (meh-TAH-tays), or concave stones, and cooked it in pottery they made with ridged surfaces. They often painted their serving bowls. "We climbed down into a *kiva*," says Landon. A *kiva* (KEE-vuh) is an underground chamber. In its floor is a *sipapu* (SEE-pah-pooh), or hole, symbolizing an opening between the physical world and the place where the Pueblo ancestors believed that life began.

"Only the men were allowed in the *kiva*," Landon says. There they held religious ceremonies and gathered to talk, perhaps about the weather, as people do today. By the late 1200s, the weather must have been on their minds a lot. Archaeologists know that for many years little rain fell in the region. By 1300 the cliff dwellings of Mesa Verde had been abandoned. "Maybe the people left because of the drought," says Leighana. Some scientists agree. They think, too, that soil erosion, warfare, and disease may have driven them away. After so many years, the mysteries remain. But the ancient people probably did not vanish. Archaeologists and modern Pueblo people believe they migrated south. Today, through their descendants—the Pueblo Indians of Arizona and New Mexico—the ancient ones live on.

VERY HANDY
Ancient artists may have pressed clay-covered palms against the wall in place of signatures.

CLUES TO LIFE
Ridges on ancient pots made them easier to grip and helped heat food evenly.

BUILT TO KEEP
Kathrine peers into a cliffside storeroom. A family may have used the structure to store its blankets and winter food supply.

COOL KIVA
From the left, Leighana, Kathrine, and Landon peer into a nine-foot-deep kiva. On the floor is a *sipapu*, or hole, a symbolic opening between the physical world and an ancient source of life.

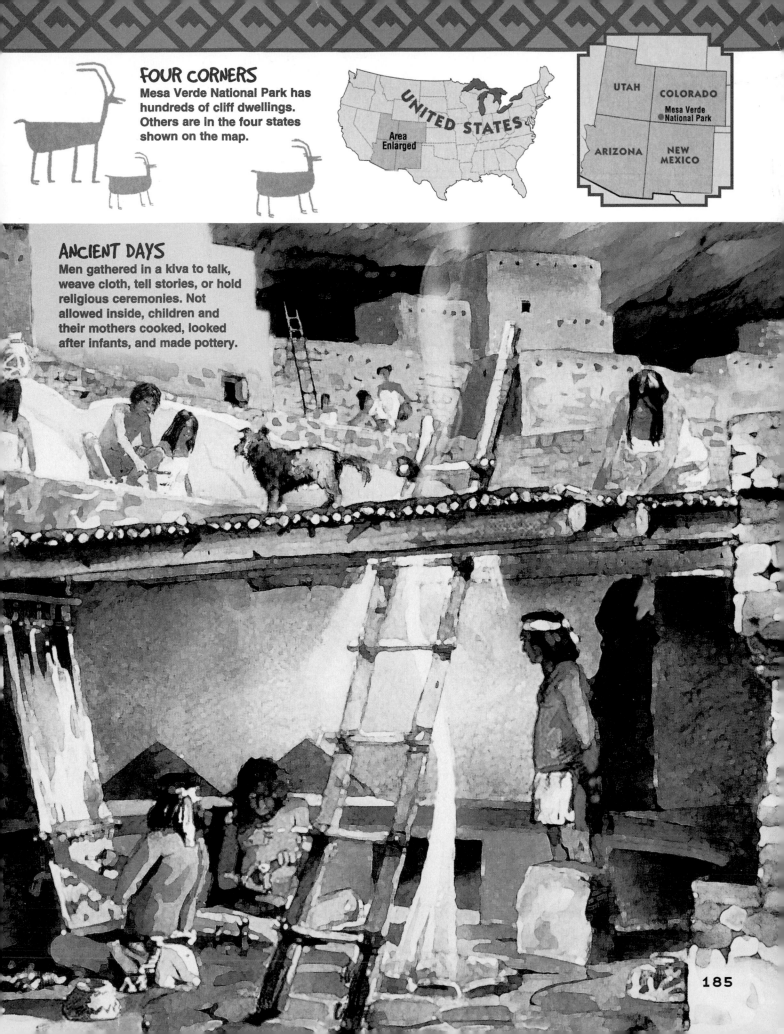

FOUR CORNERS
Mesa Verde National Park has hundreds of cliff dwellings. Others are in the four states shown on the map.

UNITED STATES

Area Enlarged

UTAH
COLORADO
Mesa Verde National Park
ARIZONA
NEW MEXICO

ANCIENT DAYS
Men gathered in a kiva to talk, weave cloth, tell stories, or hold religious ceremonies. Not allowed inside, children and their mothers cooked, looked after infants, and made pottery.

185

THINK ABOUT READING

Write your answers.

1. Why was Dr. Sara Bisel called to the ruins of the Roman town of Herculaneum in 1982?

2. Why might some people say that Dr. Bisel is a detective?

3. Which part of Dr. Bisel's job do you find most interesting? Give reasons for your answer.

4. How does the author keep you in suspense about the findings in the boat chamber?

5. What goals do the archaeologists at Herculaneum and at Mesa Verde share? What is one goal that only the Mesa Verde archaeologists have?

WRITE A TRAVEL BROCHURE

A travel brochure uses text and pictures to describe a travel destination. Imagine that you are trying to promote either Herculaneum or Mesa Verde as a travel destination for student archaeologists. Write a paragraph for this brochure in which you describe the site and tell why it would be an interesting place for young archaeologists to visit.

LITERATURE CIRCLE

Talk about the two sites studied by archaeologists—the one in Herculaneum and the one at Mesa Verde. Discuss the similarities and differences. What kinds of food did the people who once lived at each site eat? What kinds of work did they do? How was the location of Herculaneum different from Mesa Verde? How did the location influence the types of jobs people did? Make a Venn diagram to show your findings.

AUTHOR
SARA C. BISEL

Dr. Sara C. Bisel is one of the world's leading experts on ancient bones. She has worked at archaeological sites in Greece, Turkey, and Israel. In 1982, the National Geographic Society asked Dr. Bisel to examine the finds at Herculaneum. A visit that she expected to last five days has stretched into years. National Geographic based a television program on Dr. Bisel's exciting finds.

MORE BOOKS ABOUT
ANCIENT CIVILIZATIONS

- *The Buried City of Pompeii: What It Was Like When Vesuvius Exploded* by Shelley Tanaka
- *Native Americans and Mesa Verde* by Hazel Mary Martell

SKY PIONEER
A Photobiography of Amelia Earhart

PHOTOBIOGRAPHY

AWARD
WINNER

From

SKY PIONEER
A Photobiography of Amelia Earhart

by CORINNE SZABO

Amelia Earhart—one of America's most famous pilots—was born to break records. In 1928, she boarded a plane called the Friendship *and became the first woman passenger to fly across the Atlantic. There were many more record-breaking moments to come.*

Ever since her flight on the *Friendship*, Amelia had felt challenged to make her *own* solo flight across the Atlantic. This time she would not be just a passenger!

By May 20, 1932, she was ready.

Flying in her red Lockheed Vega, she set out at dusk from Harbor Grace, Newfoundland. Thirteen and a half hours later, she arrived somewhat off course in a pasture in Londonderry, Ireland. She was the first woman pilot to successfully make the Atlantic crossing.

"I taxied to the upper end of a sloping pasture and turned my plane into the shelter of some trees.... Of course, I came down in a pasture and I had to circle many other pastures to find the best one. The horses, sheep, and cows in Londonderry were not used to airplanes, and so, as I flew low, they jumped up and down and displayed certain disquiet."

During the Atlantic crossing, the Vega's engines had used up 350 gallons of gasoline. Amelia drank one can of tomato juice, which she sipped through a straw.

Amelia's record flight was an exciting one. She discovered that her altimeter was faulty, so she was unable to record the plane's height above the sea. She encountered a violent storm and, trying to climb out of it, developed ice on her wings.

She said later, "I descended to hunt for warmer air to melt the ice. Down I went until I could see the whitecaps through the fog. It was unpleasant there, because sudden heavy fog and a dip would land me in the ocean. So I climbed until the ice began to form again. Then down again to the fog above the waves." Relying on her wits, she kept the plane above the water and below the altitude where ice formed.

After landing in the Gallagher's pasture, Amelia stopped at their farmhouse to wash her face and drink some tea. The next day, once the news of her arrival had spread, she read some of the congratulatory telegrams.

Amelia's courage and persistence were matched by her spirit of adventure. Her pioneering sky voyage was acclaimed not only in the United States, but in many parts of the world.

Amelia received the National Geographic Society's Special Gold Medal from President Hoover. The ceremony was broadcast on radio so that the entire country could listen. (No TV in those days!)

Amelia received many awards that same year. Among them were the first Distinguished Flying Cross given to a woman by the United States Congress, and the Cross of the Legion of Honor from France.

President Hoover said: *"She has shown a splendid courage and skill.... She has often before demonstrated her ability to accomplish the most difficult tasks that she set herself to do. She has been modest and good humored. All these things combine to place her in spirit with the great pioneering women to whom every generation of Americans has looked up.... The nation is proud that an American woman should be the first woman in history to fly an airplane alone across the Atlantic Ocean."*

After her solo Atlantic flight, Amelia kept looking for new experiences. She loved to take to the skies, and wanted to set new records. She liked the challenge and the thrill of achieving, and she liked the fun of it.

In 1935 she began preparations for the flight that would eventually make her the first woman to fly solo across the Pacific Ocean from Hawaii to Oakland, California. Her food for the trip consisted of tomato juice, one hard-boiled egg, and a cup of delicious hot chocolate.

ABOVE: Amelia practiced inflating an emergency raft in the event of a forced landing at sea.

RIGHT: Ten thousand admirers greeted the smiling Amelia when she arrived in Oakland.

"The night I found over the Pacific was a night of stars. They seemed to rise from the sea and hang outside my cockpit window, near enough to touch, until hours later they slipped away into the dawn."

With the help of her husband, who made all the arrangements, and at the request of the Mexican government, Amelia decided to make a "goodwill" flight from Burbank, California, to Mexico. She strayed off course and landed in a village near Mexico City, startling the local inhabitants. Her plane was quickly surrounded by cowboys, villagers, cattle, goats, and chickens.

Flying on to Mexico City, Amelia was greeted by the President of Mexico. Lively festivals and colorful celebrations were the highlights of her visit.

LEFT: Amelia's official welcome in Mexico City included a gift of a traditional Mexican cowboy outfit in blue and silver and a colorful sombrero.

ABOVE: George Putnam, Amelia's husband, who had flown ahead, was waiting for her when she arrived in Mexico.

Her return trip was another record—a nonstop flight from Mexico City to Newark, New Jersey. She left Mexico after an early morning breakfast and arrived in New York at 10:30 p.m., in time for a late dinner.

Amelia attracted people wherever she went with her warm and friendly personality. She was an articulate public speaker who made hundreds of lecture tours around the country. She often expressed concern about the education of women: Why shouldn't they have the same experiences and career choices as men?

In particular, she deplored the lack of opportunities for women in aviation, and the unfairness of unequal pay for men and women who did similar work.

The President of Indiana's Purdue University, Edwin C. Elliot, was so impressed when he heard Amelia speak that he invited her to come to Purdue for part of the year as a career counselor for nearly a thousand women students.

Amelia accepted, and at age 38 she joined the faculty. Purdue had an aeronautics department and its own airfield. To Amelia's delight the university encouraged women to study mechanics and engineering.

At Purdue, Amelia's dream—to become the first woman to fly around the world—came closer to a reality. She felt she had "just one more long flight in my system."

"There was my belief that now and then women should do for themselves what men have already done—and occasionally what men have not done— thereby establishing themselves as persons, and perhaps encouraging other women toward greater independence of thought and action."

A jubilant Amelia posed with her twin-engine "flying laboratory."

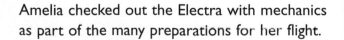

Amelia checked out the Electra with mechanics as part of the many preparations for her flight.

time when she was a baby. She had also had two teeth removed about one or two weeks before she died, probably giving her a fair bit of pain. And her life had been very hard. She had done a lot of running up and down stairs or hills, as well as having to lift objects too heavy for her delicate frame.

This girl could not have been the child of a wealthy family, like the baby. She had probably been a slave who died trying to protect the baby of the family she worked for.

shape to create more surface for the muscles to attach to. By examining the shape and weight of certain bones, we can see which muscles were used, and what kind of work or exercise a person might have done.

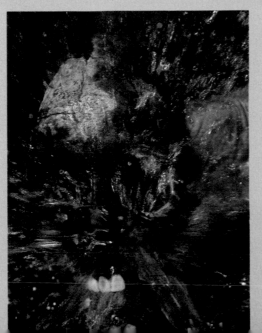

And there were many others. Near the slave girl lay the skeleton of a seven-year-old girl whose bones also showed that she had done work far too heavy for a child so young.

We found a sixteen-year-old fisherman, his upper body well developed from rowing boats, his teeth worn from holding cord while he repaired his fishing nets.

Particularly heartbreaking were the two pregnant women I examined, for we were also able to recover their tiny unborn babies, their bones as fragile as eggshells. One woman had been only about sixteen years old.

Though it is fascinating to reconstruct the life of a single person by examining his or her bones, for anthropologists and historians the most useful information comes from examining all of the skeletons of one population. This is one reason why Herculaneum is so important.

During the next few months we opened two more boat chambers. In one we discovered forty tangled human skeletons and one of a horse; in another we found twenty-six skeletons creepily lined up like a row of dominoes, as if heading in single file for the back of the chamber.

The skeletons represented a cross-section of the population of a whole town—old people, children and babies, slaves, rich and poor, men and women, the sick and the healthy. By examining all these skeletons, we can get some ideas about how the townspeople lived and what they were like physically.

We found out, for example, that the average Herculanean man was 5 feet 5 inches (165 centimeters) tall, the average woman about 5 feet 1 inch (155 centimeters). In general, they were well nourished. And we have examined enough people to know that although the rich people had easy lives, the slaves often worked so hard that they were in pain much of the time.

Studying these skeletons closely can also help medical researchers and doctors. In ancient times, many diseases could not be cured by surgery or drugs. Instead, people kept getting sicker, until they eventually died. By examining the bones of these people, we can learn a great deal about how certain diseases progress.

By the end of my stay in Herculaneum, I had examined 139 skeletons. Their bones were sorted into yellow plastic vegetable crates that lined the shelves in my laboratory. And each box of bones has a different story to tell.

Even though I can't tell the good guys from the bad, and I can't tell you whether they were happy or not, I know a great deal about these people. I can see each person plainly. I even imagine them dressed as they might have been, lounging on their terraces or in the baths if they were wealthy, toiling in a mine or in a galley if they were the most unfortunate slaves.

Most of all, I feel that these people have become my friends, and that I have been very lucky to have had a part in bringing their stories to the rest of the world.

Left: The Romans usually cremated the dead and placed their ashes in urns like this one.

Under the management of the Purdue Research Foundation, an all-metal, twin-engine Lockheed Electra 10E with the most modern equipment was built especially for her use.

Amelia was thrilled with her shiny new Electra. The plane was built to meet the challenges of the arduous journey she was planning, with enough horsepower in the engines to accommodate the weight of additional fuel tanks.

Men had flown around the world, but Amelia's plan was to take the longest route, one never tried before, along the Equator. After the flight, she planned to use the plane as a "flying laboratory" to add to aviation research.

The preparations for the trip included many hours of careful planning, trial flights to test equipment, and studying maps and charts to determine the exact route.

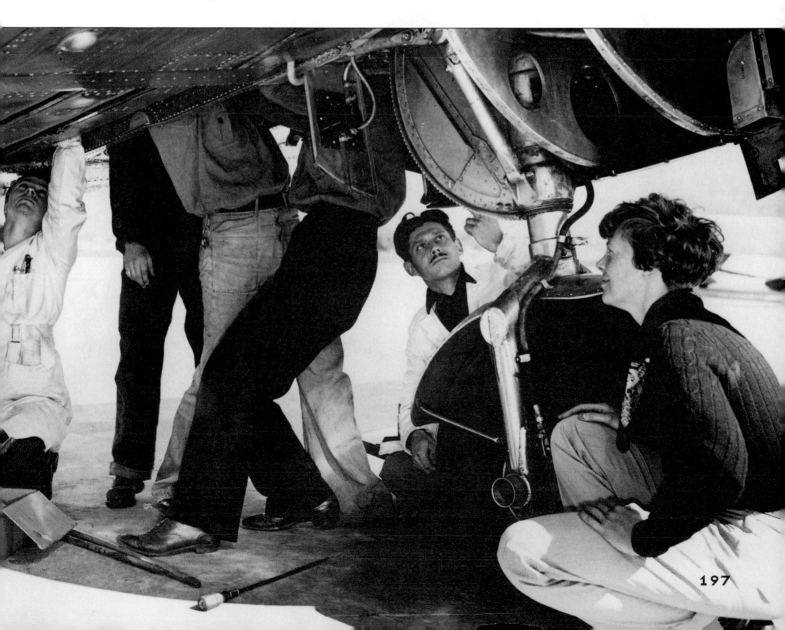

*"Living with these maps and charts
was absorbing and instructive. My knowledge of geography—
at least theoretically—increased from week to week.
To sit in the sunshine…in my California home, tracking monsoons
to their lairs and appraising rainfalls in India and
take-off conditions at African airports,
was an adventure in itself."*

ABOVE: Paul Mantz, a veteran pilot and old friend, advised Amelia on flight plans for the trip.

RIGHT: Capt. Harry Manning studies an instrument for providing celestial bearings. He was to have been the navigator on the original around-the-world flight. Because of scheduling conflicts, he reluctantly gave his job over to Fred Noonan.

Fred Noonan, a former navigator for Pan American, had made a dozen trips across the Pacific. Amelia described him as "tops among aerial navigators."

ON MARCH 17, 1937, starting from Oakland, California, on a westerly course, she arrived at her first stop, Honolulu, Hawaii. However, on takeoff from Honolulu there was a disastrous mishap, a crash which required extensive repairs. When the plane was ready again, Amelia decided to reverse her route because of seasonal changes in weather conditions. On May 21, 1937, she began for a second time the first leg of the around-the-world flight. This time she left California going east, to Miami, Florida, making several stops and testing out the plane. With her was her friend, an experienced navigator, Fred Noonan.

At the Florida airport, final mechanical checks were made, and on June 1, the sleek silver plane took off into the Miami sunrise. The equatorial flight around the world took them to Caripito, Venezuela, Amelia's first glimpse of South America, and her first sight of a jungle. Then, dipping below the Equator, they stopped in Fortaleza, Brazil.

The Electra's cockpit, with a pilot and copilot's seat, measured four feet eight inches in height, and four feet six inches in length and width. Its control board contained about fifty dials and gauges.

Honolulu •

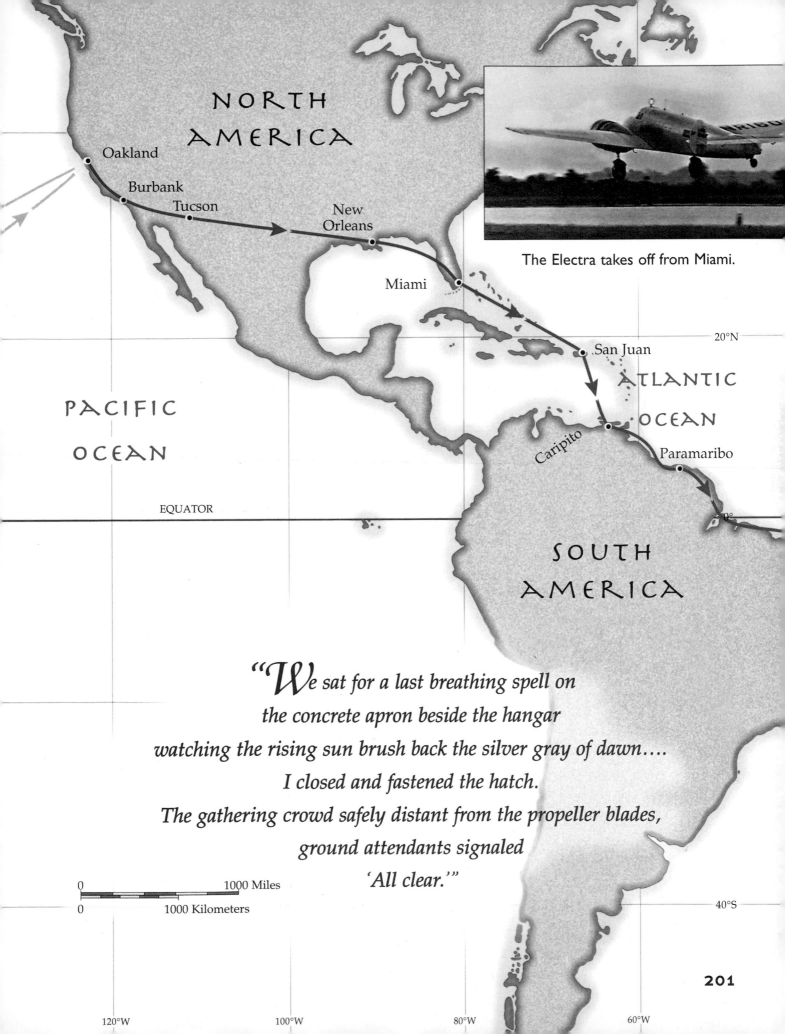

NORTH
AMERICA

Oakland

Burbank
Tucson

New
Orleans

Miami

The Electra takes off from Miami.

20°N

San Juan

ATLANTIC

OCEAN

Caripito

Paramaribo

PACIFIC

OCEAN

0°

EQUATOR

SOUTH
AMERICA

"*We* sat for a last breathing spell on
the concrete apron beside the hangar
watching the rising sun brush back the silver gray of dawn....
I closed and fastened the hatch.
The gathering crowd safely distant from the propeller blades,
ground attendants signaled
'All clear.'"

0   1000 Miles

0   1000 Kilometers

40°S

120°W   100°W   80°W   60°W

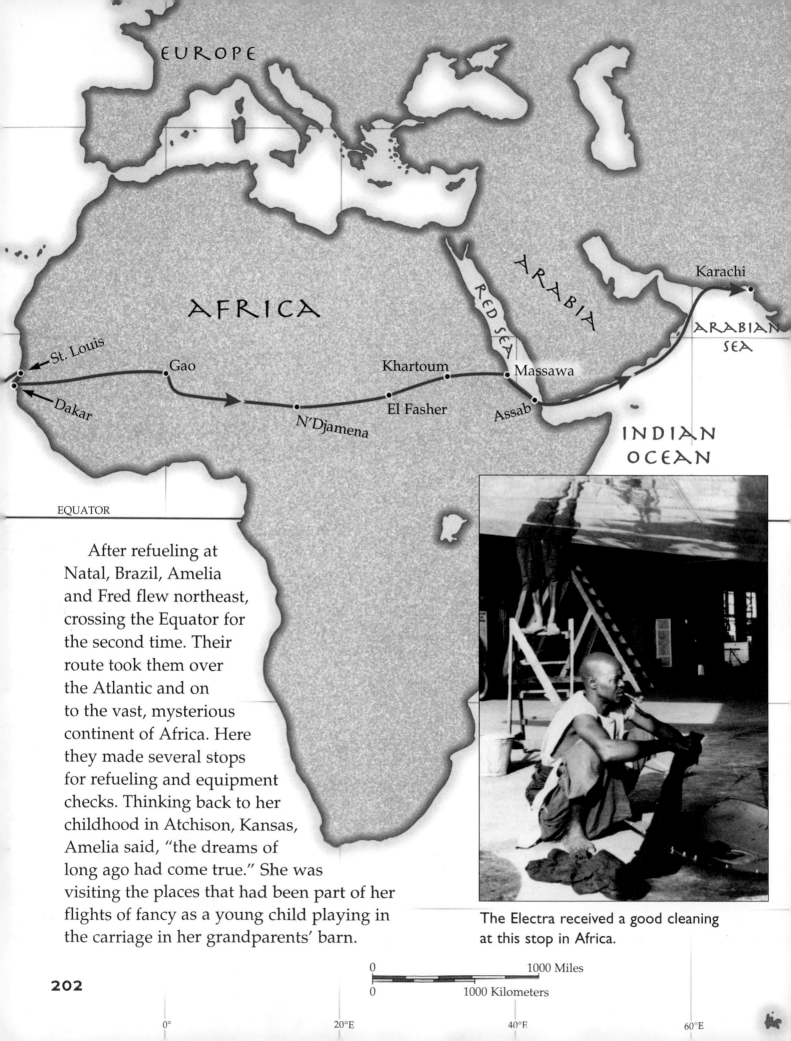

EUROPE

AFRICA

ARABIA

RED SEA

Karachi

ARABIAN SEA

St. Louis

Gao

Khartoum

Massawa

Dakar

N'Djamena

El Fasher

Assab

INDIAN OCEAN

EQUATOR

After refueling at Natal, Brazil, Amelia and Fred flew northeast, crossing the Equator for the second time. Their route took them over the Atlantic and on to the vast, mysterious continent of Africa. Here they made several stops for refueling and equipment checks. Thinking back to her childhood in Atchison, Kansas, Amelia said, "the dreams of long ago had come true." She was visiting the places that had been part of her flights of fancy as a young child playing in the carriage in her grandparents' barn.

The Electra received a good cleaning at this stop in Africa.

0   1000 Miles

0   1000 Kilometers

0°   20°E   40°E   60°E

ASIA

Beyond Africa lay the Red Sea, Arabia, and finally Karachi, in what is now Pakistan. In Karachi, while mechanics made repairs and an oil change, Amelia found time for some sightseeing. Intrigued by a bushy-bearded man in a high turban who offered rides on his camel, Amelia took the challenge in spite of Fred's teasing, "Better wear a parachute."

"Whatever his disposition, my hired steed knelt down and I climbed into the saddle swung between his two humps. It was a startling take-off as we rose.... As his hind legs unfold you are threatened with a nose-dive forward. Then with a lurch... the animal's center section hoists into the air."

With several others, Amelia went "cameling." She visited a nearby oasis, passing many other "ships of the desert" on the way. The Karachi airport was the largest she had seen, and an important stop for those flying from Europe to India and the Far East.

100°E   120°E   140°E   160°E

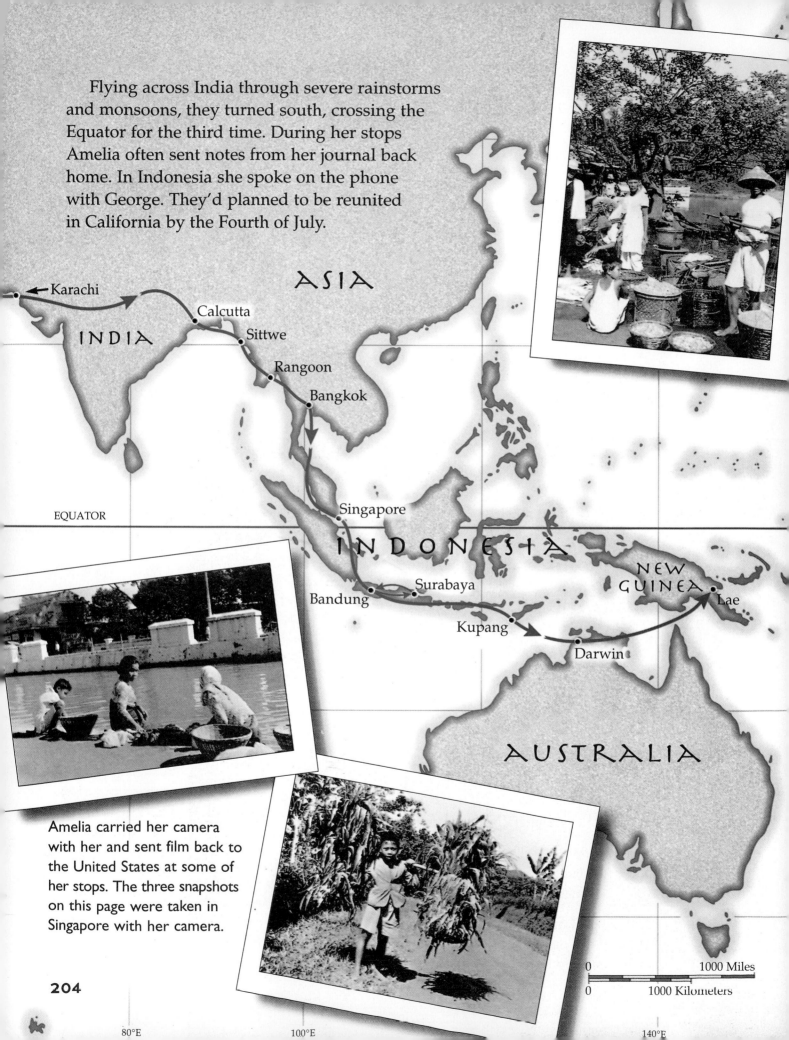

Flying across India through severe rainstorms and monsoons, they turned south, crossing the Equator for the third time. During her stops Amelia often sent notes from her journal back home. In Indonesia she spoke on the phone with George. They'd planned to be reunited in California by the Fourth of July.

ASIA

Karachi

Calcutta

Sittwe

Rangoon

Bangkok

INDIA

EQUATOR

Singapore

INDONESIA

NEW GUINEA

Bandung

Surabaya

Lae

Kupang

Darwin

AUSTRALIA

Amelia carried her camera with her and sent film back to the United States at some of her stops. The three snapshots on this page were taken in Singapore with her camera.

0   1000 Miles

0   1000 Kilometers

80°E   100°E   140°E

Fuel was siphoned from drums marked for Amelia Earhart at this stop in Indonesia.

On the 29th of June, Amelia and Fred arrived in Lae, New Guinea. They had been traveling almost six weeks and had covered the remarkable distance of 22,000 miles. But the most dangerous part of the trip lay ahead. They were to fly 2,556 miles over the Pacific Ocean to Howland Island, an island so tiny it would be difficult to locate.

EQUATOR 0°

20°S

A smiling Amelia climbed out of her plane on arrival at Lae, New Guinea, her last stop before taking off for Howland Island.

40°S

120°W

PACIFIC

OCEAN

Oakland

Honolulu

On July 2, the Electra left New
Guinea, heading toward Howland
Island. Offshore, seamen aboard
the U.S. Coast Guard cutter *Itasca*
were waiting to guide the plane in
for landing.

The *Itasca* received several radio
messages from Amelia requesting a
bearing. The crew replied each time,
but Amelia did not acknowledge
having heard them. Finally, more
than five hours after her first message,
she reported receiving their signals.

The cutter was unable to give
her a bearing because her
transmission was too brief.

*Howland
Island*

EQUATOR

The men aboard scanned the skies,
anxious for a sighting.

Amelia's last message came less
than an hour later. Attempting to find
a radio frequency where they could
make contact she said, "Listening on
6210 kilocycles. We are running north
and south."

The *Itasca* crew tried to reach her
on every possible radio frequency.

They received no further word.

There was only silence.

A massive sea and air search
followed, but no trace has ever been
found of the plane or its crew.

PACIFIC

OCEAN

0   1000 Miles

0   1000 Kilometers

160°E   180°   160°W   140°W   120°W

NORTH AMERICA

40°N

20°N

The *Itasca* desperately tried to make radio contact with Amelia to pinpoint her location.

100°W   80°W   60°W   40°W

"*Please know I am quite aware of the hazards.
I want to do it because I want to do it.
Women must try to do things as men have tried.
When they fail, failure must be but
a challenge to others.*"

AFTERWORD

When someone vanishes without a trace, it becomes a mystery clamoring to be solved. This is the stuff that legends are made of. Amelia's last frantic words were sketchy and uninformative. Without definite proof of what happened, some people question whether she really disappeared. They look for clues, for answers to the inconclusive end of the world-famous pilot.

The speculation covers a wide range of theories. Some thought that Amelia was on a spy mission for the United States. Others suggested that she landed or crashed near one of the Pacific Islands and was picked up by the Japanese who patrolled that area. Could she have been imprisoned or executed by them? There was one bizarre speculation that she was rescued by the United States after World War II, sent home disguised as someone else, and given a new identity.

These theories were followed up by investigations, but were never proven to be true. In some cases they may have been prompted by people who, feeding on sensationalist rumors, wanted to gain fame for themselves. Both President Franklin Roosevelt and his wife, Eleanor, denied that Amelia was on a spy mission. Japanese records showed no evidence that she was found by one of their ships. All reputable investigations reported that there is no convincing evidence to substantiate any of these assumptions.

The attempt to explain her disappearance brought with it a series of "What ifs?" What if she and Noonan had been more experienced with Morse code? What if they had taken the extralong antenna it was believed they left behind in Miami? What if they were not so exhausted by the time they reached Lae?

Both Amelia and Fred lacked a good working knowledge of Morse code. They had learned to fly without it. Instead they were relying on radio equipment that was exclusively based on voice contact. Being better at Morse code might have helped them to make contact with the *Itasca*. The 250-foot trailing antenna which was removed or shortened before the Electra left Miami might have made the difference in their ability to communicate and make themselves heard. Fatigue was certainly their enemy. Amelia and Fred had been traveling for more than thirty days, adjusting to different climates, often getting little sleep. This may have made it more difficult to concentrate and to use good judgment.

At best, this speculation is intriguing to read about. However, proof is something we may never entirely have. Unless someday her plane is found at the bottom of the ocean, closure may never take place.

For now, the only realistic conclusion is that her plane ran out of fuel and was lost at sea.

The real "afterward" to Amelia's story lies in a prophecy she made as she wrote about her thoughts on future air travel. She looked back more than a hundred years to the first women aeronauts, pioneers who flew in hot air balloons, and asked herself what changes in aeronautical activity would come in the next hundred years. She envisioned faster planes flying at higher altitudes, greater comfort for passengers, and the acceptance of flying as the best means of transportation for going anywhere in the world. She foresaw that "women will share in these endeavors, even more than in the past."

Amelia Earhart, sky pioneer, contributed to the fulfillment of this prophecy.

She paved the way for the thousands of women in aviation who followed her, from Air Force pilots, to captains on commercial planes, to women astronauts traveling in space.

CHRONOLOGY

Amelia at age 6

July 27, 1897	Born in Atchison, Kansas, to Edwin and Amy Otis Earhart
1908	Saw her first airplane at the Iowa State Fair
1916	Entered the Ogontz School near Philadelphia, Pennsylvania
1918	Became a nurse's aide at Spadina Military Hospital in Toronto, Canada
1919	Enrolled as a premedical student at Columbia University in New York
1920	Visited her parents in Los Angeles, and took her first airplane ride
1921	Took her first flying lessons from Neta Snook
1922	Bought her first plane
	Set women's altitude record of 14,000 feet on October 22
1923	Received pilot's license on May 16
1926	Became a social worker at Denison House in Boston
1928	Became first woman to fly across the Atlantic as a passenger, June 17–18
	Was the first woman to make a round-trip solo flight across the United States
1929	Took third place in the first Women's Air Derby
1930	Set women's speed record of 181 miles per hour
1931	Married George Putnam, February 7
	Set autogiro altitude record of 18,451 feet

1932   Became first woman to fly solo across the Atlantic, May 20–21

Received the National Geographic Society's Special Gold Medal, June 21

Set women's transcontinental speed record from Los Angeles, California, to Newark, New Jersey, August 24–25

1933   Broke her previous women's transcontinental speed record from Los Angeles, California, to Newark, New Jersey, July 7–8

1935   Became first person to fly solo from Honolulu, Hawaii, to Oakland, California, January 11–12

Became first person to fly solo from Los Angeles, California, to Mexico City, April 19–20

Became first person to fly solo from Mexico City to Newark, New Jersey, May 8

Joined the faculty of Purdue University as a career consultant to women, September 1

1937   Attempted flight around the world

from **Flying Machine**
written by **Andrew Nahum**

On the Flight Deck

THE FLIGHT DECK of a modern jetliner looks dauntingly complicated, with its array of switches, dials, and displays for such things as engine condition, hydraulics, navigational aids, and so on, not to mention the basic flight controls. Increasingly, however, computers are taking over certain functions, and the mass of dials is being replaced by neat screens called CRTs (for "cathode ray tube"), on which the pilot can change the information displayed by the flick of a button.

Landing and taxi
light switches

Engine starting
controls

Battery-powered
stand-by main flight
instruments, enabling
the pilot to land safely
in case of complete
electrical failure

Navigation
computer
equipment

Engine
speed control
(throttle)

Engine data such
as fuel flow, torque
(the force turning
the turbines), and
turbine temperature

Indicators for brakes and
hydraulic systems

Flight deck lights

TOWARD THE GLASS COCKPIT

This cockpit, from a 1980s airliner, has a "second generation" CRT display. This means that it uses both CRTs and conventional dials. Some large new airliners, such as the Boeing 747-400, have "all-glass cockpits," which means that almost all information comes up on a few CRTs.

Independent weather radar

Wing flap control

Array of warning lights, supplementing the CRT displays

Second CRT, displaying all the navigational information. It can also function as a simple compass, a radar screen, or a map display

Primary flight display CRT, combining all the functions of the main flying instruments on earlier aircraft, including artificial horizon, altimeter, airspeed indicator, course indicator, and landing approach glide scope indicator

Control yoke

Gauges for cabin pressure

THINK ABOUT READING

Write your answers.

1. What records did Amelia Earhart break?

2. How does the author convince you that Amelia Earhart had a spirit of adventure?

3. Why do you think people wanted to meet and applaud Amelia Earhart?

4. What do you think happened to Amelia Earhart's plane on the final leg of her journey?

5. Which of the instruments on a modern flight deck could have helped Amelia Earhart on her flight to tiny Howland Island?

WRITE A JOURNAL ENTRY

Write a journal entry that pilot Amelia Earhart might have written after one of her flights. Choose your own subject, such as maneuvering across the Atlantic or landing in Mexico City. Picture what might have happened as you flew the plane. Include sensory details about what you saw and heard—in the air and on the ground after you landed. Be sure express your feelings about your accomplishment.

LITERATURE CIRCLE

Discuss other real-life adventurers you have read about or have encountered in books, on television, or at the movies. What personality traits do they have in common with Amelia Earhart? How are they different from her? Were their explorations or adventures successful? Role play a conversation between one of these explorers and Amelia Earhart.

AUTHOR
CORINNE SZABO

Corinne Szabo didn't start out to write a photobiography about Amelia Earhart. However, while she was working as a photo researcher, Ms. Szabo became inspired by the sky pioneer's outlook on life and her great sense of adventure. That was when the idea for a book was born. Ms. Szabo says, "I wanted to tell young people her story."

MORE BOOKS ABOUT
SKY PIONEERS

- *The Glorious Flight* by Alice and Martin Provenson
- *Flying Free: America's Black Aviators* by Phillip S. Hart
- *Up in the Air: The Story of Bessie Coleman* by Philip S. Hart

PROJECT

How to
Prepare an Investigative Report

Use your problem-solving skills to investigate a real-life mystery!

Be a detective and investigate a real-life mystery that interests you. Perhaps you're curious about who built Stonehenge or why whales sometimes strand themselves on the beach. Whatever mystery you choose, you will research and analyze real-life clues and form a hypothesis about the solution to your mystery. Finally, you will gather your information into an investigative report.

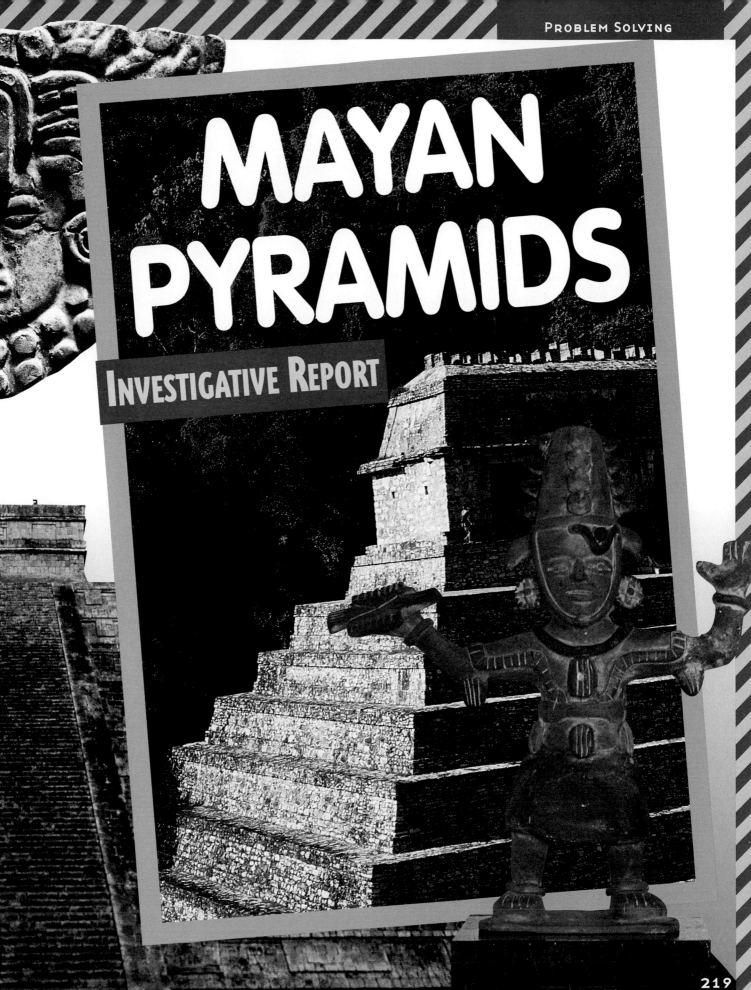

MAYAN PYRAMIDS

INVESTIGATIVE REPORT

Choose a Mystery

Mysteries have always existed and they continue to happen everyday. Why did the dinosaurs disappear? What became of the lost colony of Roanoke? Think of some other real-life mysteries of history and science. If you're having trouble coming up with ideas, you might want to do a little library research, or even check out a video about real-life mysteries. Once you've generated a list of possibilities, go over it and weed out those mysteries that may be impossible to research thoroughly. From the remaining list, select the mystery that intrigues you the most!

The Dallas Morning News

DALLAS, TEXAS, SUNDAY, JULY 4, 1937—SIXTY-SIX PAGES IN FIVE SECTIONS

FIFTY-SECOND YEAR

Earhart's Death Feared as Storm Repels Rescue Plane

International Search for Missing Aviatrix Started in Southern Pacific

Ice, Snow Prevent Navy Fliers Going In Search of Pair

City Edition — Price Ten Cents — NO. 277

20,000 Cheer Jack, Mary in Stadium Scene

Amelia's Husband Has Hunch Missing Pair Are on Reef

World Flight Last Spectacular Dash Planned by Amelia

Labor Board Gets Challenge by Ford As to Its Powers

2 Investigate the Mystery

Search for newspaper and magazine articles and nonfiction books that discuss your chosen mystery. Other possible sources of information include videos, TV programs, and people who are familiar with the subject. Find out what clues have already turned up in the search for a solution.

Make note of the hypotheses proposed by previous investigators. As you check out each source, take notes on the information you find, and file your notes in a folder. File, also, any pictures, charts, diagrams, or other visual aids that you might want to include in your report.

How Am I Doing?

Before you begin to analyze your research, take a minute to ask yourself these questions:

- Did I take clear notes on the mystery?

- Do my notes cover all possible angles?

- Did I use several sources of information so that my report will be as complete as possible?

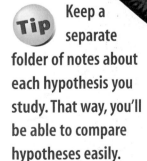

Tip Keep a separate folder of notes about each hypothesis you study. That way, you'll be able to compare hypotheses easily.

Analyze Your Research

Every investigative report includes a hypothesis, or guess, about what happened. A hypothesis is not a random guess, however, but one based on evidence. Look through your notes, and separate facts (those items which are positively known to be true) from opinions, or hypotheses.

List all the facts on the left side of a piece of paper and all the hypotheses on the right.

Look carefully at your lists. What do they tell you? By looking at the facts, can you eliminate any hypotheses? Which ones still seem possible?

Mayan stone carvings located in Rio Lacantun, Mexico, illuminated at night

4 Form Your Hypothesis

Review all the known facts about your mystery. Look once again at the hypotheses you have discarded and those that remain. Use your best judgment to come up with your own hypothesis. Check it against the facts. Is there reason to believe that your hypothesis could not possibly be correct? If so, revise it and check it against the facts once more.

5 Write Your Investigative Report

Introduce your report by describing your mystery. Next, list all the facts you've uncovered. Then, explain the different theories about solutions to the mystery, and why you did or did not discount them. If possible, enhance your report with some direct quotes, as well as with a variety of visual aids. Conclude by stating your hypothesis and explaining why you think it's the real solution! Finally, present your report to your classmates. Did other students investigate your mystery? Compare your report to theirs.

If You Are Using a Computer ...

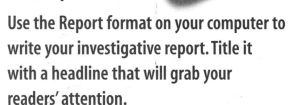

Use the Report format on your computer to write your investigative report. Title it with a headline that will grab your readers' attention.

CONGRATULATIONS

You've become the detective in a real-world mystery! Keep your problem-solving skills sharp. You're sure to use them throughout your life.

Lilly Gallman
Forensic Chemist ▶

Voyagers

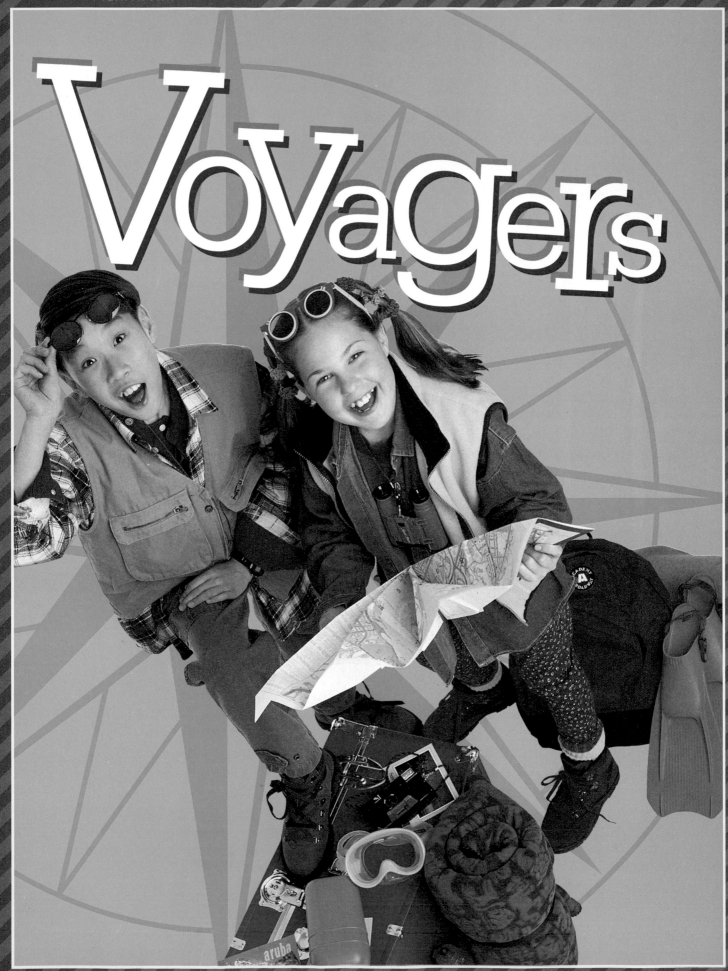

Voyagers

THEME

We depend on a network of people when we explore.

UNIT 3

Caravan
Europe
INTERNATIONAL CERTIFICATES OF VACCINATION
AS APPROVED BY
THE WORLD HEALTH ORGANIZATION
(EXCEPT FOR ADDRESS OF VACCINATOR)
PASSPORT
United States of America
U.S. DEPARTMENT OF
PUBLIC HEALTH SERVICE
GLOBUS
EUROPE & BRITAIN
COSMOS TOURAMA
EUROPE & BRITAIN
COSTA RICA
AND
BELIZE
INDEPENDENT
GREECE
PLUS TURKEY & ISRAEL
London Specials
$629.95
SOUTH AM
VACATIONS
LAS VEGAS

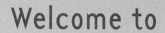

Welcome to

LITERACY PLACE

Travel Agency

We depend on
a network of people
when we explore.

AWARD
WINNER

THE BUNYANS

WRITTEN BY
AUDREY WOOD • **DAVID SHANNON**
ILLUSTRATED BY

STORYTELLER'S NOTE

Now I suppose that you have heard about the mighty logger Paul Bunyan and his great blue ox named Babe. In the early days of our country, Paul and Babe cleared the land for the settlers, so farms and cities could spring up. And you probably know that Paul was taller than a redwood tree, stronger than fifty grizzly bears, and smarter than a library full of books. But you may not know that Paul was married and had two fine children.

ONE DAY WHEN PAUL BUNYAN WAS OUT CLEARING A ROAD THROUGH

THE FORESTS of Kentucky, a great pounding began to shake the earth. Looking around, Paul discovered an enormous hole in the side of a hill. The lumberjack pulled up an acre of dry cane and fashioned a torch to light his way.

Paul climbed inside the hole and followed the sound underground for miles, until he came to a large cavern glistening with crystals. By the flickering light of his torch, he saw a gigantic woman banging a behemoth pickax against a wall.

It was love at first sight.

"I'm Carrie McIntie," the gigantic woman said. "I was sitting on the hill when my lucky wishbone fell down a crack into the earth. I've been digging all day trying to find it."

With a grin on his face as wide as the Missouri River, Paul reached into his shirt pocket. "I've got one too," he said, pulling out *his* lucky wishbone. "Marry me, Carrie, and we'll share mine."

Carrie agreed, and their wedding invitations were mailed out right away.

The invitations were so large, only one needed to be sent to each state. Everyone could read them for miles!

The invitations said: *You are cordially invited to the mammoth wedding of Paul Bunyan and Carrie McIntie.* The couple were married in the enormous crystal chamber that Carrie had carved, and after the ceremony, folks began to call it "Mammoth Cave." The giantess had dug more than two hundred miles, making it the longest cave in the world, so the name fit perfectly.

Paul and Carrie settled down on a farm in Maine, and soon there were two new Bunyans. While Pa Bunyan traveled with his logging crew, Ma Bunyan worked the farm and cared for their jumbo boy, named Little Jean, and their gigantic girl, named Teeny.

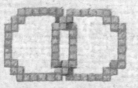

One morning when Pa Bunyan was home between jobs, Ma Bunyan cooked up a hearty breakfast of pancakes and syrup. Teeny was wrestling with her big purple puma named Slink and accidentally dumped a silo of syrup on her head. Teeny's hair was so sweet, bears crawled into it and burrowed deep in her curls. Try as they might, Pa and Ma Bunyan couldn't wash them out.

"We'll need a forceful shower of water to get rid of those varmints!" Ma Bunyan declared.

Pa Bunyan had an idea. He placed his daughter on Babe, and he led them to the Niagara River in Canada. The gargantuan father scooped out a huge hole in the middle of the riverbed. As the great river roared down into the deep hole, Teeny cried out in delight, "Niagara falls!" Teeny showered in the waterfall, and the pesky bears were washed downstream.

When Little Jean was five, he wanted to work too, so he followed his pa out to his logging camp in Montana. Thinking his son was too young to do much of anything, Paul set Little Jean down in a barren canyon in Utah to play for the day. When the lumberjack went to fetch him, he couldn't believe his eyes. Little Jean had carved the canyon into a wonderland of fanciful shapes.

Pa Bunyan got tongue-tied and said, "That's a mighty *brice* nanyon, coy, I mean, a mighty nice canyon, boy!" Somehow part of the mix-up stuck.

To this day the canyon is known as Bryce Canyon.

After all that sculpting, Little Jean's shoes were full of sand. Pa knew Ma Bunyan wouldn't want her clean floors dirtied up, so he told Little Jean to sit down and empty out his shoes.

The sand from Little Jean's shoes blew away on the eastern wind and settled down a state away. It covered a valley ten miles long, making sand dunes eight hundred feet high. Everyone knows that's how the Great Sand Dunes of Colorado came to be.

One summer, Little Jean and Teeny wanted to go to the beach. Ma Bunyan told them to follow a river to the ocean. But all the rivers flowed west back then, so they missed the Atlantic Ocean and ended up on the other side of the country instead.

Ma Bunyan tracked them out to the Pacific Ocean, where she found Teeny riding on the backs of two blue whales and Little Jean carving out fifty zigzag miles of the California coast.

When Ma Bunyan saw what her son had done, she exclaimed, "What's the big idea, sir!?" From that time on, the scenic area was known as Big Sur.

Ma Bunyan knew she had to put up a barrier to remind her children not to wander off too far. So, on the way home, everyone pitched in and built the Rocky Mountains. Teeny gathered up and sorted out all the rivers, letting some flow east and others west. After that, the children had no trouble following the eastern rivers down to the Atlantic Ocean. And when they wanted to go out exploring, Ma Bunyan would call out, "Now don't cross the Continental Divide, children!"

The best thing about camping is sleeping outdoors, and the worst thing is not having enough hot water. That's why the Bunyans always camped in Wyoming. By the time their camping years were over, Ma Bunyan had poked more than three hundred holes in the ground with her pickax and released tons of hot water from geysers. But Ma got tired of poking so many holes, so she made a geyser that blew every hour on the hour. After that, there was a steady supply of hot water to keep the giants' clothes and dishes sparkling clean.

Teeny named the geyser Old Faithful, and to this day, Old Faithful still blows its top every hour in Yellowstone National Park.

As our great country grew up, so did the Bunyan children. When the kids left home, Ma and Pa Bunyan retired to a wilderness area, where they still live happily.

Teeny hitched a ride on a whale over to England and became a famous fashion designer. Her colorful skirts made from air balloons and her breezy blouses cut from ship sails were a sensation at the first World's Fair in London.

Little Jean traveled to Venice, Italy, where he studied astronomy and art. Every day, the gondoliers would take their passengers down the Grand Canal to watch the giant artist chiseling his marble sculptures.

After graduation, Little Jean decided to explore new lands, as his parents had done. So he took two great jumps and one flying leap and bounded up into outer space.

In 1976, the year of our country's bicentennial, a spacecraft sent by the National Aeronautics and Space Administration was on a mission to study Mars. The spacecraft was named *Viking I*, and it took many photographs of the surface of the planet. One mysterious photo looked like a face carved out of colossal rock.

Some say the photograph is not a face, but an illusion caused by light and shadows on the rock. Others think the famous "Martian face" is just the spitting image of Little Jean Bunyan. If that's so, who knows what he's up to on the other planets.

Only time will tell!

from USA FROM SPACE
by Anne-Catherine Fallen

Satellites collect data about the Earth's surface using radar, and infrared and thermal imaging. This information can be compiled and layered to create "living maps" like these of the Grand Canyon and Yellowstone National Park.

The Grand Canyon

A rafting trip through the Grand Canyon is an exciting way to get a close look at the canyon walls, where the Earth's geologic history is exposed in layers of rock. Rafters can also discover the ruins of ancient Anasazi communities.

A deep blue line etched in pink rock, the Colorado River winds southwest through the Grand Canyon in Arizona. One mile deep and up to 18 miles wide, the canyon is so big that it can be seen even from high in space. Figuring in all the twists of the river, it is 277 miles long.

At sunrise and sunset, when light accents the colors and shapes the shadows, the rock walls of the Grand Canyon retell the ancient and dramatic story of the Earth's formation. The powerful Colorado River carved the Grand Canyon over the past 5 or 6 million years. Sand and gravel carried by the rushing water acted like a scrub brush, gouging away the rock inch by inch. The canyon walls are striped with horizontal layers of colored rock. Each layer represents a geologic era, when volcanoes and seas, sediment and erosion shaped the land. Some of the oldest rocks on the planet, close to 2 billion years old, are found at the bottom of the canyon. At the top, almost 8,000 feet above sea level, is a layer of limestone formed from marine animals.

Erosion is also responsible for the spectacular variety of shapes in the Grand Canyon. Harder rocks, such as sandstone and limestone, erode into vertical cliffs. Softer rocks, such as shale, form slopes and terraces.

The countryside surrounding the Grand Canyon is high plateau, a mostly flat, dry land. The tops of the plateaus, covered with sparse vegetation, show up as broad green areas in this satellite image. Most of the canyon is preserved as a national park, which is bordered by Indian reservations and national forests. At the far left, the dark waters of Lake Mead mark the western boundary of the Grand Canyon.

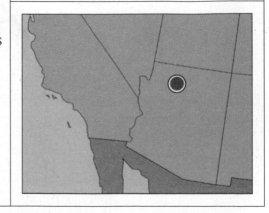

Yellowstone

Old Faithful is not the biggest or most powerful of Yellowstone's many geysers, but it is the most dependable, erupting to heights of 100 feet and more every 40 to 80 minutes. Old Faithful has performed on schedule since it was first observed by trappers over a century ago.

This view from space is too far away to capture the boiling, steaming, rumbling attractions of Yellowstone National Park. Taking up the northwest corner of Wyoming and crossing into Montana and Idaho, Yellowstone became the world's first national park in 1872. Best-known for its spouting geysers and grazing bison, the park preserves a unique geologic environment and is an important sanctuary for wildlife.

Yellowstone Lake, the big lake in the center of the image, is the largest lake in North America above 7,000 feet. The light blue line of the Yellowstone River curves northwest from the north shore of the lake. The park sits on top of the Continental Divide that separates rivers flowing east into the Mississippi River and the Gulf of Mexico from those running west into the Pacific. The Continental Divide zigzags from lower right to upper left, passing just beneath Yellowstone Lake.

The peaks, canyons, and lakes of Yellowstone were created over the past 2 million years by violent volcanic forces. Yellowstone sits inside a huge caldera, a collapsed crater so big it can't be seen from the ground. Two chambers filled with magma lie beneath the caldera, and a column of hot rock goes down 125 miles into the Earth's core. The heat from the rocks and magma is what causes geysers to erupt. Water collects in cracks underground and begins to heat up. Expanding steam forces the water upward, building pressure. When the balance between temperature and pressure reaches a critical point, the remaining water turns instantly into steam and shoots out of the ground. This spectacular display is repeated at dozens of spots throughout Yellowstone. Nearly two-thirds of the world's active geysers and hot springs are concentrated here.

Think About Reading

Answer the questions and then complete the chart.

CHARACTERS AND SETTING

1. Who are the characters in the story?
2. Where and when does the story take place?

NATURAL WONDER	WHO MADE IT?	HOW DID IT HAPPEN?
Mammoth Cave	Carrie McIntie (Ma Bunyan)	She was digging to find her lucky wishbone.
Niagara Falls	Teeny and Pa Bunyan	3.
Bryce Canyon	4.	5.
Great Sand Dunes of Colorado	6.	7.
The Continental Divide	8.	9.
Old Faithful	10.	11.

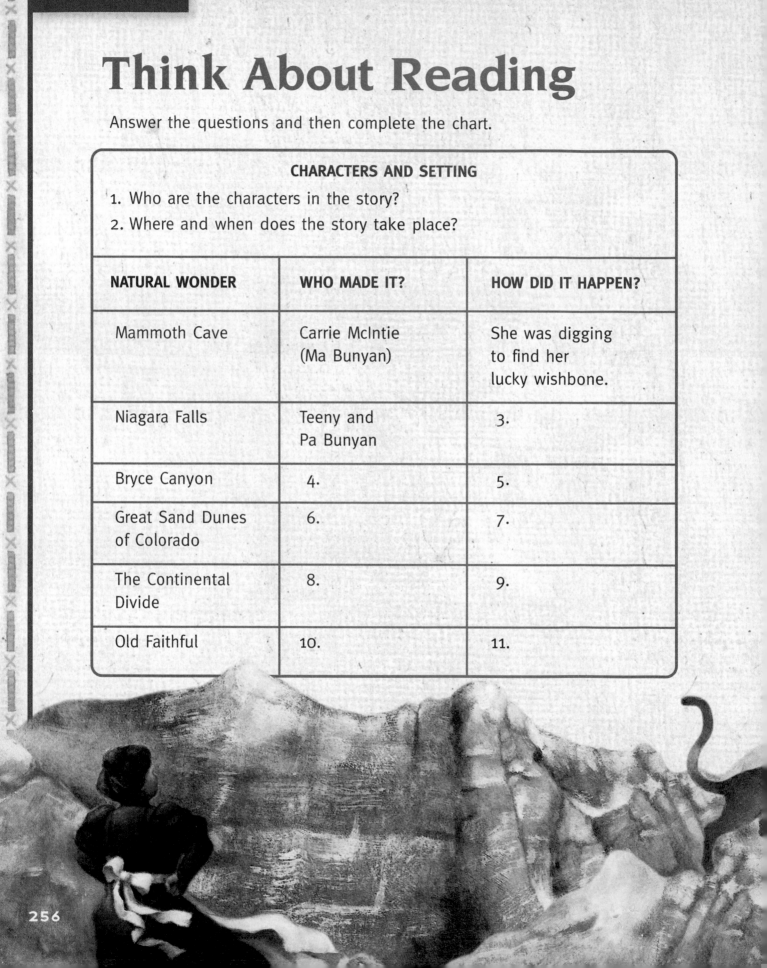

Write an Introduction

Pa Bunyan is presenting a speech to a group of geologists who study natural wonders in North America. Write an introduction for Pa. Tell what kind of guy he is. Give a quick rundown of some of his most important contributions to the North American landscape. Make your introduction lively and fun so the audience will look forward to hearing Pa speak.

Literature Circle

A picture is worth a thousand words! Discuss how David Shannon's great illustrations help you understand and appreciate the story of the Bunyans. What added information and details are pictured in the illustrations? How do the illustrations make you feel? Then discuss how the images from *USA From Space* help you picture the natural wonders mentioned in *The Bunyans*.

AUTHOR AND ILLUSTRATOR
Audrey Wood and David Shannon

As a child, Audrey Wood watched her father paint circus murals and listened to the stories her mother made up to go with them. She says, "By fourth grade, I had two burning ambitions: to live in Doctor Dolittle's house and to write and illustrate children's books." Wood certainly has reached her second goal with over 30 children's books to her credit.

Award-winning illustrator David Shannon is known for his clever and colorful paintings. He lives in Los Angeles, California and loves the sun.

MORE BOOKS BY
Audrey Wood

- *Rude Giants*
- *The Rainbow Bridge: Inspired by a Chumash Tale*

SHIP

David Macaulay

JOURNAL

from

SHIP

by David Macaulay

In SHIP, *a fictional team of underwater archaeologists has been recovering and studying artifacts from a sunken caravel— a type of small wooden sailing ship. Then, one member of the team discovers an early-sixteenth-century journal that describes in detail the building of a caravel. The following journal entries tell how the main body of the ship was built and launched.*

The Seventh day of January in the Year of Our Lord — 1504

Although my brother Garcia and I are presently enjoying great success importing dyewood and pearls from the Indies, it seems only prudent to be searching for new sources of these precious commodities before we run out (or someone else finds them). We have therefore commissioned the building of a caravel. Such a ship, although quite small, is surprisingly capacious. It is also of modest draft and can be heavily armed, making it ideal for the uncertainties of exploration.

This latest addition to the Vergara fleet is to be built by the Guerra shipyard, which continues to flourish under the watchful eye of the widow Guerra. Prices remain high, but so too does the quality of the work, all of which is overseen by master shipwright Alonso de Fonseca. Because my personal life in Seville has grown somewhat complicated, Garcia has agreed that I should sail with the ship on its maiden voyage. For my own peace of mind, therefore, I have taken it upon myself to observe and record all aspects of the vessel's construction.

The Ninth day of January

Master Alonso looks favorably upon my quest and promises that no detail shall be overlooked. We passed this rainy afternoon reviewing the list of timbers required for the hull, all of which, I am pleased to report, will be the finest white oak. Once a year, Alonso and his master carpenter, José de Arbora, visit the forests to select lumber for their ships. In the winter, the trees they have marked are felled and sent on their way.

The Eleventh day of January

Alonso, José and I passed much of this morning with two lumber merchants who were attempting to justify their high prices. They complained incessantly about the difficulty of transporting wood to the city. Alonso countered their claims by suggesting that the Guadalquivir River does all the work. "It flows directly from the mountains to the sea and passes right by our shipyard on its way. All you have to do is throw the logs in and, two hundred miles later, pull them out!"

The Eighteenth day of January

By the time I reached the yard, José and his able apprentices were already shaping the keel—the very backbone of our ship, which, incidentally, we have named *Magdalena*. "Once the rough shape has been established with the ax," he informed me, "each face of the timber will be smoothed with the short strokes of the adze." José is reputed to be one of the finest adze men in the city, although his apprenticeship was not without personal cost. His right foot carries only four toes.

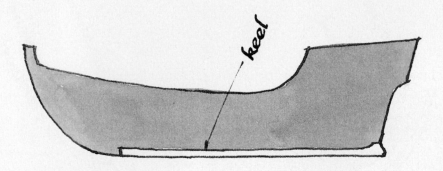

The Thirtieth day of January

Not surprisingly, my arrival this morning was greeted with greater than usual enthusiasm. As the sun, which has been rare of late, added its blessing to that of the good friar, *Magdalena*'s finished keel was levered up and onto its supports. This event, according to our contract, marks the day upon which my brother and I are bound to pay the first of three sums of money to the shipyard. This we did at the inn, in the presence of Alonso and the Señora's eldest son, Diego. After toasting the continued success of our venture, Master Alonso bade me accompany him to the blacksmith's. There he ordered large quantities of iron nails and bolts as well as two dozen spikes almost the length of my arm.

The Fifteenth day of February

The curved stempost that will lead *Magdalena* through the waves is now secured to the keel. A generous coating of pitch was applied to the adjoining surfaces before they were permanently fastened—a procedure that, Alonso assures me, will be repeated throughout construction to prevent rot. This afternoon a large curved brace called a deadwood was hoisted onto the keel where it fit with perfection into the curve of the stempost.

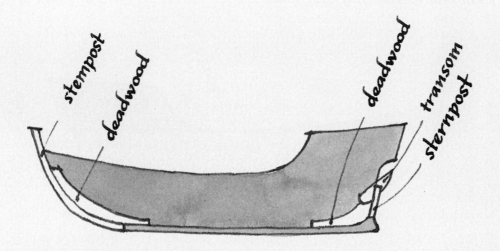

The Twenty-ninth day of February

The yard is very busy these days, and Alonso has been much distracted. One of Their Royal Highnesses' ships has been hauled over onto its side for repairs to the hull, and the cargo vessel that sits next to *Magdalena* is already being caulked in preparation for its launch. At the opposite end of *Magdalena*'s keel from the stempost, the sternpost and its deadwood are now in place. Together they support a fine broad transom. As I was leaving the yard, I found Alonso threatening one of the lumber merchants with all manner of legal retribution if the merchant did not immediately provide the promised timbers. "Did the Lord create lumber merchants simply to impede the shipwright's progress?" he shouted. "It is truly a miracle that Noah finished his work in time and that we were not all lost to the Great Flood."

The First day of March

From *Magdalena*'s sturdy spine, her ribs must now be built. After making a series of complicated calculations, which, he tells me, all begin with the length of the keel, Alonso creates two patterns from which all the largest ribs will be traced. Every rib is to be built in three pieces. The bottommost section, called the floor, will sit directly on the keel or deadwoods. Secured to the ends of each floor are the futtocks, which will support the sides of the ship. By slightly adjusting the pieces of the pattern for each one, Alonso and his apprentices trace the shapes of the first thirteen ribs.

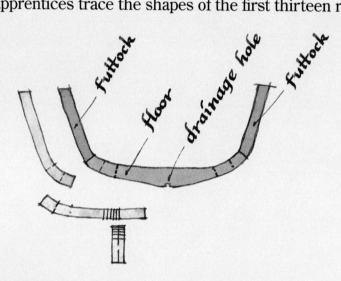

The Twentieth day of March

It has been some time since I put pen to paper. I was confined to my bed for two weeks with a terrible fever, although now, thanks be to God, I have regained my strength. Much has happened in my absence. The cargo ship that once stood next to *Magdalena* has been launched and now awaits its masts. Not only is our vessel free from its shadow, but the first of *Magdalena*'s ribs have been assembled and hoisted into place on the keel.

Because all ships, even those built by Alonso de Fonseca, are bound to leak, he has instructed that a small notch be cut at the base of each floor to direct water to the pump. I can tell you, having personally ventured into the holds of ships where this refinement was overlooked, the result is a most foul-smelling stew.

The Twenty-second day of March

This morning Alonso, José, and two apprentices began tacking thin strips of wood called ribbands between the posts and ribs on one side of the ship. Only after several hours of adjusting and readjusting did the two master craftsmen seem satisfied with the resulting shape. The curvature of each ribband was then carefully measured so that it could be replicated exactly on the opposite side of the ship. When all the ribbands are in place, a pattern will be made for each remaining rib.

The Twenty-fourth day of March

The keelson, an impressive piece of timber, is now installed. It rests upon the ribs directly above the keel. Because of its size and great weight, it was slipped into the hull before all the futtocks were attached.

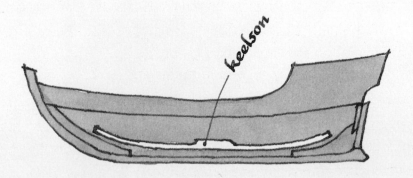

Easter Week

When the last of the ribs are in place, the tops of each futtock are then tied together by two heavy planks called wales. Each wale has been slowly bent over a hot fire so that it follows the curvature of the hull. Starting at the stempost on one side of the ship, carpenters move along the scaffolding, first drilling holes and then securing each connection with both iron nails and wooden pegs called treenails. It is José's desire to install both wales before the Easter fair, since leaving only one in place, even for a week, could cause the entire frame to become twisted.

The Twenty-fourth day of April

The keelson is notched to fit snugly over every floor and is held in place with long iron spikes. The wooden skeleton is further secured by two additional pieces of timber called stringers. These, too, are notched and extend from bow to stern along both sides of the keelson.

The Twenty-seventh day of April

Garcia chided me today for spending too much time at the shipyard. We have three ships leaving within the month, and there are still contracts to be drawn up and supplies to be gathered. I can barely force myself to confront the endless columns of figures that cover the pages of our ledgers, but as my elder brother points out, it is those endless columns which are paying for my current pleasure.

The Twenty-ninth day of April

It appears that Alonso has finally conquered the lumber men. Wood arrives every day, and much of it is immediately dragged to the saw pits for cutting. Piles of planks now lay waiting along both sides of the ship. José's carpenters have been sheathing the hull below the wales. They painstakingly measure and trim each plank to create the tightest possible seam before drilling and securing it to the ribs.

The Twenty-eighth day of May

Curved beams required to support the deck and ensure its drainage are now in place. José has begun framing a large hatch in the center of the deck so that cargo can be easily stored below. To increase the amount of deck space and provide some protection from the elements, a second, smaller deck is under construction at the stern.

The Thirty-first day of May

I was introduced today to Vincente Albene, a master caulker. He and his crew will seal the hull and later the deck by pounding strands of tar-soaked hemp called oakum into every seam. As a further precaution against leakage, Master Alonso has asked that a thin strip of lead be tacked over the oakum in those seams which will lie below the water line. No matter how well Albene does his work, however, some water will most certainly find its way into the hold. To return it to the sea as quickly as possible, Alonso has installed a pump that rises from the depths of the hold up through the main deck.

The Twenty-third day of June

The past two days have been spent getting ready for the launch. Once Albene and Alonso were satisfied with the caulking, the hull was coated with pitch. *Magdalena* was then carefully lowered onto two parallel wooden tracks that extend to the river. Tomorrow they will be covered with a thick coating of animal fat to help the ship slide more easily. The keel will travel freely in a trench dug between the tracks. This afternoon Alonso supervised the placement of many stones on the floor of the hold to help steady the ship as it enters the water.

The Twenty-fourth day of June

At about two o'clock Alonso gave the order from the bow to remove the remaining supports. At first there was no movement. Then, as people along both sides gently rocked the hull, it gradually slid onto the greased portion of the tracks. Cheers filled the air as the ship glided whole into the same river that only a few months earlier had delivered her in pieces.

Sea Fever

I must go down to the seas again, to the lonely sea and the sky,

And all I ask is a tall ship and a star to steer her by;

And the wheel's kick and the wind's song and the white sail's shaking,

And the gray mist on the sea's face, and a gray dawn breaking.

I must go down to the seas again, for the call of the running tide

Is a wild call and a clear call that may not be denied;

And all I ask is a windy day with the white clouds flying,

And the flung spray and the blown spume, and the seagulls crying.

I must go down to the seas again, to the vagrant gypsy life,

To the gull's way and the whale's way where the wind's like a whetted knife;

And all I ask is a merry yarn from a laughing fellow-rover,

And quiet sleep and a sweet dream when the long trick's over.

by John Masefield

illustrated by Raul Colon

Think About Reading

Write your answers.

1. Why is the journal writer having a ship built?

2. How does shipwright Master Alonso show that he takes great care with his work?

3. What do you think is the most challenging part of building the *Magdalena*? Why?

4. David Macaulay used a fictional journal to explain the design of a sixteenth-century caravel. How else might he have explained how a caravel was built? Which method do you think is more interesting?

5. How do the brothers in *Ship* feel about the sea? How are their feelings similar to or different from the narrator's in "Sea Fever"?

Write an Invitation

The owners of the *Magdalena* are having a party to celebrate the ship's completion. Write an invitation to the party that they will send to friends and business acquaintances. Include the party's date and time. Give a brief summary of events the owners have planned for the guests. Be sure to include the date, a greeting and a closing in the invitation.

Literature Circle

What kind of person is the journal writer? Discuss his character traits. What are his strong points and what are his weaknesses? How do you know? Do you think he is a good businessperson? How do you think the other characters in the story feel about him? Record your ideas on a character web.

AUTHOR AND ILLUSTRATOR
David Macaulay

Before David Macaulay began creating books, he earned a degree in architecture. Now Macaulay uses words and pictures to take his readers on fascinating architectural tours of places such as medieval castles and the Egyptian pyramids. His knowledge of design has also helped him to write and illustrate books such as *Ship* and *The Way Things Work*. Macaulay continues to create award-winning books that please readers everywhere.

MORE BOOKS BY
David Macaulay

- *Pyramid*
- *Cathedral*
- *The Way Things Work*

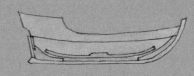

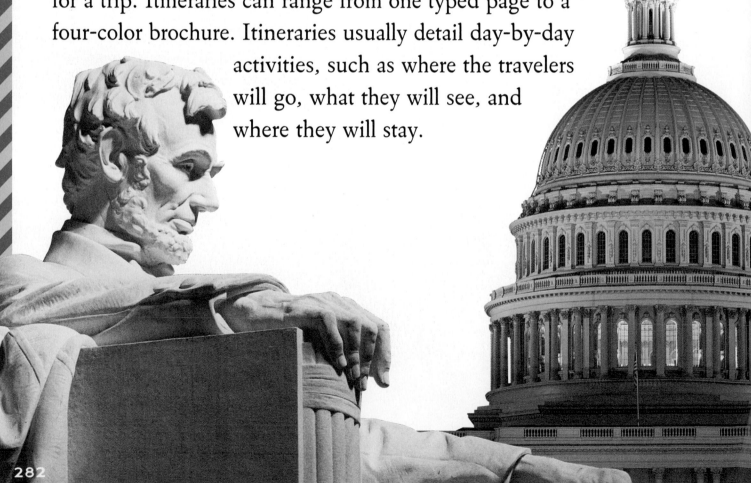

WORKSHOP

How to Develop an Itinerary

Itineraries indicate the length of the trip.

The places visited on the tour appear at the top of the itinerary.

Each day is described in detail.

Successful travel requires teamwork and planning. Time spent working with others to develop an itinerary helps to make a trip safe and enjoyable.

What is an itinerary? An itinerary is a plan or an outline for a trip. Itineraries can range from one typed page to a four-color brochure. Itineraries usually detail day-by-day activities, such as where the travelers will go, what they will see, and where they will stay.

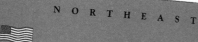

3 DAYS/2 NIGHTS ESCORTED

ITD3WA6

Points of Interest: • Baltimore Inner Harbor • Arlington National Cemetery • White House • Vietnam Veterans Memorial • Tomb of the Unknown Soldier • U.S. Capitol • Smithsonian Institution • Georgetown • Embassy Row

Washington, D.C. Getaway

Originates/Ends: New York, New Jersey, Pennsylvania
PASSENGERS MAY JOIN TOUR IN WASHINGTON, D.C.

Included Tour Features:
• Superior accommodations for 2 nights
• Narrated sightseeing tour in Washington, D.C.
• Professional tour director throughout
• Deluxe, air-conditioned motorcoach transportation
• Tourmobile in Arlington National Cemetery
• Visit of historic Baltimore Harbor
• All hotel taxes and luggage handling

1st Day
(Tour departs Monday, Friday & Saturday)
New York - Baltimore Inner Harbor - Washington, D.C.
Our deluxe motorcoach takes us on a relaxing ride to historic Baltimore, Maryland. There is ample time to stroll through the Inner Harbor with its beautiful Marina and the Harborplace before continuing to Washington, D.C. Accommodations for 2 nights are reserved. (Those passengers wishing to join the tour in Washington, D.C. will meet the group this evening at the hotel.) **Hotel: Washington Renaissance Hotel**

2nd Day
Washington, D.C. - Capitol Building - Arlington - White House
Today, enjoy a unique view of America's capital city. Our guided tour takes us to the White House (when available), the U.S. Capitol and the Washington Monument. We'll view the Vietnam Veterans Memorial and the Jefferson Memorial. In the afternoon, our escort takes us to Arlington National Cemetery, where we ride the Tourmobile and view the Kennedy gravesite. The remainder of the day is ours to visit Georgetown and Embassy Row or explore the famous Washington Mall. **Hotel: Washington Renaissance Hotel**

3rd Day
Washington, D.C. - Smithsonian Institution - New York
The last day of our Washington tour is devoted to the Smithsonian Institution, where we are free to visit the Museum of Natural History, the Museum of American History and the National Air and Space Museum, the most visited museum in the world. Or, we may choose to visit the Holocaust Memorial Museum. In the late afternoon we travel homeward, arriving this evening with wonderful memories of America's impressive capital city. On holiday weekends itinerary subject to change.

Washington Monument

Tour Rate Includes:
Deluxe motorcoach transportation, services of a professional tour director, 2 nights' accommodations at a superior hotel, narrated tour of Washington, D.C., admission to Tourmobile in Arlington National Cemetery, and gratuities for luggage handling.

Optional Meal Plan:
3 Meals $49 per person
Plan includes two (2) Full American breakfasts and one (1) dinner (Day 2). All taxes and gratuities included. Must be pre-purchased with tour program.

Pre And Post Tour Accommodations:
For hotel accommodations in New York, New Jersey & Pennsylvania before/after tour, see page 7. For passengers joining in Washington, D.C., additional hotel nights can be reserved before tour at:

	Twin	Single	Triple
Washington Renaissance Washington, D.C.	$54	$108	$36

Rates are per person, per night.

Air Fare:
Air fare is available to cities where tour begins, see page 6.

Approximate Miles On Tour:
Day 1 - 226
Day 3 - 226

Sabre: TODDM2831
Worldspan: G/PTS/DTX/WAS3
Domenico Tours

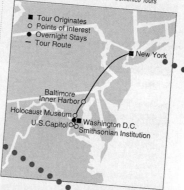
Lincoln Memorial

■ Tour Originates
○ Points of Interest
● Overnight Stays
— Tour Route

New York
Baltimore Inner Harbor
Holocaust Museum
U.S. Capitol
Washington D.C.
Smithsonian Institution

DEPARTURES

	TWIN	SINGLE	TRIPLE
MAR 24			
APR 7, 14, 21, 28			
MAY 5, 12, 19, 27			
JUN 2, 9, 16, 23			
SEP 8, 15,✦22,✦29			
OCT ✦7,✦13,✦20, 27			
NOV 3, 10, 17, 24	$259	$349	$239
JUL 1, 7, 10, 14, 17, 21, 24, 28, 31			
AUG 4, 7, 11, 14, 18, 21, 25, 28			
SEP 2	$269	$359	$249

✦ = Fall Foliage Departure.

28

A list gives information about services provided by the tour company.

A map shows the route of the tour. Daily mileage is listed above.

The fact box lists all the departure dates for one year, along with rates for twin, single, and triple hotel rooms.

Photographs show some of the sights seen on the tour.

1 Brainstorm

Where would you go, and what would you do, if you could travel anywhere in the world? With your team, choose a destination for a week's vacation. You can stay in one place or visit several spots. Decide what sort of vacation activity you'd like to focus on. Will you visit a theme park? take a ski trip? tour museums or historic sites? backpack through the wilderness?

Remember, you have only seven days to complete your travel!

TOOLS

- paper and pencil

- folder

- photographs and maps

- art supplies

2 Divide the Work

Make a list of the questions you'll need to answer to put together your travel itinerary. Depending on the size of your team, assign each team member to research one or two items. Your list will probably include questions such as the following:

- Transportation: How do we get from place to place?

- Recreation and sightseeing: What can we do at each place?

- Dining: Where do we eat?

- Lodging: Where do we sleep?

  - Weather: What is the best time of the year for this trip?

  - Budget: How much will the trip cost?

3 Research

Research the questions on your list. There are many sources of information about world destinations. You might want to try some of these:

- atlases and encyclopedias
- travel sections of libraries
- state tourist boards
- travel magazines
- travel sections of newspapers
- travel agencies or an automobile association
- other people who have traveled to your location

Take notes on the information you find. File them in a folder.

Tip Communication among team members is essential. For instance, your "transportation director" must be in touch with your "sightseeing planner" in order to arrange transportation to each sight you'll visit.

4 Complete Your Plans

Gather your research information. Use it to make group decisions about your trip: what forms of transportation you'll use, where you'll stay, how you'll spend each day, and what you'll do about meals.

Write your itinerary. Check it to make sure you haven't left out any times, dates, or other important details. Add any maps, charts, or illustrations you want to include.

Share your itinerary with your class. Would you like to trade your team's vacation for any of the others?

If You Are Using a Computer . . .

Create a separate journal entry for each item you need to research. Record the information you find and share it with others on-line.

THINK

What kind of planning is involved when you take a class trip?

Marie French
Travel Agent ▶

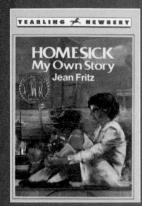

MEMOIR

Homesick
My Own Story

by Jean Fritz

illustrated by Tom Boll

Twelve-year-old Jean has lived her entire life in China. Now it is 1927, and she's sailing home to America. As she steps aboard ship, Jean begins to miss her Chinese nanny Lin Nai-Nai but also looks forward to meeting all her relatives in faraway Pennsylvania. During the long Pacific crossing, Jean and her friend Andrea endlessly talk about America—an America of 48 states where John Gilbert is the reigning Hollywood movie star.

On the whole, Andrea and I had a good time on the *President Taft.* In the evenings we often watched movies. In the afternoons we made pigs of ourselves at tea where we had our pick of all kinds of dainty sandwiches, scones, macaroons, chocolate bonbons, and gooey tarts. Actually, I even liked going to bed on shipboard. I'd lie in my bunk and feel the ship's engines throbbing and know that even when I fell asleep I wouldn't be wasting time. I'd still be on the go, moving closer to America every minute.

Still, my "in-between" feeling stayed with me. One evening after supper I took Andrea to the top deck and told her about the feeling. Of course the "in-betweenness" was stronger than ever in the dark with the circle of water rippling below and the night sky above spilling over with stars. I had never seen so many stars. When I looked for a spot where I might stick an extra star if I had one, I couldn't find any space at all. No matter how small, an extra star would be out of place, I decided. The universe was one-hundred-percent perfect just as it was.

And then Andrea began to dance. She had slipped off her shoes and stockings and she was dancing what was obviously an "in-between" dance, leaping up toward the stars, sinking down toward the water, bending back toward China, reaching forward toward America, bending back again and again as if she could not tear herself away, yet each time dancing farther forward, swaying to and fro. Finally, her arms raised, she began twirling around, faster and faster, as if she were trying to outspin time itself. Scarcely breathing, I sat beside a smokestack and watched. She was making a poem and I was inside the poem with her. Under the stars, in the middle of the Pacific Ocean. I would never forget this night, I thought. Not if I lived to be one hundred.

Only when we came to the international date line did my "in-between" feeling disappear. This is the place, a kind of imaginary line in the ocean, where all ships going east add an extra day to that week and all ships going west drop a day. This is so you can keep up with the world turning and make time come out right. We had two Tuesdays in a row when we crossed the line and after that when it was "today" for me, I knew that Lin Nai-Nai was already in "tomorrow." I didn't like to think of Lin Nai-Nai so far ahead of me. It was as if we'd suddenly been tossed on different planets.

On the other hand, this was the first time in my life that I was sharing the same day with my grandmother.

Oh, Grandma, I thought, ready or not, here I come!

It was only a short time later that Edward saw a couple of rocks poking out of the water and yelled for us to come. The rocks could hardly be called land, but we knew they were the beginning of the Hawaiian Islands and we knew that the Hawaiian Islands were a territory belonging to the United States.

Of course it wasn't the same as one of the forty-eight states; still, when we stepped off the *President Taft* in Honolulu (where we were to stay a couple of days before going on to San Francisco), we wondered if we could truthfully say we were stepping on American soil. I said no. Since the Hawaiian Islands didn't have a star in the flag, they couldn't be one-hundred-percent American, and I wasn't going to consider myself on American soil until I had put my feet flat down on the state of California.

We had a week to wait. The morning we were due to arrive in San Francisco, all the passengers came on deck early, but I was the first. I skipped breakfast and went to the very front of the ship where the railing comes to a point. That morning I would be the "eyes" of the *President Taft*, searching the horizon for the first speck of land. My private ceremony of greeting, however, would not come until we were closer, until we were sailing through the Golden Gate. For years I had heard about the Golden Gate, a narrow stretch of water connecting the Pacific Ocean to San Francisco Bay. And for years I had planned my entrance.

Dressed in my navy skirt, white blouse, and silk stockings, I felt every bit as neat as Columbus or Balboa and every bit as heroic when I finally spotted America in the distance. The decks had filled with passengers by now, and as I watched the land come closer, I had to tell myself over and over that I was HERE. At last.

Then the ship entered the narrow stretch of the Golden Gate and I could see American hills on my left and American houses on my right, and I took a deep breath of American air.

"'Breathes there the man, with soul so dead,'" I cried,

"'Who never to himself hath said,

This is my own, my native land!'"

I forgot that there were people behind and around me until I heard a few snickers and a scattering of claps, but I didn't care. I wasn't reciting for anyone's benefit but my own.

Next for my first steps on American soil, but when the time came, I forgot all about them. As soon as we were on the dock, we were jostled from line to line. Believe it or not, after crossing thousands of miles of ocean to get here, we had to prove that it was O.K. for us to come into the U.S.A. We had to show that we were honest-to-goodness citizens and not spies. We had to open our baggage and let inspectors see that we weren't smuggling in...anything...illegal. We even had to prove that we were germ-free, that we didn't have smallpox or any dire disease that would infect the country. After we had finally passed the tests, I expected to feel one-hundred-percent American. Instead, stepping from the dock into the city of San Francisco, I felt dizzy and unreal, as if I were a made-up character in a book I had read too many times to believe it wasn't still a book. As we walked the Hulls to the car that their Aunt Kay had driven up from Los Angeles, I told Andrea about my crazy feeling.

"I'm kind of funny in the head," I said. "As if I'm not really me. As if this isn't really happening."

"Me too," Andrea agreed. "I guess our brains haven't caught up to us yet. But my brains better get going. Guess what?"

"What?"

"Aunt Kay says our house in Los Angeles is not far from Hollywood."

Then suddenly the scene speeded up and the Hulls were in the car, ready to leave for Los Angeles, while I was still stuck in a book without having said any of the things I wanted to. I ran after the car as it started.

"Give my love to John Gilbert," I yelled to Andrea.

She stuck her head out the window. "And how!" she yelled back.

My mother, father, and I were going to stay in a hotel overnight and start across the continent the next morning, May 24, in our new Dodge. The first thing we did now was to go to a drugstore where my father ordered three ice-cream sodas. "As tall as you can make them," he said. "We have to make up for lost time."

My first American soda was chocolate and it was a whopper. While we sucked away on our straws, my father read to us from the latest newspaper. The big story was about America's new hero, an aviator named Charles Lindbergh who had just made the first solo flight across the Atlantic Ocean. Of course I admired him for having done such a brave and scary thing, but I bet he wasn't any more surprised to have made it across one ocean than I was to have finally made it across another. I looked at his picture. His goggles were pushed back on his helmet and he was grinning. He had it all over John Gilbert, I decided. I might even consider having a crush on him—that is, if and when I ever felt the urge. Right now I was coming to the bottom of my soda and I was trying to slurp up the last drops when my mother told me to quit; I was making too much noise.

The rest of the afternoon we spent sight-seeing, riding up and down seesaw hills in cable cars, walking in and out of American stores. Every once in a while I found myself smiling at total strangers because I knew that if I were to speak to them in English, they'd answer in English. We were all Americans. Yet I still felt as if I were telling myself a story. America didn't become completely real for me until the next day after we'd left San Francisco and were out in the country.

My father had told my mother and me that since he wasn't
used to our new car or to American highways, we should be
quiet and let him concentrate. My mother concentrated too.
Sitting in the front seat, she flinched every time she saw
another car, a crossroad, a stray dog, but she never said a word.
I paid no attention to the road. I just kept looking out the
window until all at once there on my right was a white picket
fence and a meadow, fresh and green as if it had just this
minute been created. Two black-and-white cows were grazing
slowly over the grass as if they had all the time in the world, as
if they knew that no matter how much they ate, there'd always
be more, as if in their quiet munching way they understood that
they had nothing, nothing whatsoever to worry about. I poked
my mother, pointed, and whispered, "Cows." I had never seen
cows in China but it was not the cows themselves that
impressed me. It was the whole scene. The perfect greenness.

The washed-clean look. The peacefulness. Oh, *now*! I thought.
Now I was in America. Every last inch of me.

By the second day my father acted as if he'd been driving
the car all his life. He not only talked, he sang, and if he felt
like hitching up his trousers, he just took his hands off the
wheel and hitched. But as my father relaxed, my mother became
more tense. "Arthur," she finally said, "you are going forty-five."

My father laughed. "Well, we're headed for the stable,
Myrtle. You never heard of a horse that dawdled on its way
home, did you?"

My mother's lips went tight and thin. "The whole point of
driving across the continent," she said, "was so we could see
the country."

"Well, it's all there." My father swept his hand from one
side of the car to the other. "All you have to do is to take your
eyes off the road and look." He honked his horn at the car in
front of him and swung around it.

At the end of the day, after we were settled in an overnight cabin, my father took a new notebook from his pocket. I watched as he wrote: "May 24. 260 miles." Just as I'd suspected, my father was out to break records. I bet that before long we'd be making 300 miles or more a day. I bet we'd be in Washington, P.A., long before July.

The trouble with record breaking is that it can lead to Narrow Squeaks, and while we were still in California we had our first one. Driving along a back road that my father had figured out was a shortcut, we came to a bridge with a barrier across it and a sign in front: THIS BRIDGE CONDEMNED. DO NOT PASS. There was no other road marked DETOUR, so obviously the only thing to do was to turn around and go back about five miles to the last town and take the regular highway. My father stopped the car. "You'd think they'd warn you in advance," he muttered. He slammed the door, jumped over the barrier, and walked onto the bridge. Then he climbed down the riverbank and looked up at the bridge from below. When he came back up the bank, he pushed the barrier aside, got in the car, and started it up. "We can make it," he said.

It hadn't occurred to me that he'd try to drive across. My mother put her hand on his arm. "Please, Arthur," she begged, but I didn't bother with any "pleases." If he wanted to kill himself, he didn't have to kill Mother and me too. "Let Mother and me walk across," I shouted. "Let us out. Let us OUT."

My father had already revved up the motor. "A car can have only one driver," he snapped. "I'm it." He backed up so he could get a flying start and then we whooped across the bridge, our wheels clattering across the loose boards, space gaping below. Well, we did reach the other side and when I looked back, I saw that the bridge was still there.

"You see?" my father crowed. "You see how much time we saved?"

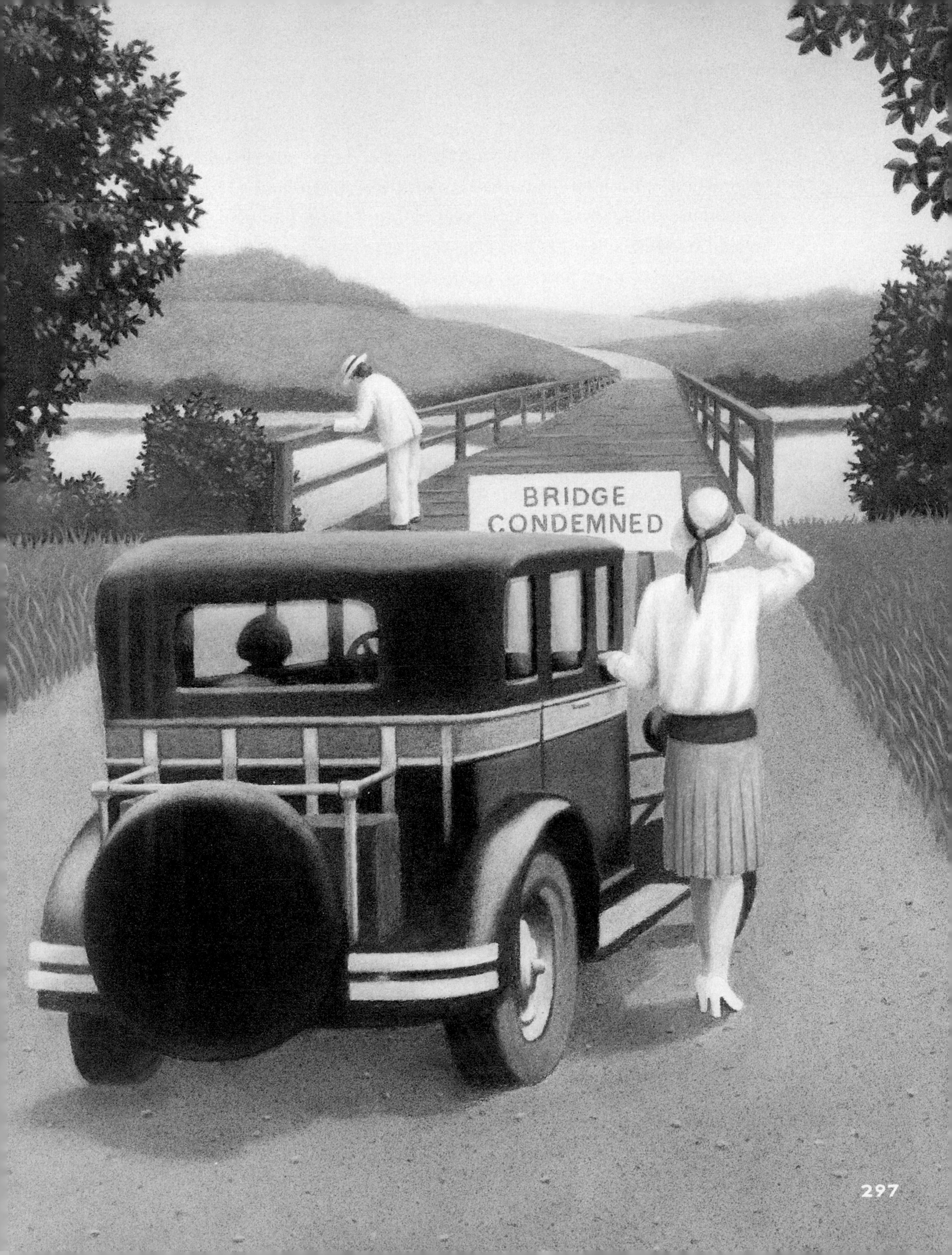
BRIDGE
CONDEMNED

All I could see was that we'd risked our lives because he was so pigheaded. Right then I hated my father. I felt rotten hating someone I really loved but I couldn't help it. I knew the loving would come back but I had to wait several hours.

There were days, however, particularly across the long, flat stretches of Texas, when nothing out-of-the-way happened. We just drove on and on, and although my father reported at the end of the day that we'd gone 350 miles, the scenery was the same at the end as at the beginning, so it didn't feel as if we'd moved at all. Other times we ran into storms or into road construction and we were lucky if we made 200 miles. But the best day of the whole trip, at least as far as my mother and I were concerned, was the day that we had a flat tire in the Ozark Mountains. The spare tire and jack were buried in the trunk under all our luggage, so everything had to be taken out before my father could even begin work on the tire. There was no point in offering to help because my father had a system for loading and unloading which only he understood, so my mother and I set off up the mountainside, looking for wild flowers.

"Watch out for snakes," my mother said, but her voice was so happy, I knew she wasn't thinking about snakes.

As soon as I stepped out of the car, I fell in love with the day. With the sky—fresh, blotting-paper blue. With the mountains, warm and piney and polka-dotted with flowers we would never have seen from the window of a car. We decided to pick one of each kind and press them in my gray geography book which I had in the car. My mother held out her skirt, making a hollow out of it, while I dropped in the flowers and she named them: forget-me-not, wintergreen, pink, wild rose. When we didn't know the name, I'd make one up: pagoda plant, wild confetti, French knot. My mother's skirt was atumble with color when we suddenly realized how far we'd walked. Holding her skirt high, my mother led the way back, running and laughing.

We arrived at the car, out of breath, just as my father was loading the last of the luggage into the trunk. He glared at us, his face streaming with perspiration. "I don't have a dry stitch on me," he said, as if it were our fault that he sweat so much. Then he looked at the flowers in Mother's skirt and his face softened. He took out his handkerchief and wiped his face and neck and finally he smiled. "I guess I picked a good place to have a flat tire, didn't I?" he said.

The farther we went, the better mileage we made, so that by the middle of June we were almost to the West Virginia state line. My father said we'd get to Washington, P.A., the day after the next, sometime in the afternoon. He called my grandmother on the phone, grinning because he knew how surprised she'd be. I stood close so I could hear her voice.

"Mother?" he said when she answered. "How about stirring up a batch of flannel cakes?"

"Arthur!" (She sounded just the way I knew she would.) "Well, land's sakes, Arthur, where are you?"

"About ready to cross into West Virginia."

My grandmother was so excited that her words fell over each other as she tried to relay the news to my grandfather and Aunt Margaret and talk over the phone at the same time.

The next day it poured rain and although that didn't slow us down, my mother started worrying. Shirls Avenue, my grandparents' street, apparently turned into a dirt road just before plunging down a steep hill to their house and farm. In wet weather the road became one big sea of mud which, according to my mother, would be "worth your life to drive through."

"If it looks bad," my mother suggested, "we can park at the top of the hill and walk down in our galoshes."

My father sighed. "Myrtle," he said, "we've driven across the Mohave Desert. We've been through thick and thin for over three thousand miles and here you are worrying about Shirls Avenue."

The next day the sun was out, but when we came to Shirls Avenue, I could see that the sun hadn't done a thing to dry up the hill. My father put the car into low, my mother closed her eyes, and down we went, sloshing up to our hubcaps, careening from one rut to another, while my father kept one hand down hard on the horn to announce our arrival.

By the time we were at the bottom of the hill and had parked beside the house, my grandmother, my grandfather, and Aunt Margaret were all outside, looking exactly the way they had in the calendar picture. I ran right into my grandmother's arms as if I'd been doing this every day.

"Welcome home! Oh, welcome home!" my grandmother cried.

I hadn't known it but this was exactly what I'd wanted her to say. I needed to hear it said out loud. I was home.

PREAMBLE TO THE CONSTITUTION OF THE UNITED STATES

We, the people of the United States, in order to form a more perfect union, establish justice, insure domestic tranquility, provide for the common defence, promote the general welfare, and secure the blessings of liberty to ourselves and our posterity, do ordain and establish this Constitution for the United States of America.

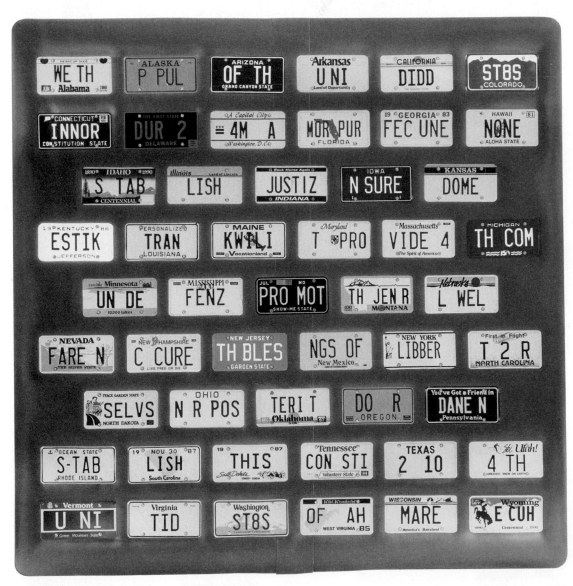

PREAMBLE
MIKE WILKENS

National Museum of Art, Smithsonian Institution

MENTOR

Marie French

Travel Agent

Marie French and her team work hard to make traveling easy.

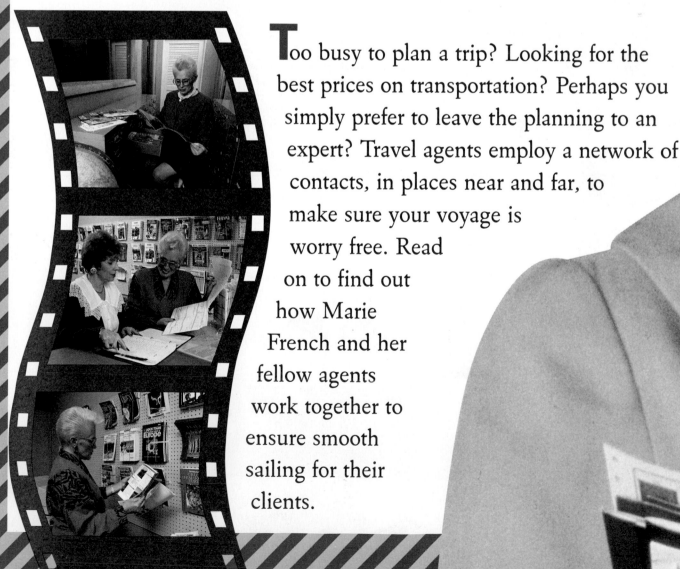

Too busy to plan a trip? Looking for the best prices on transportation? Perhaps you simply prefer to leave the planning to an expert? Travel agents employ a network of contacts, in places near and far, to make sure your voyage is worry free. Read on to find out how Marie French and her fellow agents work together to ensure smooth sailing for their clients.

PROFILE

Name: Marie French

Occupation: travel agent

Education: Harper College

Interests: interior design, photography

Favorite travel destination: Rome and Israel for history, Greek islands for relaxation

Favorite travel magazine: *Travel Weekly*

Favorite travel movie: *Raiders of the Lost Ark*

Souvenir collection: polished stones from all over the world

QUESTIONS
for Marie French

Find out how Marie French and her colleagues make plans for people on the go.

Q When a client asks you to plan a trip, what do you do?

A It depends on what the client wants. If she or he needs an airline ticket, the procedure is simple. We make at least three calls to find the best possible rate. If the client wants to rent a car or reserve a hotel room, we arrange those things, too.

Q How do you and your colleagues at the agency split up the work?

A Everyone does everything, but each of us has special knowledge of certain places. My belief is that if I don't know something, somebody else does. We are a team and we depend on each other. On really large projects, two agents work together so that there is always someone to follow up if needed.

Q How do you and your colleagues communicate?

A We hold daily meetings before the agency opens to talk about future concerns, discuss outside organizations we're using, and review any problems our clients have experienced.

Q What tools do you depend on the most in your office?

A The telephone and the computer. We use them all the time. Everything we do for our clients goes into a computer database. We also rely on maps, timetables, and currency exchange charts.

Q Do you make out itineraries for your clients?

A Every client gets an itinerary listing everything that has been arranged and paid for: car rentals, airline tickets, hotel rooms, and more. Every move the client will make is listed.

Q How do you communicate with organizations in other countries?

A Fax machines are essential. If you call an organization in a foreign country, you might not reach anyone who speaks your language.

But if you send a fax, there is always someone who can translate. My colleagues speak a total of six different languages, so we can usually translate incoming faxes here in our office.

Q If you could travel anywhere in the world, where would you go?

A Every year I take a trip to a different place. This year I am going to Jordan.

Marie French's Tips
for Group Travelers

1 Split up the research and planning for your trip.

2 If you're visiting a foreign country, learn a few words and phrases in the language of that country.

3 Take turns suggesting things to do. Don't be afraid to try new things.

4 Respect the culture and customs of the place you visit.

305

Think About Reading

Write the answers.

1. What is Jean's first experience in America after she and her family check into the hotel?

2. When Jean is on the ship, she says that she has an "in-between feeling." What does she mean?

3. Which part of Jean's journey do you find most exciting? Why?

4. How does author Jean Fritz make the journey across the United States interesting for the reader?

5. Through which states shown on the license plates in *Preamble* do you think Jean and her family travelled?

Write a Friendly Letter

Imagine that you are Jean, the narrator of *Homesick*. Write a friendly letter to your friend Andrea. Describe your journey across the United States, including highlights of the trip as well as your thoughts and feelings during the journey. Be sure to tell Andrea how you felt when you finally reached your grandparents' house.

Literature Circle

Discuss some of the ways that Marie French and her fellow travel agents could have helped Jean and her parents before they made their trip from China to San Francisco and then across the United States. Imagine that you were helping Jean's family plan their trip. What are some places you would suggest they stop at along the way? List your ideas on a chart.

AUTHOR
Jean Fritz

Jean Fritz was born in China and lived there until 1927, when she was twelve. *Homesick: My Own Story* is based on her childhood experiences. Even though Fritz spent her childhood in China, her parents' glowing memories and letters from relatives made her feel homesick for America. Today Jean Fritz is widely recognized for her historical biographies of famous Americans. She says: "My interest in writing about American history stemmed originally, I think, from a subconscious desire to find roots."

MORE BOOKS BY
Jean Fritz

- *China Homecoming*
- *And Then What Happened, Paul Revere?*
- *Shh! We're Writing the Constitution*

WILMA UNLIMITED

How Wilma Rudolph Became the World's Fastest Woman

BY

KATHLEEN KRULL

ILLUSTRATED BY

DAVID DIAZ

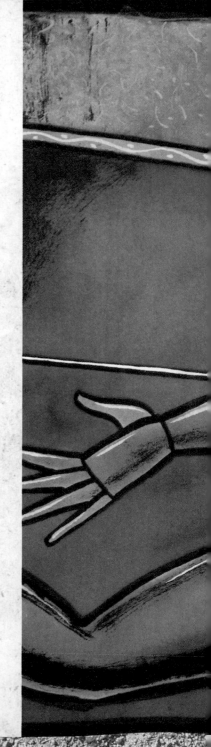

No one expected such a tiny girl to have a first birthday. In Clarksville, Tennessee, in 1940, life for a baby who weighed just over four pounds at birth was sure to be limited.

But most babies didn't have nineteen older brothers and sisters to watch over them. Most babies didn't have a mother who knew home remedies and a father who worked several jobs. Most babies weren't Wilma Rudolph.

Wilma did celebrate her first birthday, and everyone noticed that as soon as this girl could walk, she ran or jumped instead.

She worried people, though—she was always so small and sickly. If a brother or sister had a cold, she got double pneumonia. If one of them had measles, Wilma got measles, too, plus mumps and chicken pox.

Her mother always nursed her at home. Doctors were a luxury for the Rudolph family, and anyway, only one doctor in Clarksville would treat black people.

Just before Wilma turned five, she got sicker than ever. Her sisters and brothers heaped all the family's blankets on her, trying to keep her warm.

During that sickness, Wilma's left leg twisted inward, and she couldn't move it back. Not even Wilma's mother knew what was wrong.

The doctor came to see her then. Besides scarlet fever, he said, Wilma had also been stricken with polio. In those days, most children who got polio either died or were permanently crippled. There was no cure.

The news spread around Clarksville: Wilma, that lively girl, would never walk again.

But Wilma kept moving any way she could. By hopping on one foot, she could get herself around the house, to the outhouse in the backyard, and even, on Sundays, to church.

Wilma's mother urged her on. Mrs. Rudolph had plenty to do— cooking, cleaning, sewing patterned flour sacks into clothes for her children, now twenty-two in all. Yet twice every week, she and Wilma took the bus to the nearest hospital that would treat black patients, some fifty miles away in Nashville. They rode together in the back, the only place blacks were allowed to sit.

Doctors and nurses at the hospital helped Wilma do exercises to make her paralyzed leg stronger. At home, Wilma practiced them constantly, even when it hurt.

To Wilma, what hurt most was that the local school wouldn't let her attend because she couldn't walk. Tearful and lonely, she watched her brothers and sisters run off to school each day, leaving her behind. Finally, tired of crying all the time, she decided she had to fight back—somehow.

Wilma worked so hard at her exercises that the doctors decided she was ready for a heavy steel brace. With the brace supporting her leg, she didn't have to hop anymore. School was possible at last.

But it wasn't the happy place she had imagined. Her classmates made fun of her brace. During playground games she could only sit on the sidelines, twitchy with impatience. She studied the other kids for hours—memorizing moves, watching the ball zoom through the rim of the bushel basket they used as a hoop.

Wilma fought the sadness by doing more leg exercises. Her family always cheered her on, and Wilma did everything she could to keep them from worrying about her. At times her leg really did seem to be getting stronger. Other times it just hurt.

One Sunday, on her way to church, Wilma felt especially good. She and her family had always found strength in their faith, and church was Wilma's favorite place in the world. Everyone she knew would be there—talking and laughing, praying and singing. It would be just the place to try the bravest thing she had ever done.

She hung back while people filled the old building. Standing alone, the sound of hymns coloring the air, she unbuckled her heavy brace and set it by the church's front door. Taking a deep breath, she moved one foot in front of the other, her knees trembling violently. She took her mind off her knees by concentrating on taking another breath, and then another.

Whispers rippled throughout the gathering: Wilma Rudolph was *walking*. Row by row, heads turned toward her as she walked alone down the aisle. Her large family, all her family's friends, everyone from school—

each person stared wide-eyed. The singing never stopped; it seemed to
burst right through the walls and into the trees. Finally, Wilma reached
a seat in the front and began singing too, her smile triumphant.

Wilma practiced walking as often as she could after that, and when she was twelve years old, she was able to take off the brace for good. She and her mother realized she could get along without it, so one memorable day, they wrapped the hated brace in a box and mailed it back to the hospital.

As soon as Wilma sent that box away, she knew her life was beginning all over again.

After years of sitting on the sidelines, Wilma couldn't wait to throw herself into basketball, the game she had most liked to watch. She was skinny but no longer tiny. Her long, long legs would propel her across the court and through the air, and she knew all the rules and all the moves.

In high school, she led her basketball team to one victory after another. Eventually, she took the team all the way to the Tennessee state championships. There, to everyone's astonishment, her team lost.

Wilma had become accustomed to winning. Now she slumped on the bench, all the liveliness knocked out of her.

But at the game that day was a college coach. He admired Wilma's basketball playing but was especially impressed by the way she ran. He wanted her for his track-and-field team.

With his help, Wilma won a full athletic scholarship to Tennessee State University. She was the first member of her family to go to college.

Eight years after she mailed her brace away, Wilma's long legs and years of hard work carried her thousands of miles from Clarksville, Tennessee. The summer of 1960 she arrived in Rome, Italy, to represent the United States at the Olympic Games—as a runner.

Just participating in the Olympics was a deeply personal victory for Wilma, but her chances of winning a race were limited. Simply walking in Rome's shimmering heat was a chore, and athletes from other countries had run faster races than Wilma ever had. Women weren't thought to run very well, anyway; track-and-field was considered a sport for men. And the pressure from the public was intense—for the first time ever, the Olympics would be shown on television, and all the athletes knew that more than one hundred million people would be watching. Worst of all, Wilma had twisted her ankle just after she arrived in Rome. It was still swollen and painful on the day of her first race.

Yet once it was her turn to compete, Wilma forgot her ankle and everything else. She lunged forward, not thinking about her fear, her pain, or the sweat flying off her face. She ran better than she ever had before. And she ran better than anyone else.

Grabbing the attention of the whole world, Wilma Rudolph of the United States won the 100-meter dash. No one else even came close. An Olympic gold medal was hers to take home.

So when it was time for the 200-meter dash, Wilma's graceful long legs were already famous. Her ears buzzed with the sound of the crowd chanting her name. Such support helped her ignore the rain that was beginning to fall. At the crack of the starting gun, she surged into the humid air like a tornado. When she crossed the finish line, she had done it again. She finished far ahead of everyone else. She had earned her second gold medal. Wet and breathless, Wilma was exhilarated by the double triumph. The crowd went wild.

The 400-meter relay race was yet to come. Wilma's team faced the toughest competition of all. And as the fourth and final runner on her team, it was Wilma who had to cross the finish line.

Wilma's teammates ran well, passed the baton smoothly, and kept the team in first place. Wilma readied herself for the dash to the finish line as her third teammate ran toward her. She reached back for the baton—and nearly dropped it. As she tried to recover from the fumble, two other runners sped past her. Wilma and her team were suddenly in third place.

Ever since the day she had walked down the aisle at church, Wilma had known the power of concentration. Now, legs pumping, she put her mind to work. In a final, electrifying burst of speed, she pulled ahead. By a fraction of a second, she was the first to blast across the finish line. The thundering cheers matched the thundering of her own heart. She had made history. She had won for an astounding third time.

At her third ceremony that week, as the band played "The Star-Spangled Banner," Wilma stood tall and still, like a queen, the last of her three Olympic gold medals hanging around her neck.

Wilma Rudolph, once known as the sickliest child in Clarksville, had become the fastest woman in the world.

AUTHOR'S NOTE

Wilma Rudolph became, at age twenty, the first American woman to win three gold medals at a single Olympics. When she returned home from Rome, her family was waiting for her, and so was all of Clarksville, Tennessee. The huge parade and banquet held in her honor were the first events in the town's history to include both blacks and whites.

During the time of Wilma's childhood in the 1940s, polio, also known as infantile paralysis, was the world's most dreaded disease. A cure for it was not found until 1955. By then it had killed or crippled 357,000 Americans, mostly children — only 50,000 fewer than the number of Americans who had died in World War II.

After she retired from her career as a runner in 1962, Wilma became a second-grade teacher and a high school coach. She remained a much-admired celebrity, but to prove that there was more to her than just running, she started a company called Wilma Unlimited that gave her opportunities to travel, lecture, and support causes she believed in. Later she founded the nonprofit Wilma Rudolph Foundation to nurture young athletes and teach them that they, too, can succeed despite all odds against them. The story of all she overcame in order to win at the Olympics has inspired thousands of young athletes, especially women.

Wilma Rudolph died in 1994.

from GUINNESS RECORD BREAKERS
by KAREN ROMANO YOUNG

Because It's There

Sometimes you're inspired to do something great. Why? Because it fills you with awe. Because you love it. Because it's there.

Extra Young

In 1997, **Tara Lipinski**, age 14, became the youngest figure skater to win the World Championship. "I was just happy that it happened," she says. "It didn't matter about age." In 1998, she went on to win a gold medal in the Winter Olympics.

Cheri Becerra was one of a record 3,300 athletes with disabilities who competed at the 1996 Paralympics Games in Atlanta, Georgia. 225 new world records were set.

Youngest to Climb All 50 Peaks

At 14, Joshua Stewart was the youngest person to climb to the highest point in each of the 50 states.

How He Did It

Granite Peak, in Montana, was Joshua's first state peak. From there, Joshua's climbing took him and his father (who is the 50th person to climb all the peaks) zig-zagging around the United States. Not all the "peaks" were tough climbs: "Florida's—435 feet—is just a hill off the side of a road." But Mount McKinley, in Alaska, was a different story. "We were on it for three weeks," Joshua recalls. "Sometimes we had to stay in our tent for five days at a time, because of the snowstorms. We had to go out and shovel the snow off our tent or we'd suffocate." When Joshua reached the top, he would be the youngest to climb Mount McKinley—or so he thought. On the way up, he met a girl three weeks younger, who was just coming down.

Dream Record

"I'm working on climbing the highest mountains in each continent. I've already done Kilimanjaro in Africa and Mt. McKinley in North America."

THINK ABOUT READING

Write your answers.

1. Why was participating in the 1960 Olympic Games a personal victory for Wilma Rudolph?

2. What kind of person was Wilma Rudolph? How do you know?

3. Who or what in Wilma's life do you think influenced her the most? Why do you think so?

4. How might Wilma's life be different if she were growing up today? How might it be the same?

5. What characteristics do the athletes featured in "Because It's There" share with Wilma Rudolph?

WRITE AN ACCEPTANCE SPEECH

Write an acceptance speech that Wilma Rudolph might have given when she received one of her three gold medals at the 1960 Olympic Games. Tell what the medal means to her and why. Be sure to include a thank you to each person who inspired and helped her.

LITERATURE CIRCLE

Talk about what may have motivated Wilma Rudolph, Joshua Stewart, Tara Lipinski, and others to do something no one else had done before. Discuss why you think some people want to become record breakers. Why are people around the world such big fans of record breakers? How do the feats of athletes like Wilma Rudolph make you feel?

AUTHOR AND ILLUSTRATOR
KATHLEEN KRULL
AND DAVID DIAZ

As a child, author Kathleen Krull thought books were the most important things in the world. Now she writes them. She especially enjoys creating biographies for young people. She says, "I love the chance to explore subjects I'm passionate about." The story of Wilma Rudolph came out of her admiration for strong women.

David Diaz's illustrations have been called "remarkable" and "dazzling." In 1995, during a trip down Brazil's Amazon, he began developing the bold painting style that eventually won him a Caldecott Medal.

MORE BOOKS ILLUSTRATED BY
DAVID DIAZ

- *December* by Eve Bunting
- *Going Home* by Eve Bunting
- *Neighborhood Odes* by Gary Soto

PROJECT

How to
Publish a Travel Magazine

Build a publishing team and create a magazine that will entice others to travel.

Visitors to a travel agency will find plenty of travel magazines to browse through. Travel magazines provide pictures and articles about vacation spots around the world. Travelers might read travel magazines for ideas about where to travel or for information about destinations they've already chosen. It takes a team of writers, artists, and researchers to publish a really exciting travel magazine.

TERRIFIC TRAVEL

In this issue:

Top Ten Dream Vacations

Page 10

Choose a Focus

What would you like to read about in a travel magazine? With your team, decide on a focus for your magazine. Perhaps each teammate could write an article about his or her dream vacation. Or you might focus on one destination, with each teammate exploring something different about it. You could devote your magazine to budget travel, or to a comparison of great theme parks. For more ideas, browse through some travel magazines and think about what makes them particularly appealing or useful. Think also about what sort of audience you'd like your magazine to target.

Tip If you completed the Workshop, you might want to publish a travel magazine article about the destination you chose for your itinerary.

2 Plan Your Magazine

Make a list of all the articles and features you'd like to include in your magazine—first-person travel narratives; interviews with well-traveled friends; well-researched articles about dream destinations; charts, graphs, and maps; and so on. Decide how each teammate will contribute. Some of you might research and write articles while others locate photographs or create illustrations to accompany the articles. One or two teammates might take charge of laying out the finished contributions and making a cover and a table of contents. If you find yourself with more jobs than teammates, decide as a group which features to drop. Make a list of each teammate's assignment to use as a checklist when it's time to publish the magazine. Review the list to make sure you haven't neglected any important jobs.

How Am I Doing?

Before your team begins to put your magazine together, take a minute to ask yourself these questions:

- Has the team decided on a focus for the magazine?

- Have all the articles, columns, and features been assigned?

- Does everyone on the team have an assignment?

Do Your Part

Complete your magazine assignment. If you are writing an article or looking for photos, you might have to go to the library to do some research. Here are a few more suggestions.

Writers: Ask your teammates for ideas. Look at their travel brochures and itineraries for information.

Illustrators/Photo Researchers: If you're looking for photos or drawing illustrations for a specific article, make sure you know what it's about! Post-cards might make good illustrations. See if you have any at home, and ask your teammates to bring some, too.

Cover artists: Try to think up a cover design or illustration that will tie together everything inside the magazine. Explain your ideas to your teammates and get their feedback.

Everyone: Make sure your completed assignments are neat, clean, and ready to be published!

4 Publish Your Magazine

When all of your magazine copy is complete and the illustrations are ready, it's time to publish your travel magazine. Those team members who are in charge of layout should collect all of the articles and illustrations, and work together to come up with a creative and appealing layout for the magazine. When they are ready to put everything together, they might call a meeting of the whole team, to get their teammates' final input before publishing the magazine.

When all of the teams in your class have published their magazines, hold a Travel Day. Present your magazine in class, and exchange magazines with the other teams. Discover new places you'd like to explore!

If You Are Using a Computer ...

Create your travel magazine on the computer, using the Newsletter format. Browse through clip art to find maps for your magazine.

CONGRATULATIONS

You've found out how teammates can work together to plan a successful voyage or explore a new destination.

Marie French
Travel Agent ▶

IN THE SPOTLIGHT

IN THE SPOTLIGHT

THEME
We use our
creativity to reach
an audience.

UNIT 4

Welcome to

LITERACY PLACE

Actor's Workshop

We use our creativity to reach an audience.

FROM **BASEBALL IN APRIL
AND OTHER STORIES**
BY GARY SOTO

AWARD
WINNER

Manuel was the fourth of seven children and looked like a lot of kids in his neighborhood: black hair, brown face, and skinny legs scuffed from summer play. But summer was giving way to fall: the trees were turning red, the lawns brown, and the pomegranate trees were heavy with fruit. Manuel walked to school in the frosty morning, kicking leaves and thinking of tomorrow's talent show. He was still amazed that he had volunteered. He was going to pretend to sing Ritchie Valens's "La Bamba" before the entire school.

Why did I raise my hand? he asked

ILLUSTRATED BY JOSÉ ORTEGA

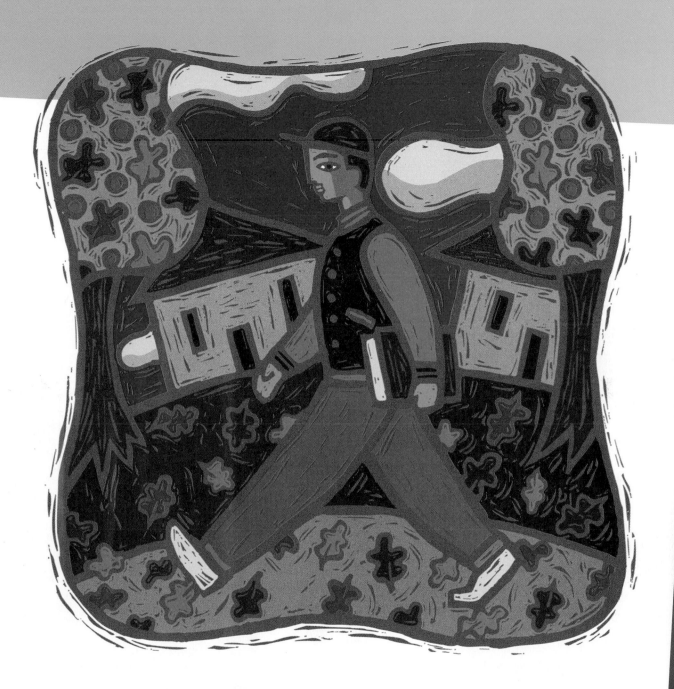

himself, but in his heart he knew the answer. He yearned for the limelight. He wanted applause as loud as a thunderstorm, and to hear his friends say, "Man, that was bad!" And he wanted to impress the girls, especially Petra Lopez, the second-prettiest girl in his class. The prettiest was already taken by his friend Ernie. Manuel knew he should be reasonable, since he himself was not great-looking, just average.

Manuel kicked through the fresh-fallen leaves. When he got to school he realized he had forgotten his math workbook. If the teacher found out, he would have to stay after school and miss practice for the talent show. But fortunately for him, they did drills that morning.

During lunch Manuel hung around with Benny, who was also in the talent show. Benny was going to play the trumpet in spite of the fat lip he had gotten playing football.

"How do I look?" Manuel asked. He cleared his throat and started moving his lips in pantomime. No words came out, just a hiss that sounded like a snake. Manuel tried to look emotional, flailing his arms on the high notes and opening his eyes and mouth as wide as he could when he came to "*Para bailar la baaaaammmba.*"

After Manuel finished, Benny said it looked all right, but suggested Manuel dance while he sang. Manuel thought for a moment and decided it was a good idea.

"Yeah, just think you're like Michael Jackson or someone like that," Benny suggested. "But don't get carried away."

During rehearsal, Mr. Roybal, nervous about his debut as the school's talent coordinator, muttered under his breath when the lever that controlled the speed on the record player jammed.

"Darn," he growled, trying to force the lever. "What's wrong with you?"

"Is it broken?" Manuel asked, bending over for a closer look. It looked all right to him.

Mr. Roybal assured Manuel that he would have a good record player at the talent show, even if it meant bringing his own stereo from home.

Manuel sat in a folding chair, twirling his record on his thumb. He watched a skit about personal hygiene, a mother-and-daughter

violin duo, five first-grade girls jumping rope, a karate kid breaking boards, three girls singing, and a skit about the pilgrims. If the record player hadn't been broken, he would have gone after the karate kid, an easy act to follow, he told himself.

As he twirled his forty-five record, Manuel thought they had a great talent show. The entire school would be amazed. His mother and father would be proud, and his brothers and sisters would be jealous and pout. It would be a night to remember.

Benny walked onto the stage, raised his trumpet to his mouth, and waited for his cue. Mr. Roybal raised his hand like a symphony conductor and let it fall dramatically. Benny inhaled and blew so loud that Manuel dropped his record, which rolled across the cafeteria floor until it hit a wall. Manuel raced after it, picked it up, and wiped it clean.

"Boy, I'm glad it didn't break," he said with a sigh.

That night Manuel had to do the dishes and a lot of homework, so he could only practice in the shower. In bed he prayed that he wouldn't mess up. He prayed that it wouldn't be like when he was a first-grader. For Science Week he had wired together a C battery and a bulb, and told everyone he had discovered how a flashlight worked. He was so pleased with himself that he practiced for hours pressing the wire to the battery, making the bulb wink a dim, orangish light. He showed it to so many kids in his neighborhood that when it was time to show his class how a flashlight worked, the battery was dead. He pressed the wire to the battery, but the bulb didn't respond. He pressed until his thumb hurt and some kids in the back started snickering.

But Manuel fell asleep confident that nothing would go wrong this time.

The next morning his father and mother beamed at him. They were proud that he was going to be in the talent show.

"I wish you would tell us what you're doing," his mother said. His father, a pharmacist who wore a blue smock with his name on a plastic rectangle, looked up from the newspaper and sided with his wife. "Yes, what are you doing in the talent show?"

"You'll see," Manuel said with his mouth full of Cheerios.

The day whizzed by, and so did his afternoon chores and dinner.

Suddenly he was dressed in his best clothes and standing next to Benny backstage, listening to the commotion as the cafeteria filled with school kids and parents. The lights dimmed, and Mr. Roybal, sweaty in a tight suit and a necktie with a large knot, wet his lips and parted the stage curtains.

"Good evening, everyone," the kids behind the curtain heard him say. "Good evening to you," some of the smart-alecky kids said back to him.

"Tonight we bring you the best John Burroughs Elementary has to offer, and I'm sure that you'll be both pleased and amazed that our little school houses so much talent. And now, without further ado, let's get on with the show." He turned and, with a swish of his hand, commanded, "Part the curtain." The curtains parted in jerks. A girl dressed as a toothbrush and a boy dressed as a dirty gray tooth walked onto the stage and sang:

> Brush, brush, brush
> Floss, floss, floss
> Gargle the germs away—
> hey! hey! hey!

After they finished singing, they turned to Mr. Roybal, who dropped his hand. The toothbrush dashed around the stage after the dirty tooth, which was laughing and having a great time until it slipped and nearly rolled off the stage.

Mr. Roybal jumped out and caught it just in time. "Are you OK?"

The dirty tooth answered, "Ask my dentist," which drew laughter and applause from the audience.

The violin duo played next, and except for one time when the girl got lost, they sounded fine. People applauded, and some even stood up. Then the first-grade girls maneuvered onto the stage while jumping rope. They were all smiles and bouncing ponytails as a hundred cameras flashed at once. Mothers "awhed" and fathers sat up proudly.

The karate kid was next. He did a few kicks, yells, and chops, and finally, when his father held up a board, punched it in two. The audience clapped and looked at each other, wide-eyed with respect. The boy bowed to the audience, and father and son ran off the stage.

Manuel remained behind the stage shivering with fear. He mouthed the words to "La Bamba" and swayed from left to right. Why did he raise his hand and volunteer? Why couldn't he

more sweaty than before, took Manuel's forty-five record and placed it on a new record player.

"You ready?" Mr. Roybal asked.

"Yeah..."

Mr. Roybal walked back on stage and announced that Manuel Gomez, a fifth-grader in Mrs. Knight's class, was going to pantomime Richie Valens's classic hit "La Bamba."

The cafeteria roared with applause. Manuel was nervous but loved the noisy crowd. He pictured his mother and father applauding loudly and his brothers and sisters also clapping, though not as energetically.

Manuel walked on stage and the song started immediately. Glassy-eyed from the shock of being in front of so many people, Manuel moved his lips and swayed in a made-up dance step. He couldn't see his parents, but he could see his brother Mario, who was a year younger, thumb-wrestling with a friend. Mario was wearing Manuel's favorite shirt; he would deal with Mario later. He saw some other kids get up and head for the drinking fountain, and a baby sitting in the middle of an aisle sucking her thumb and watching him intently.

have just sat there like the rest of the kids and not said anything? While the karate kid was on stage, Mr. Roybal,

What am I doing here? thought Manuel. This is no fun at all. Everyone was just sitting there. Some people were moving to the beat, but most were just watching him, like they would a monkey at the zoo.

But when Manuel did a fancy dance step, there was a burst of applause and some girls screamed. Manuel tried another dance step. He heard more applause and screams and started getting into the groove as he shivered and snaked like Michael Jackson around the stage. But the record got stuck, and he had to sing

Para bailar la bamba
Para bailar la bamba
Para bailar la bamba
Para bailar la bamba

again and again.

Manuel couldn't believe his bad luck. The audience began to laugh and stand up in their chairs. Manuel remembered how the forty-five record had dropped from his hand and rolled across the cafeteria floor. It probably got scratched, he thought, and now it was stuck, and he was stuck dancing and moving his lips to the same words over and over. He had never been so embarrassed. He would have to ask his parents to move the family out of town.

After Mr. Roybal ripped the needle across the record, Manuel slowed his dance steps to a halt. He didn't know what to do except bow to the audience, which applauded wildly, and scoot off the stage, on the verge of tears. This was worse than the homemade flashlight. At least no one laughed then, they just snickered.

Manuel stood alone, trying hard to hold back the tears as Benny, center stage, played his trumpet. Manuel was jealous because he sounded great, then mad as he recalled that it was Benny's loud trumpet playing that made the forty-five record fly out of his hands. But when the entire cast lined up for a curtain call, Manuel received a burst of applause that was so loud it shook the walls of the cafeteria. Later, as he mingled with the kids and parents, everyone patted him on the shoulder and told him, "Way to go. You were really funny."

Funny? Manuel thought. Did he do something funny?

Funny. Crazy. Hilarious. These were the words people said to him. He was confused, but beyond caring. All he knew was that people were paying attention to him, and his brother and sisters looked at him with a mixture of jealousy and awe. He was going to pull Mario aside and punch him in the arm for wearing his shirt, but he cooled it. He was enjoying the limelight. A teacher brought him cookies and punch, and the popular kids who had never before given him the time of day now clustered around him. Ricardo, the editor of the school bulletin, asked him how he made the needle stick.

"It just happened," Manuel said, crunching on a star-shaped cookie.

At home that night his father, eager to undo the buttons on his shirt and ease into his La-Z-Boy recliner, asked Manuel the same thing, how he managed to make the song stick on the words "*Para bailar la bamba.*"

Manuel thought quickly and reached for scientific jargon he had read in magazines. "Easy, Dad. I used laser tracking with high optics and low functional decibels per channel." His proud but confused father told him to be quiet and go to bed.

"Ah, *que niños tan truchas,*" he said as he walked to the kitchen for a glass of milk. "I don't know how you kids nowadays get so smart."

Manuel, feeling happy, went to his bedroom, undressed, and slipped into his pajamas. He looked in the mirror and began to pantomime "La Bamba," but stopped because he was tired of the song. He crawled into bed. The sheets were as cold as the moon that stood over the peach tree in their backyard.

He was relieved that the day was over. Next year, when they asked for volunteers for the talent show, he wouldn't raise his hand. Probably.

MENTOR

José García

Drama Coach

This coach teaches kids how to act up!

When you watch a movie, TV show, or play, the actors' performances often seem perfect. How do actors learn the tricks of their trade? If they're lucky, they have the help of a good drama coach like José García. García works with professional actors. He also teaches young people about acting and helps them prepare to give school presentations.

PROFILE

Name: José García

Occupation: drama coach

Previous jobs: substitute teacher, actor, set designer, maskmaker

Favorite actors: James Caan and Geraldine Page

Favorite play: *The Blood Wedding* by Federico García Lorca

Favorite story as a fifth grader: *The Lord of the Rings* by J.R.R. Tolkien

Most embarrassing moment on stage: "While showing off during a high school singing concert, I pushed my voice so much that I went flat."

QUESTIONS

for José García

Here's how drama coach José García trains performers to exercise their creativity.

Q When did you first become interested in acting?

A I created my own skits with friends as early as second grade. I even won the sixth-grade talent show at my school!

Q Who attends your acting workshops?

A I coach professional actors preparing for roles. I also work with kids who want to learn about acting, or who are preparing for school plays or other presentations.

Q Do all actors need coaches?

A Like any skill, acting is easier for some people than for others, but training is always important.

Q Many of your students have no acting experience. How do you get them started?

A I put them through a lot of exercises. I want them to be able to work with their whole bodies, from the tips of their toes to their hair follicles! Actors cannot work effectively unless their whole bodies are loose.

Q What kinds of exercises do you do?

A One favorite exercise involves masks. The students and I put on masks and move our heads and bodies silently. We try to convey the feeling of the masks through body language. As time goes on, we add sound, and eventually speech.

Q How do you help students prepare to perform in plays?

A We begin by reading through the script. We spend time analyzing the characters. Actors need to know their characters inside and out. Then they can begin to "play" with the roles and make them their own.

Q What's the most important skill an actor can have?

A I'd have to say sincerity. You have to believe in the role you are playing. If you are sincere, you will win over your audience.

Q Many people worry about stage fright. What is it?

A Butterflies in the stomach, trembling, anxiety, and fear of failure. It can be scary, but without it you don't have the edge. It's that excitement that allows an artist to work on a heightened level.

Q Besides working with actors, what things might you do in a typical day?

A I write plays and screenplays, and I spend time researching them. I also have to promote myself as an actor and drama coach. It takes a lot of work to get work! When I have time left over, I design masks and drama sets.

José García's Tips for Young Performers

1 Learn everything you can about your craft. There's always room to learn and improve.

2 Discover your own natural talents and strive to expand them. Don't try to be like someone else.

3 Don't allow others to discourage you. Believe in yourself.

THINK ABOUT READING

Answer the questions in the story map.

SETTING

1. Where does the story take place?

2. When does the story take place? How do you know?

CHARACTERS

3. Who is the main character in the story?

BEGINNING

4. How does Manuel feel about volunteering to sing "La Bamba" at the talent show?

5. What happens to the "La Bamba" recording during the dress rehearsal?

MIDDLE

6. Why is Manuel nervous the night before the talent show?

7. What happens during Manuel's performance that upsets him?

8. How does the crowd react?

ENDING

9. How does Manuel feel right after his performance? How does he feel a little later?

WRITE A FLYER

The school talent show is full of fun and entertainment! Write a flyer that announces and advertises the event. Tell the date, the time, and the location. Then spotlight some of the most interesting and unusual acts. Be sure to tell about Manuel's "La Bamba" pantomime, too.

LITERATURE CIRCLE

Talk about how drama coach José García might have been able to help Manuel practice for his performance at the talent show. Describe some activities and skills that he would suggest and how they might help Manuel. Then imagine that you could have a chance to work with José García. What would you want to work on with him?

AUTHOR
GARY SOTO

Gary Soto hasn't forgotten his childhood in Fresno, California. In fact, his memories of growing up in a close-knit Mexican American community show up in many of his poems, stories, and novels. As a child, Soto never dreamed that he would become a writer. Then he began to write poetry while he was in college. Soto says, "Writing is my one talent. There are a lot of people who never discover what their talent is. I am very lucky to have found mine."

MORE BOOKS BY
GARY SOTO

- *Pacific Crossing*
- *Chato's Kitchen*
- *Too Many Tamales*

THE HOME

"The Homecoming," by Laurence Yep, is a story from The Rainbow People, a collection of 20 Chinese folk tales. In this book Yep retells traditional stories that were collected and translated in the 1930s by a researcher who worked with Chinese Americans living in Oakland, California.

Once there was a woodcutter who minded everyone's business but his own. If you were digging a hole, he knew a better way to grip the shovel. If you were cooking a fish, he knew a better recipe. As his village said, he knew a little of everything and most of nothing.

If his wife and children hadn't made palm leaf fans, the family would have starved. Finally his wife got tired of everyone laughing at them. "You're supposed to be a woodcutter. Go up to the hill and cut some firewood."

COMING

by Laurence Yep
illustrations
by Chi Chung

"Any fool can do that." The woodcutter picked up his hatchet. "In the mountains there's plenty of tall oak. That's what burns best."

His wife pointed out the window. "But there's a stand of pine just over the ridgetop."

Her husband looked pained. "Pine won't sell as well. I'll take my load into town, where folk are too busy to cut their own. Then I'll come back with loads of cash." With a laugh, he shouldered his long pole. After he cut the wood, he would tie it into two big bundles and place each at the end of the pole. Then he would balance the load on his shoulder.

Waving good-bye to his children, he left their house; but his wife walked right with him. "What are you doing?" he asked.

His wife folded her arms as they walked along. "Escorting you."

He slowed down by a boy who was making a kite out of paper and rice paste. "That thing will never fly. You should—"

His wife caught his arm and pulled him along. "Don't be such a busybody."

"If a neighbor's doing something wrong, it's the charitable thing to set that person straight." He tried to stop by a man who was feeding his ducks. "Say, friend. Those ducks'll get fatter if—"

His wife yanked him away and gave him a good shake. "Do I have to blindfold you? We have two children to feed."

"I'm not lazy," he grumbled.

She kept dragging him out of the village. "I never said you were. You can do the work of two people when no one else is around. You're just too easily distracted."

She went with him to the very edge of the fields and sent him on his way. "Remember," she called after him. "Don't talk to anyone."

He walked with long, steady strides through the wooded hills. "I'll show her. It isn't how often you do something, it's how you do it. I'll cut twice the wood and sell it for double the price and come back in half the time."

Complaining loudly to himself, he moved deep into the mountains. I want just the right sort of oak, he thought to himself. As he walked along, he kept an eye out for a likely tree.

He didn't see the funny old man until he bumped into him. "Oof, watch where you're going," the old man said.

The old man had a head that bulged as big as a melon. He was dressed in a yellow robe embroidered with storks and pine trees.

Playing chess with the old man was another man so fat he could not close his robe. In his hand he had a large fan painted with scenes.

The fat man wagged a finger at the old man. "Don't try to change the subject. I've got you. It's checkmate in two moves."

The funny old man looked back at the chessboard. The lines were a bright red on yellow paper, and the chess pieces were flat disks with words painted in gold on their tops.

"Is it now, is it now?" the funny old man mused.

The woodcutter remembered his wife's warning. But he said to himself, "I'm not actually talking to them. I'm advising them." So he put down his hatchet and pole. "Actually, if you moved that piece"—he jabbed at a disk—"and moved it there"—he pointed at a spot on the board—"you'd have him."

But the old man moved a different disk.

The fat man scratched the top of his bald head. "Now how'd you think of that?"

The woodcutter rubbed his chin. "Yes, how *did* you think of that?" But then he nodded his head and pointed to one of the fat man's disks. "Still, if you shifted that one, you'd win."

However, the fat man ignored him as he made another move.

"Well," the woodcutter said to the old man, "you've got him now."

ut the old man paid him no more mind than the fat man. "Hmmm," he murmured, and set his chin on his fist as he studied the board.

The woodcutter became so caught up in the game that he squatted down. "I know what you have to do. I'll be right here just in case you need to ask."

Neither man said anything to the woodcutter. They just went on playing, and as they played, the woodcutter became more and more fascinated. He forgot about chopping wood. He even forgot about going home.

When it was night, the funny old man opened a big basket and lifted out a lantern covered with stars. He hung it from a tree and the game went on. Night passed on into day, but the woodcutter was as involved in the game now as the two men.

"Let's take a break." The old man slipped a peach from one big sleeve. The peach was big as the woodcutter's fist, and it filled the woods with a sweet aroma.

"You're just stalling for time," the fat man said. "Move."

"I'm hungry," the old man complained, and took a big bite. However, he shoved a piece along the board. When he held the peach out to the fat man, the fat man bit into it hungrily.

Alternating moves and bites, they went on until there was nothing left of the peach except the peach stone. "I feel much better now," the old man said, and threw the stone over his shoulder.

As the two men had eaten the peach, the woodcutter had discovered that he was famished, but the only thing was the peach stone. "Maybe I can suck on this stone and forget about being hungry. But I wish one of them would ask me for help. We could finish this game a lot quicker."

He tucked the stone into his mouth and tasted some of the peach juices. Instantly, he felt himself filled with energy. Goodness, he thought, I feel like there were lightning bolts zipping around inside me. And he went on watching the game with new energy.

After seven days, the old man stopped and stretched. "I think we're going to have to call this game a draw."

The fat man sighed. "I agree." He began to pick up the pieces.

The woodcutter spat out the stone. "But you could win easily."

The old man finally noticed him. "Are you still here?"

The woodcutter thought that this was his chance now to do a good deed. "It's been a most interesting game. However, if you—"

But the old man made shooing motions with his hands. "You should've gone home long ago."

"But I—" began the woodcutter.

The fat man rose. "Go home. It may already be too late."

That's a funny thing to say, the woodcutter thought. He turned around to get his things. But big, fat mushrooms had sprouted among the roots of the trees. A brown carpet surrounded him. He brushed the mushrooms aside until he found a rusty hatchet blade. He couldn't find a trace of the hatchet shaft or of his carrying pole.

Puzzled, he picked up the hatchet blade. "This can't be mine. My hatchet was practically new. Have you two gentlemen seen it?" He turned around again, but the two men had disappeared along with the chessboard and chess pieces.

"That's gratitude for you." Picking up the rusty hatchet blade, the woodcutter tried to make his way back through the woods; but he could not find the way he had come up. "It's like someone rearranged all the trees."

Somehow he made his way out of the mountains. However, fields and villages now stood where there had once been wooded hills. "What are you doing here?" he asked a farmer.

"What are you?" the farmer snorted, and went back to working in his field.

The woodcutter thought about telling him that he was swinging his hoe wrong, but he remembered what the two men had said. So he hurried home instead.

The woodcutter followed the river until he reached his own village, but as he walked through the fields, he didn't recognize one person. There was even a pond before the village gates. It had never been there before. He broke into a run, but there was a different house in the spot where his home had been. Even so, he burst into the place.

Two strange children looked up from the table, and a strange woman picked up a broom. "Out!"

The woodcutter raised his arms protectively. "Wait, I live here."

But the woman beat the woodcutter with a broom until he retreated into the street. By now, a crowd had gathered. The woodcutter looked around desperately. "What's happened to my village? Doesn't anyone know me?"

The village schoolteacher had come out of the school. He asked the woodcutter his name, and when the woodcutter told him, the schoolteacher pulled at his whiskers. "That name sounds familiar, but it can't be."

With the crowd following them, he led the woodcutter to the clan temple. "I collect odd, interesting stories." The schoolteacher got out a thick book. "There's a strange incident in the clan book." He leafed through the book toward the beginning and pointed to a name. "A woodcutter left the village and never came back." He added quietly. "But that was several thousand years ago."

"That's impossible," the woodcutter insisted. "I just stayed away to watch two men play a game of chess."

The schoolteacher sighed. "The two men must have been saints. Time doesn't pass for them as it does for us."

And at that moment, the woodcutter remembered his wife's warning.

But it was too late now.

The Art of

Most traditional stories were passed along orally for generations before anyone wrote them down. Today, modern storytellers from diverse cultures continue the oral tradition. They share traditional tales and personal stories with audiences around the globe.

The National Storytelling Association, headquartered in Jonesborough, Tennessee, is dedicated to preserving and expanding the art of storytelling. Each year, the NSA holds a National Storytelling Festival. Some of the most renowned storytellers in the world perform there. You will meet some of them on these pages.

Storyteller	Childhood Home
 **DEREK BURROWS**	Burrows was born and raised in Nassau, Bahamas. He also spent a great deal of time on his grandparents' farm on Long Island, Bahamas.
 **DONALD DAVIS**	Davis grew up in the mountains of North Carolina, in an area settled by people from Scotland. His rural community had no radios, electricity, or other modern conveniences until the 1950s.
 **OLGA LOYA**	Loya grew up in a Mexican-American neighborhood in Los Angeles, California, where her neighbors spoke a lively mixture of English and Spanish.

Storytelling

Why he/she became a storyteller	Origin of his/her stories	Special Techniques
While studying music, Burrows played with a group that performed ballads based on old European stories. Learning all those old stories made him think back to the stories he had heard as a child. He began to research the stories he remembered and to collect new tales from Bahamian friends. Today, Burrows uses stories and music to share his rich cultural heritage with others.	Burrows' stories come from the Caribbean. They contain elements of African stories, as well as elements of stories told by the Arawak—the first people to live on the Bahama Islands. Many of the stories are about traditional characters called B'Anase and B'Boukee.	Burrows likes to have his audience participate in his stories. He sometimes asks the audience to add phrases to a story or to respond to "Boonday," a traditional Bahamian storyteller's chant. Burrows often includes music in his performances, playing one or more of the fifteen instruments he has learned. He sometimes teaches the audience to sing parts of the songs he plays.
Wherever he went, new acquaintances asked Davis many questions about his rather unusual childhood. He found that the best way to answer them was by sharing childhood stories. When he returned home for visits, Davis collected additional stories from friends and neighbors.	Many of Davis's stories are traditional Appalachian stories called Jack Tales, which are based on ancient Scottish tales. Davis has also crafted a number of stories based on events from his own childhood.	Davis believes that stories are made of pictures. When he tells a story, he is trying to help the audience under-stand the pictures inside his head. Therefore, he uses lots of body language and descriptive language to tell his stories. Davis tailors his words and gestures to the audience at hand.
During Loya's childhood, story-telling was a part of everyday life. While working as a community organizer, Loya decided to plan a storytelling festival as a fundraiser for her community. She found herself not only organizing but performing as well.	Loya uses people and books as sources for traditional stories from all over the world. She also enjoys studying history and uses storytelling to share important stories from the past.	Loya uses sound effects to add humor or suspense to a tale. She likes to use some Spanish when she tells stories to an English-speaking audience, so that listeners can appreciate the music of the language. Using Spanish also helps Loya convey the authentic voices of traditional Hispanic story characters, such as Coyote and Tía Miseria.

Think About Reading

Write your answers.

1. Why does the woodcutter's wife decide to escort him out of the village?

2. Why has the blade of the woodcutter's hatchet become rusty and lost its handle?

3. What advice would you give the woodcutter after he returns?

4. What elements of this story show you that it is a folk tale?

5. If you were performing "The Homecoming" at a storytelling festival, which special techniques described in "The Art of Storytelling" would you use?

WRITE A HUMAN-INTEREST ARTICLE

The woodcutter has quite a story to tell. Write a human-interest article about him that will appear in the local newspaper of his village. Describe what happened to him and tell what kind of person he is. Include some quotes by him and some of the people in the village who meet him after he reappears.

LITERATURE CIRCLE

Discuss the way "The Homecoming" is told. Who is telling the story? How would the story change if the woodcutter's wife told it? What if the woodcutter told it? Consider whether or not the lesson that is taught would change or remain the same with a different narrator.

AUTHOR
LAURENCE YEP

When Laurence Yep was a boy in San Francisco, he read comic books—lots of them—as well as fantasy and science fiction stories. The writing bug first bit him when he was in high school. He has been publishing award-winning stories and books ever since. When Yep writes, he sometimes feels as if he's looking through a window and describing what is outside. He says, "I think of writing as a way of seeing. It's a way of bringing out the specialness of ordinary things."

MORE BOOKS BY
LAURENCE YEP

- *The Lost Garden*
- *Dragonwings*
- *Later, Gator*
- *Tree of Dreams*

WORKSHOP

How to
Tell a Story

Storytellers use gestures and different expressions to help tell a story.

Storytellers' gestures are often written into their story script.

Storytelling is a tradition that began in ancient cultures. Early storytellers passed their tales down orally from generation to generation. Many of those stories still exist today.

What is a storyteller? A storyteller is someone who can tell stories in ways that make them come alive. Some storytellers change the sound of their voices, wear costumes, use props, sing, or speak in rhyme as they tell their stories.

Music or sound effects can help set a mood or feeling for a story.

from
"HOW THE COYOTE GETS HIS NAME"
by Jerry Tello

...so all the animals gathered their young and took them back to where they slept and as the coyote was walking up (*walking motion*) the hill, he was thinking, "How can I be first...how can I be first??!!" (*Make pensive face— look at extended finger.*)

By this time, the Sun (*look up*) had finished his cycle and touched (*tap-on-the-shoulder motion with index finger*) the Moon on the shoulder and Ms. Moon began sharing her brilliance.

And there sat (*sitting action*) the coyote on top of the hill, under a tree, still thinking how he could be first (*index finger to temple, as if thinking*), when he had a brilliant idea!

(*Eyes wide, mouth open*) "I'll just stay up all night! That way, I'll see Mr. Sun as he awakes and I can be first!"

Well, several hours passed and as hard as the coyote tried, he was still getting tired (*eyes drooping*). In his struggle to keep awake, he glanced up (*look up*) at the tree branches and had a good idea and thought to himself, "I'll just break two small branches and put one in each eyelid to keep me awake!"

So the coyote did just that (*motion of reaching up, breaking branches*)... except that in a short time, the coyote was fast asleep with his eyes wide open. (*index finger and thumb of each hand, holding eyes wide open*)

The moon finished her cycle and several hours later, the coyote finally awoke and ran to the circle (*running motion*), where he saw no one except the big brown animal standing on the rock. Thinking he was first, the coyote said, (*stand up straight*) "OK, I'm ready to pick and I want to be the Bear so I can stand on the rock and make all the announcements!"

1 Write Your Script

Choose a story that you would like to tell others. It could be a well-known fairy tale, a myth, or an experience from your own life. Create a script to help you learn your story. Organize it in a way that is useful to you. Some storytellers like to work from an outline that lists the major events of the story, then fill in the details orally. Others like to write down the whole story, using their own words. Write your first draft. Try to keep it short—about one or two pages.

TOOLS

- paper and pencil
- story to tell
- props and music (optional)

2 Plan Your Delivery

Look over your script. Think about the effect you want the story to have on your audience. Is your story happy or sad, funny or scary? You will want to create the right mood for your audience. Traditionally, storytellers have used many different methods to bring their stories to life. They make gestures, use props, change their voices, and use sound effects. Revise the first draft of your script by adding directions for yourself in the appropriate places. When you tell your story, you'll know just when to include special effects.

3 Practice Your Story

Practice telling your story. Refer to your script at first to make sure that you get the story right and that you know exactly when the gestures, props, music, or sound effects come into the story. Practice telling your story in front of a mirror so you can watch your movements. Tell it to a friend or a member of your family. Eventually you'll be able to tell the story from memory using all the special effects and props you've planned.

Tip Tape-record your special effects. Ask a helper to play the tape for you. Provide him or her with a marked script that shows when the tape should be played.

4 Tell Your Story

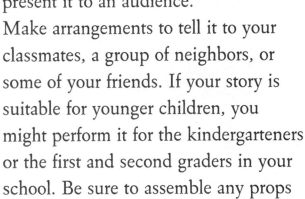

When you're happy with the way you tell the story, you will want to present it to an audience. Make arrangements to tell it to your classmates, a group of neighbors, or some of your friends. If your story is suitable for younger children, you might perform it for the kindergarteners or the first and second graders in your school. Be sure to assemble any props or costumes you will need.

If You Are Using a Computer ...

Use the Record and Playback tools to practice your story as you write it. Edit your story as you listen to how it sounds.

THINK
In what other situations might you use the storytelling skills you have learned?

José García
Drama Coach ▶

FROM MISS IDA'S PORCH

by SANDRA BELTON

illustrated by FLOYD COOPER

There's a very best time of day on Church Street. My street. It begins when the sky and my feelings match, both kind of rosy around the edges.

You can hear all the best-time noises—Shoo Kate and Mr. Fisher laughing from their kitchen. Reginald and T-Bone slamming out their back door. Mr. Porter coming home from work in his noisy ole car, calling out to everybody he passes on the street. Netta practicing on her piano (mostly to get out of washing dinner dishes), and Mr. Willie making his just-checkin'-on call to Mrs. Jackson, his ninety-year-old mama.

The noises feel good.

Most of the big kids are getting ready to hang out somewhere, like at the drugstore down on the corner, or on the steps in front of the church. Those are some of their favorite pretending places—the boys pretending not to see the girls, and the girls pretending to ignore the boys. . . . Like my sister Sylvia pretending to ignore Peewee.

Most of the little kids are getting ready to get ready for bed. Getting ready for bed takes a long time for the little kids. Some of them can make it last all the way to the end of the best time. Especially the Tolver kids.

"Just five more minutes, Mama, please!" they say. Then after five minutes they hide somewhere in the yard for five more minutes. Then they start pleading all over again for five more minutes.

But most of the kids on Church Street are in-between kids. Like Freda and me.

Some of the best times we just sit on her porch or mine, playing jacks or reading comics. Sometimes we play statues with Rosetta and Punkin and Rodney. Sometimes T-Bone plays, too.

$\mathcal{M}$ost of the best times, though, just about all of us end up at Miss Ida's. Sitting on her porch.

Miss Ida's house is halfway down Church Street. That's probably one reason folks end up there a lot. Another reason is Miss Ida herself. She and the best time are kind of alike. Soft, peaceful.

But the biggest reason we all end up there is that Miss Ida's porch is a telling place.

Usually Mr. Fisher comes over to sit on the porch about the same time we do. It's about the time the sky is getting rosy all over. You know then that the best time is settling in.

Miss Ida calls Mr. Fisher "Poissant" because they both come from Louisiana, and that's what people there used to call him.

Mr. Fisher has been all over. It's hard to tell how old he is. But from all the stuff he's done, he could be really old. He doesn't look old at all, though. Especially when he walks. He sorta bounces. Miss Ida always says, "Poissant has a jaunty step."

Mr. Fisher has lots of memories about the places he's been and things he's seen. Almost *anything* can make him think about something he saw or heard or did a while back. He'll start out, "Puts my mind on the time . . . ," and we know what's coming.

"Tell us about that time, Poissant," Miss Ida will say to Mr. Fisher when he begins his remembering.

And he will.

Like the time Freda and Punkin were arguing about what Mrs. Jackson had said when she was over at Punkin's house, visiting Miss Esther, Punkin's aunt.

"Lena Horne ain't never visited Miz Jackson, Punkin," Freda said. "Miz Jackson was just talking outta her head, girl. You know she ninety years old. You crazy for believing her."

"You don't know nothing, Freda." Punkin was getting angry. "Just 'cause Miz Jackson's ninety don't mean she talking outta her head. Most time Miz Jackson make more sense than you!"

Punkin and T-Bone almost fell over laughing. Me, too. And this made Freda fighting mad.

"Hold on there, Miss Lady," said Mr. Fisher, taking hold of one of Freda's hands. "Don't press ugly on that pretty face. Tell me now, how come you think Lena Horne couldn't have stayed at Mrs. Jackson's house?"

"'Cause Lena Horne is famous. Why would she want to stay at Miz Jackson's?"

"Why not?" Mr. Fisher settled back in his chair.

I had a feeling that some remembering was getting started.

Used to be that most all the famous black folks who came to town stayed at somebody's house."

"How come, Mr. Fisher?" Freda sat on the stoop in front of Mr. Fisher.

"Nowhere else for them to stay! Couldn't stay in hotels. Hotels didn't allow no black guests! Famous or not. When our folk came to town to give a speech, put on a show, or whatever they came to do, we had to be the ones to give 'em a bed.

"Puts my mind on a time back in thirty-nine. I was working in West Virginia then. Working in the mines. Lived in a nice town close to where I worked. Lots of good folks there, working hard to make a life for themselves and their children."

Mr. Fisher's remembering was making him smile.

"Anyhow, a big dance took place in the town every year. Folks came from all around to go to this dance. That year, 1939, the dance was *really* going to be special. Duke Ellington was coming to town. The great bandsman himself was coming to play for the dance."

"Was Duke Ellington famous?" I bet none of us knew who Duke Ellington was. Punkin was brave enough to ask.

Mr. Fisher almost jumped out of his chair. "Don't they teach you children nothin' in school? Duke Ellington *famous*?" Mr. Fisher was almost shouting.

"Don't get bothered now, Poissant." Miss Ida put her hand on Mr. Fisher's arm. She was speaking in that peaceful way she has.

"Can't expect anybody to listen if you shouting, now can you," said Miss Ida. "Just tell the children about Duke Ellington. Tell them about the sound of that band. A sound that made your feet get a life of their own on the dance floor. Tell them how he not only led the band from his piano but also wrote most of the songs they played. How you could hum your little baby to sleep with some of those pretty songs. And how some of those songs were played by big orchestras and sung by huge choirs in halls all over the world."

Mr. Fisher had a big smile on his face. "I ain't got to tell them, Miss Ida. You doin' a fine job, a mighty fine job!"

The sky was starting to look like the never-tell blue blanket on Big Mama's bed. "Never-tell blue is light enough to still be blue but dark enough to hide the dirt," Big Mama says.

The best-time noises were still there, but they had changed. You could hear the chirping bugs. One of the Tolver kids was crying. Probably asking for something he couldn't have. Mr. Willie was playing his radio. Jazz.

Mr. Fisher was still remembering.

"Yessir. The great Duke Ellington was coming to play for us, for our dance, and there was not one hotel in the state that would put him up and take his money for doin' it. If he had a mind to rest himself in a bed, it was goin' have to be in the home of some black person."

"Did he stay with you, Mr. Fisher?" Punkin asked.

"Not with me, exactly, but in the house where I was living. Mrs. Lomax's house. Mrs. Lomax had a big, fine house, and she kept it real nice. I rented a room on the third floor."

Mr. Fisher started to grin. Like he always did when he got to a part he liked to tell.

"I was there when the great man arrived with three of his bandsmen."

"So you got to meet Duke Ellington?" T-Bone was impressed. We all were.

"I not only met him, I was there when he sat at the piano in Mrs. Lomax's parlor. Duke's playing heated up that little room. I'm telling you it did. He was some kinda good!"

Mr. Fisher grew quiet. A remembering quiet. He stopped smiling, too.

"Humph. Imagine that. A man like that. Talented, famous, everything! Not being able to pay his *own* money to sleep in a crummy little hotel room, just because he was black."

After that we were all quiet. I was wishing I knew more about what Mr. Fisher was remembering. I bet Freda was wishing so, too.

venin', everybody. Must be some powerful thinking over here tonight, 'cause everybody's deep into it."

Shoo Kate was climbing the steps to the porch. I hadn't even heard her coming up the walk. Nobody else must have either.

"Hey, Shoo Kate. Come over here by me." Miss Ida patted the place on the swing beside her.

Shoo Kate is Mr. Fisher's wife. Her name is really Mrs. Kate Fisher, but just about everybody calls her Shoo Kate. She told us one time that when she was little she used to tease her baby brother, telling him that their mama said he had to call her Sugar Kate 'cause she was so sweet. The name came out Shoo Kate when her baby brother said it. Then everybody started calling her that. She even told us kids to call her Shoo Kate instead of Mrs. Fisher.

After she sat down Shoo Kate reached over and poked Mr. Fisher. "What you been telling these folks, Fisher, to make everybody so quiet?"

"I ain't been tellin' them nothing you don't already know, darlin'." Mr. Fisher and Shoo Kate smiled at each other. They always seemed to be smiling and laughing together.

"Did any famous people stay in your house, Shoo Kate?" T-bone asked.

"Now I know what talking's been over here," Shoo Kate said, laughing. "Fisher, you been telling them about that time Duke Ellington came and stayed at the place in West Virginia where you were living."

"I sure was," said Mr. Fisher. "No reason to keep that fine bit of history a secret."

"So it's history now, is it, Poissant," said Miss Ida. I think she was teasing. All the grown-ups laughed.

"Well, T," said Shoo Kate, "I never made history like Fisher here, but I *was* somewhere one time when history was being made."

"Shoo Kate, I bet I know what you're talking about. Go on, tell the children." Miss Ida sounded excited.

The sky was really getting dark. I like the best time most of all when the sky is dark. You can imagine that almost anything is out there. You can imagine almost anything.

Shoo Kate began her story.

"Around the same time Fisher was living in West Virginia, I was living with my family in Washington, D.C. My papa worked for the railroad. He was a train-car porter, so he had to travel most of the time. All of us looked forward to Papa's days off, the days he was going to be home.

"Oh, those were the best days—the days when Papa was home. He made sure we all did something special on those days. All of us together, Papa, Mama, and each one of us kids. We didn't have much money, but we had enough. And as shut out as we were in Washington, we could still find lots of things to do."

"What do you mean 'shut out,' Shoo Kate?" Freda asked.

"Just what the words say, sugar. Black folks were shut out.

We couldn't go to the movie theaters, the big restaurants, just about anyplace you think folks ought to be able to go if the place is open to the public and folks have the inclination to go. Why, when my papa was growing up in Washington, black folks couldn't even go to the national monuments!"

Punkin looked at Shoo Kate kind of funny. "But Washington is the capital city," she said. "That's where they make laws for the whole country. How could they break the law, keeping folks from going places just 'cause they was black?"

Freda had been waiting all evening to get back at Punkin, and her chance had finally come.

"Now look who's talking outta her head! Girl, don't you know nothing? Used to be that the *law* said it was okay to keep black folks out," she said.

"Don't you two get started now. Freda's right about the laws, of course," Miss Ida said, pulling Punkin down to sit beside her. "But that's another story. A long story for another time. Go on, Shoo Kate, please."

Shoo Kate did.

"Anyhow, this one time we were all real excited because Papa was going to be home for Easter. He wasn't always able to be there for holidays. So we were all looking forward to having him home and being able to dress up in our new clothes and go to church together.

"But it wasn't Papa's plan for us to go to church that Easter Sunday. After we were all dressed and ready to leave the house, Papa said we were going to catch the trolley car.

"Then we really got excited. Catching the trolley car! We knew that Papa must be planning something special because we didn't need to catch the trolley to go to our church. We only had to walk a couple of blocks to get there."

Shoo Kate sat up straighter. It was like her remembering was pushing at her back.

"How grand we were, riding on the trolley that Easter Sunday morning. And even grander when Papa explained that we were on our way to the Lincoln Memorial. That was exciting enough. Then he went on to tell us that we were going there to hear one of the greatest voices in America!"

"Who were you going to hear, Shoo Kate?" Freda asked the question this time.

"We were going to hear Marian Anderson. A grand, grand singer—a voice more magnificent than you could *ever* imagine!

"But there was more to it than just going to hear Marian Anderson sing. Much more."

Shoo Kate wiggled down to the edge of her chair and moved her face closer to us.

"It was like this. Several months before that Easter Sunday, a concert had been arranged. It was arranged for Marian Anderson to sing at Constitution Hall. Constitution Hall was the big concert stage in Washington, where all the famous musicians appeared. People from all over the world.

"Marian Anderson was certainly famous. *And* she had sung all over the world. Didn't matter, though. Marian Anderson's concert was not going to take place in Constitution Hall. You see, Marian Anderson was black. The people who owned the hall said no black musician was going to perform on their stage!"

Shoo Kate sat back in her chair. Her eyes got narrow.

"While we rode on the trolley, Papa told us what had happened. A lot of people in Washington were furious about Miss Anderson not being able to sing at Constitution Hall. The wife of the president of the United States was one of these furious people. So she and some others got together to arrange for Miss Anderson to sing somewhere else."

Shoo Kate started moving her hands as she talked. Her smile started coming back.

"Constitution Hall with its white columns and high-up ceiling wouldn't welcome Marian Anderson. But the Lincoln Memorial would! There would be no walls to keep people out. And the sky would be the ceiling! On Easter Sunday morning just about anybody who wanted to would be able to hear and *see* Marian Anderson sing. Including my entire family!"

Shoo Kate's smile was all over her face.

"At first we thought it might rain. We had gotten there early, very early, hoping to get close enough to see. While we waited, we kept looking up at the sky, wishing for the sun to come out.

"The crowd grew and grew. So many people, all kinds of people. Black folks, white folks, standing there together in front of the Lincoln Memorial, waiting to hear Marian Anderson sing."

Mr. Fisher started grinning himself. What Shoo Kate was about to say must have been his favorite part of the story.

"It was time for the concert to start. Then, just as Marian Anderson was getting ready to walk out onto the place she was gonna sing from, the sun came out. Yes, it did!"

Shoo Kate's voice grew softer. So soft we moved closer to hear her.

"When the concert started, our papa took turns holding the little ones up so they could get a better look. When he reached down to get my baby brother Jimmy, I saw tears rolling down his cheeks.

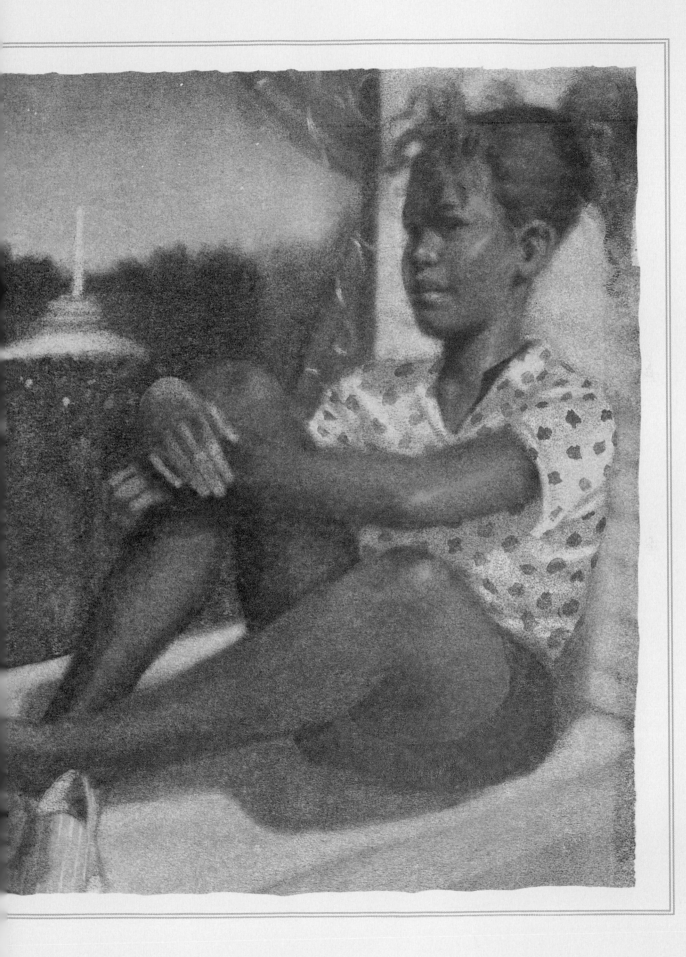

"I asked my mama if Papa was crying 'cause he was happy. This is what Mama said to us sometimes when we caught her crying. Mama said that some of Papa's tears were happy tears, but some were not. Some were tears of sadness, and maybe even anger.

"Mama said to me, 'Listen to the words she sings, Kate.' Miss Anderson was singing a song I knew, 'My Country, 'Tis of Thee.' I recognized the words:

'. . . *From every mountainside*
Let freedom ring'

"'Your papa's thinking about those words and what they should mean,' Mama said. 'Thoughts like that might be making him feel good and bad at the same time. That's probably why there are tears on your papa's face.'"

Shoo Kate sat back in her chair. Her voice got almost regular.

"So you see, on that Easter Sunday I saw history being made there at the Lincoln Memorial. I also saw my papa cry with pride and sadness at the same time. It was a day that will live in my memory forever."

Shoo Kate's remembering had kind of put a spell on us. On everybody listening. Even Punkin was real still, and she was usually moving around like a doll on strings. When my father and my sister Sylvia walked up on the porch, we all jumped. Nobody had heard them coming.

"Goodness, you all gave me a fright." Miss Ida got up. "Hi, Sylvia. Here, take my seat, J.S.," she said to Daddy. "I'll get more chairs from the house."

"No need, Ida," Daddy said. "A few folks are going to be leaving very soon and there'll be plenty of room."

Daddy looked over at me and Freda. I knew that the very best time was about to be over for us.

"Hey, J.S., what you been up to?" Daddy and Mr. Fisher were shaking hands.

"I just been walking down to the corner to make sure Sylvia and her friends know it's time to come home."

"Sylvia don't know nothing when Peewee's around." I just had to say that. My sister thinks she's something special just 'cause bony ole Peewee said she was cute.

"Shut up!" Sylvia wanted to hit me. I just knew it.

"Don't speak that way to your sister," Daddy said to Sylvia. "And you, missy," he said pointing to me, "if you want to get your extra few minutes here, I think you'd better have kinder thoughts for Sylvia."

"There's been some wonderful thoughts on this porch tonight, folks. Let's keep the good words going." Miss Ida always makes things okay.

"J.S.," she said, "you missed a wonderful story. Shoo Kate was telling us about the time she saw Marian Anderson."

"Oh, yeah," Daddy said, like he was remembering something. "You told me a little about that, Shoo Kate. I wish I had been here to hear the whole story."

"Tell him the story, Shoo Kate. We'd love to hear it again. Right, Freda?" I wanted so much to make the best time last.

"Good try, baby, but it won't work tonight." Daddy hardly ever let my tricks work on him.

"I have another chapter for that story, however. Want to hear it?" While he was talking, Daddy winked at Shoo Kate. I thought he was fooling.

Miss Ida sat up in her seat. Like she felt the same as me. Wanting the evening to go on.

"Come on, J.S., sit down and take your turn this evening." Miss Ida motioned for us to make room for Daddy.

Then my daddy started his remembering.

I had an uncle—Uncle Henry—who lived in Washington," Daddy began. "He taught at Howard University there, for many years.

"Uncle Henry was a big man, well over six feet tall. He had wide, full eyebrows that came together like a hairy *V* whenever he frowned. And Uncle Henry frowned easily. Especially when one of us was messin' up. His voice was like a drum—booming, deep.

His voice, his frown, and his attitude could put the fear of God in you. Uncle Henry didn't play!"

Daddy chuckled.

"I dearly loved Uncle Henry, though. We all did. In fact, he was probably the favorite of everybody in the family. Whenever there was going to be a family gathering, we all wanted it to be at Uncle Henry's. At Uncle Henry's you knew there would be lots to do, lots to eat, and best of all, lots and lots of Uncle Henry."

Daddy has a deep voice, too. A good telling voice.

"Uncle Henry had worked hard to get where he wanted to be in life. And he was one of the lucky ones: He got there. Yep, Uncle Henry was a grand old guy. One of those people you hope will go on forever."

Daddy looked out into the darkness. I think he was seeing Uncle Henry in his mind. I think I was, too.

"Whenever us nephews and nieces were gathered around the breakfast or dinner table, Uncle Henry would claim the floor, but we didn't mind at all. Uncle Henry was a magnificent storyteller! And though we didn't know it then, his stories were like fuel for our young minds.

"Uncle Henry firmly believed that the knowledge of our history—the history of black folks—was the most important story that we could ever be told. I can just hear him now: 'You can know where you are going in this world only if you know where you've been!'"

Mr. Fisher slapped his hand on his leg. "Now that's a man after my own heart!" he said.

"*Shhhhh*, Fisher. Let J.S. go on," Shoo Kate said.

Daddy did. "Uncle Henry held us spellbound with his stories. He told us about the great civilizations of Africa that existed thousands of years ago, and—"

"Tell us about that!" T-Bone moved real close to Daddy.

"That's a story for another time, T," Daddy said. "I'll be sure to tell you, but I'd better get on with this one now.

"One of Uncle Henry's stories described how he had been there that Easter Sunday at the Lincoln Memorial. But that same story had another part, a part that told something that had happened *before* that famous Sunday.

"You see, another important event had taken place in that same spot seventeen years earlier—the dedication of the Lincoln Memorial. Uncle Henry had been there then, too."

"Wow!" said T-Bone and Punkin. I knew how they felt.

"It wasn't as much of a 'wow' as you might think, kids. At the dedication of this monument to the man known as the Great Emancipator, the black folks who came had to stand in a special section. A section off to the left of the monument. Away from the white folks, who could stand dead center, right in front."

Daddy had started breathing hard. It sounded loud. Everything else was quiet. Except Daddy's breathing.

"Anyhow, during one of our visits to Uncle Henry, Marian Anderson was going to be giving another concert. It was very important to Uncle Henry that all the nieces and nephews have a chance to go."

"So, you heard a concert at the Lincoln Memorial, too, right?" T-Bone sure was making it hard for Daddy to get on with his story. I wanted to put some tape over his mouth.

Daddy smiled. "No, as a matter of fact, I didn't. The concert I went to was held at Constitution Hall."

"What?" All of us were surprised at this twist.

"That's right," Daddy said. His breathing wasn't so loud now. "It was 1965, over twenty-five years since that concert at the Lincoln Memorial. Marian Anderson was now at the end of her career as a singer. This concert was taking place so she could say farewell to Washington audiences.

"Constitution Hall was still one of the finest concert stages in Washington, a stage now open to all performers, no matter what their color. It had been that way for years. But that concert and that magnificent singer were special. Very special."

Everybody was looking at Daddy as he went on.

"Many of the people in the hall that night were African Americans. Some of these black people had also been standing on the grass under the sky that Easter Sunday morning. And some, like Uncle Henry, had been out there on the grass for the dedication in 1922. Now these same people were sitting in the forbidden hall, some of them in the best seats in the house!

"When Marian Andersen came onto the stage, the applause of the crowd was like the roar of a thousand pounding seas. It went on and on and on. But above the noise, there was one thing I heard very clearly."

"You heard your Uncle Henry, right?" Miss Ida was smiling at Dad. And her eyes were sparkly. Like raindrops are sparkly when I can look through them on my window and see the sun.

My dad's voice was real soft. "I did, Ida. I could hear Uncle Henry. But I think I would have known what he was saying even if I hadn't heard him. Just like I can hear him right now: 'You can know where you are going in this world only if you know where you've been!'"

In the quiet after Daddy stopped talking, I looked out into the velvet black sky. I tried to imagine the sound of a thousand pounding seas. I tried to imagine some other things, too. Like how it might have been to ride on a trolley. Or to spend the night in the same house with a famous person. Or to go to a famous monument and not be able to stand where I wanted to.

My dad's story brought the end to the very best time that evening.

Like we always did, Freda, T, Punkin, and I said good-night to all the grown-ups and walked each other home. I walked Freda home and then she walked me home, and then I walked her home again. Sylvia told on us like she usually does, so I finally went home for good to go to bed.

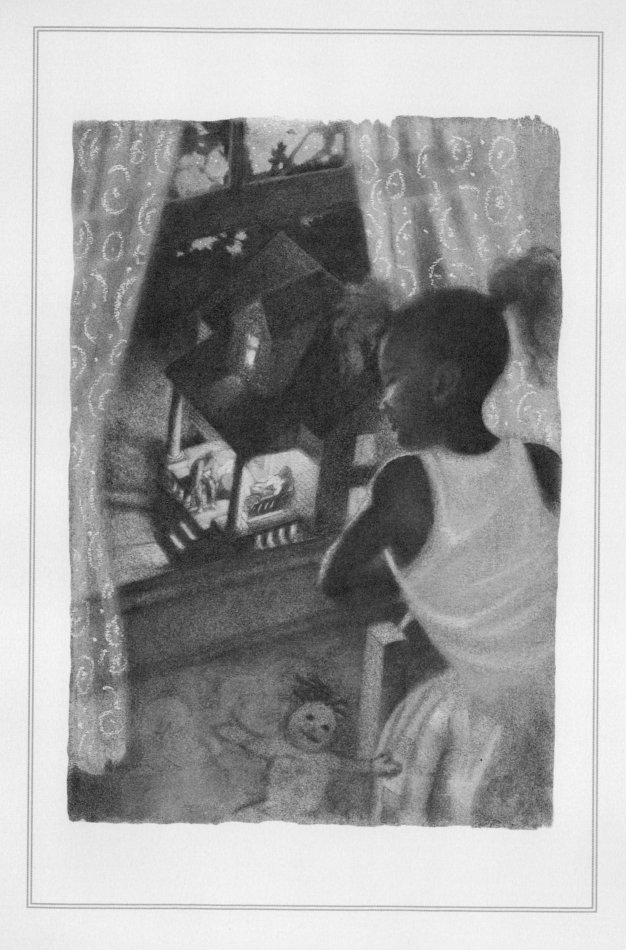

Just before I go to sleep is the very, very last part of the very best time. After I'm in bed and my light is turned off, I can look out my bedroom window and see Miss Ida's porch.

Most of the time the grown-ups are still there. I can hear them talking and laughing, but it's soft and far away.

These sounds feel good. They keep the very best times close. So close that they're with me when my eyelids stop cooperating and just drop. I think the very best times go with me into my dreams. . . .

A FEW

APPROPRIATE

'REMARKS'

BY
HAROLD HOLTZER

ILLUSTRATED BY
STEPHEN ALCORN

As Union and Confederate forces battled ferociously at Gettysburg, the Union's Commander in Chief, Abraham Lincoln, waited in Washington for news from the front.

Hour after hour during those anxious days and nights, an eyewitness remembered, Lincoln's tall form could be found at the War Department, bent over stacks of telegrams from the battle. On the third day, his burden grew even heavier: His fragile wife, Mary, was thrown from her carriage in a freak accident and suffered a head injury.

Finally, after seventy-two hours of unrelieved tension, Lincoln learned that the North had prevailed at Gettysburg. Privately, he was disappointed that his generals did not follow up their victory by pursuing the Confederates as they fled south. Publicly, he sent the army the "highest honors" for their "great success." He seemed to sense that, flawed or not, the Battle of Gettysburg would be a turning point in the Civil War.

The citizens of Pennsylvania, also aware of their new place in history, moved quickly to create a national cemetery for the thousands of casualties at Gettysburg. A dedication ceremony was planned, and Lincoln received an invitation to attend. He was not, however, asked to deliver the major speech of the day. That

Edward Everett gave a two-hour oratory before Lincoln's speech.

honor was given to a New England statesman and professional orator named Edward Everett. Lincoln, one

organizer worried, was incapable of speaking "upon such a great and solemn occasion." The president was asked merely to give "a few appropriate remarks." Yet aware that the event was momentous, Lincoln accepted the halfhearted invitation.

As the day grew near, Lincoln's wife urged him to reconsider. Their young son, Tad, had fallen ill, and Mrs. Lincoln was near hysteria. (Only a year earlier, their middle child, Willie, had died.) On the morning of his father's departure, Tad was so sick he could not eat breakfast. Lincoln himself felt unwell, but he decided to go anyway. With little fanfare, he boarded a train for the slow journey to Gettysburg.

The legend that the president waited until he was on the train to prepare his speech and then scribbled it on the back of an envelope is untrue. Lincoln carefully wrote at least one version of his speech on White House stationery before he left and probably rewrote it in his bedroom in Gettysburg the night before delivering it.

On Thursday, November 19, a balmy, Indian summer day, the six-feet-four Lincoln mounted an

Lincoln rides to the cemetery on an undersized horse.

undersized horse and joined a mournful procession through the town and toward the new cemetery near the battlefield. An immense throng had gathered there, and as Lincoln arrived on the speakers' platform, every man in the crowd respectfully removed his hat. The president was greeted with "a perfect silence."

For two hours, Edward Everett held the spectators spellbound with his rich voice and soaring words. A hymn followed, then Lincoln rose to speak. "Four score and seven years ago," Lincoln began in a high-pitched voice. He spoke for barely three minutes, ending with the words "government of the people, by the people, for the people, shall not perish from the earth."

Almost as soon as he had begun, he sat down. Some eyewitnesses recalled a smattering of applause, but others heard "not a word, not a cheer, not a shout." A stenographer leaned over to Lincoln and asked, "Is that all?" Embarrassed, Lincoln replied, "Yes—for the present." A photographer in the crowd, fussing with his camera, had not even had time to take a picture.

Lincoln thought his speech was a failure. "People are disappointed," he grimly told the man who had introduced him. To add to his misery, he came down with a mild case of smallpox on the trip back to Washington.

Lincoln addresses the crowd at Gettysburg.

Many who listened to the speech felt differently, however. While some newspapers dismissed the speech as "silly," "dull," and "commonplace," another correctly predicted the Gettysburg Address would "live among the annals of man." Perhaps the best compliment of all came from Edward Everett. A few days after they both had spoken at Gettysburg, he wrote to Lincoln,

saying he wished he had come "as close to the central idea of the occasion, in two hours, as you did in two minutes." Lincoln replied, telling Everett how pleased he was that "the little I did say was not entirely a failure."

Today, one hundred twenty-five years later, Abraham Lincoln's Gettysburg Address is remembered as one of the great speeches of all time.

Address Delivered at the Dedication of the Cemetery at Gettysburg

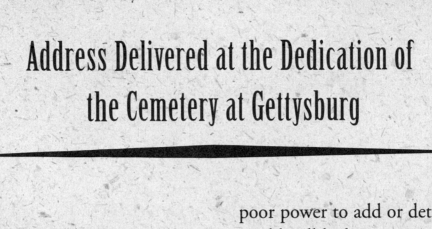

Four score and seven years ago our fathers brought forth on this continent, a new nation, conceived in liberty, and dedicated to the proposition that all men are created equal.

Now we are engaged in a great civil war, testing whether that nation or any nation so conceived, and so dedicated, can long endure. We are met on a great battle-field of that war. We have come to dedicate a portion of that field, as a final resting place for those who here gave their lives, that that nation might live. It is altogether fitting and proper that we should do this.

But, in a larger sense, we can not dedicate—we can not consecrate—we can not hallow—this ground. The brave men, living and dead, who struggled here, have consecrated it, far above our poor power to add or detract. The world will little note, nor long remember what we say here, but it can never forget what they did here. It is for us the living, rather, to be dedicated here to the unfinished work which they who fought here have thus far so nobly advanced. It is rather for us to be here dedicated to the great task remaining before us—that from these honored dead we take increased devotion to that cause for which they gave the last full measure of devotion—that we here highly resolve that these dead shall not have died in vain—that this nation, under God, shall have a new birth of freedom—and that government of the people, by the people, for the people, shall not perish from the earth.

Abraham Lincoln
November 19, 1863

THINK ABOUT READING

Write your answers.

1. What happens most evenings on Miss Ida's porch?

2. Why do you think the narrator believes the time on Miss Ida's porch is the very best part of the day?

3. What would you like best about evenings on Church Street?

4. Uncle Henry said, "You can know where you are going in this world only if you know where you've been." How do the stories told on Miss Ida's porch help the young characters in the story know where they've been?

5. How do authors Sandra Belton and Harold Holtzer feel about the historical figures they describe? How do you know?

WRITE A FIRST-PERSON ACCOUNT

Imagine that you were present when President Lincoln gave his Gettysburg Address or that you attended one of Marian Anderson's concerts in Washington, D.C. Write a personal account of the event. Describe what you experienced and how you felt. Be sure to include why the event was significant to you.

LITERATURE CIRCLE

The selections—*From Miss Ida's Porch* and "A Few Appropriate Remarks"—both tell about historical events. Compare the ways each author deals with historical material. What is each author's purpose? How is the material presented? Talk about which method of presentation is more effective and why. Record your ideas on a Venn diagram.

AUTHOR

SANDRA BELTON

Sandra Belton grew up in a small West Virginia town. As a girl, she loved to listen to the stories that were told on front porches along her street. She says, "The things I heard on those porches helped me know who I was and where I came from. They—and the energy of those wonderful mountains— also helped me figure out where it was possible for me to go." Now Sandra Belton not only listens to stories; she also entertains young readers with the ones she writes.

MORE BOOKS BY

SANDRA BELTON

- *Ernestine & Amanda*
- *Members of the Club*
- *Summer Camp, Ready or Not!*

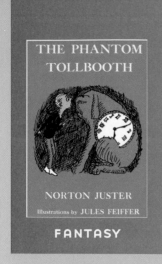
from

THE PHANTOM TOLLBOOTH

by Norton Juster

illustrations by Jules Feiffer

When Milo drives his small electric automobile through a toy tollbooth, he suddenly finds himself speeding toward adventure in a strange land called the Kingdom of Wisdom. With two new-found friends—the ill-mannered Humbug and the ticking watchdog Tock—Milo embarks on an exciting journey. Along the way, the threesome meet a boy named Alec who takes them to an evening concert unlike anything they have ever experienced.

The sun was dropping slowly from sight, and stripes of purple and orange and crimson and gold piled themselves on top of the distant hills. The last shafts of light waited patiently for a flight of wrens to find their way home, and a group of anxious stars had already taken their places.

"Here we are!" cried Alec, and, with a sweep of his arm, he pointed toward an enormous symphony orchestra. "Isn't it a grand sight?"

There were at least a thousand musicians ranged in a great arc before them. To the left and right were the violins and cellos, whose bows moved in great waves, and behind them in numberless profusion the piccolos, flutes, clarinets, oboes, bassoons, horns, trumpets, trombones and tubas were all playing at once. At the very rear, so far away that they could hardly be seen, were the percussion instruments, and lastly, in a long line up one side of a steep slope, were the solemn bass fiddles.

On a high podium in front stood the conductor, a tall, gaunt man with dark deep-set eyes and a thin mouth placed carelessly between his long pointed nose and his long pointed chin. He used no baton, but conducted with large, sweeping movements which seemed to start at his toes and work slowly up through his body and along his slender arms and end finally at the tips of his graceful fingers.

"I don't hear any music," said Milo.

"That's right," said Alec; "you don't listen to this concert— you watch it. Now, pay attention."

As the conductor waved his arms, he molded the air like handfuls of soft clay, and the musicians carefully followed his every direction.

"What are they playing?" asked Tock, looking up inquisitively at Alec.

"The sunset, of course. They play it every evening, about this time."

"They do?" said Milo quizzically.

"Naturally," answered Alec; "and they also play morning, noon, and night, when, of course, it's morning, noon, or night. Why, there wouldn't be any color in the world unless they played it. Each instrument plays a different one," he explained, "and depending,

of course, on what season it is and how the weather's to be, the conductor chooses his score and directs the day. But watch: the sun has almost set, and in a moment you can ask Chroma himself."

The last colors slowly faded from the western sky, and, as they did, one by one the instruments stopped, until only the bass fiddles, in their somber slow movement, were left to play the night and a single set of silver bells brightened the constellations. The conductor let his arms fall limply at his sides and stood quite still as darkness claimed the forest.

"That was a very beautiful sunset," said Milo, walking to the podium.

"It should be," was the reply; "we've been practicing since the world began." And, reaching down, the speaker picked Milo off the ground and set him on the music stand. "I am Chroma the Great," he continued, gesturing broadly with his hands, "conductor of color, maestro of pigment, and director of the entire spectrum."

"Do you play all day long?" asked Milo when he had introduced himself.

"Ah yes, all day, every day," he sang out, then pirouetted gracefully around the platform. "I rest only at night, and even then *they* play on."

"What would happen if you stopped?" asked Milo, who didn't quite believe that color happened that way.

"See for yourself," roared Chroma, and he raised both hands high over his head. Immediately the instruments that were playing stopped, and at once all color vanished. The world looked like an enormous coloring book that had never been used. Everything appeared in simple black outlines, and it looked as if someone with a set of paints the size of a house and a brush as wide could stay happily occupied for years. Then Chroma lowered his arms. The instruments began again and the color returned.

"You see what a dull place the world would be without color?" he said, bowing until his chin almost touched the ground. "But what pleasure to lead my violins in a serenade of spring green or hear my trumpets blare out the blue sea and then watch the oboes tint it all in warm yellow sunshine. And rainbows are best of all—and blazing neon signs, and taxicabs with stripes, and the soft, muted tones of a foggy day. We play them all."

As Chroma spoke, Milo sat with his eyes open wide, and Alec, Tock, and the Humbug looked on in wonder.

"Now I really must get some sleep." Chroma yawned. "We've had lightning, fireworks, and parades for the last few nights, and I've had to be up to conduct them. But tonight is sure to be quiet." Then, putting his large hand on Milo's shoulder, he said, "Be a good fellow and watch my orchestra till morning, will you? And be sure to wake me at 5:23 for the sunrise. Good night, good night, good night."

With that he leaped lightly from the podium and, in three long steps, vanished into the forest.

"That's a good idea," said Tock, making himself comfortable in the grass as the bug grumbled himself quickly to sleep and Alec stretched out in mid-air.

And Milo, full of thoughts and questions, curled up on the pages of tomorrow's music and eagerly awaited the dawn.

One by one, the hours passed, and at exactly 5:22 (by Tock's very accurate clock) Milo carefully opened one eye and, in a moment, the other. Everything was still purple, dark blue, and black, yet scarcely a minute remained to the long, quiet night.

He stretched lazily, rubbed his eyelids, scratched his head, and shivered once as a greeting to the early-morning mist.

"I must wake Chroma for the sunrise," he said softly. Then he suddenly wondered what it would be like to lead the orchestra and to color the whole world himself.

The idea whirled through his thoughts until he quickly decided that since it couldn't be very difficult, and since they probably all knew what to do by themselves anyway, and since it did seem a shame to wake anyone so early, and since it might be his only chance to try, and since the musicians were already poised and ready, he would—but just for a little while.

And so, as everyone slept peacefully on, Milo stood on tiptoes, raised his arms slowly in front of him, and made the slightest movement possible with the index finger of his right hand. It was now 5:23 A.M.

As if understanding his signal perfectly, a single piccolo played a single note and off in the east a solitary shaft of cool lemon light flicked across the sky. Milo smiled happily and then cautiously crooked his finger again. This time two more piccolos and a flute joined in and three more rays of light danced lightly into view. Then with both hands he made a great circular sweep in the air and watched with delight as all the musicians began to play at once.

The cellos made the hills glow red, and the leaves and grass were tipped with a soft pale green as the violins began their song. Only the bass fiddles rested as the entire orchestra washed the forest in color.

Milo was overjoyed because they were all playing for him,
and just the way they should.

"Won't Chroma be surprised?" he thought, signaling the
musicians to stop. "I'll wake him now."

But, instead of stopping, they continued to play even louder
than before, until each color became more brilliant than he
thought possible. Milo shielded his eyes with one hand and
waved the other desperately, but the colors continued to grow
brighter and brighter and brighter, until an even more curious
thing began to happen.

As Milo frantically conducted, the sky changed slowly from blue to tan and then to a rich magenta red. Flurries of light-green snow began to fall, and the leaves on the trees and bushes turned a vivid orange.

All the flowers suddenly appeared black, the gray rocks became a lovely soft chartreuse, and even peacefully sleeping Tock changed from brown to a magnificent ultramarine. Nothing was the color it should have been, and yet, the more he tried to straighten things out, the worse they became.

"I wish I hadn't started," he thought unhappily as a pale-blue blackbird flew by. "There doesn't seem to be any way to stop them."

He tried very hard to do everything just the way Chroma had done, but nothing worked. The musicians played on, faster and faster, and the purple sun raced quickly across the sky. In less than a minute it had set once more in the west and then, without any pause, risen again in the east. The sky was now quite yellow and the grass a charming shade of lavender. Seven times the sun rose and almost as quickly disappeared as the colors kept changing. In just a few minutes a whole week had gone by.

At last the exhausted Milo, afraid to call for help and on the verge of tears, dropped his hands to his sides. The orchestra stopped. The colors disappeared, and once again it was night. The time was 5:27 A.M.

"Wake up, everybody! Time for the sunrise!" he shouted with relief, and quickly jumped from the music stand.

"What a marvelous rest," said Chroma, striding to the podium. "I feel as though I'd slept for a week. My, my, I see we're a little late this morning. I'll have to cut my lunch hour short by four minutes."

He tapped for attention, and this time the dawn proceeded perfectly.

"You did a fine job," he said, patting Milo on the head. "Someday I'll let you conduct the orchestra yourself."

Tock wagged his tail proudly, but Milo didn't say a word, and to this day no one knows of the lost week but the few people who happened to be awake at 5:23 on that very strange morning.

from **The Young Person's Guide to the Orchestra**
written by **Anita Ganeri**

What is an Orchestra?

The concert hall buzzes with voices as the audience takes their seats. Snatches of music rise from the orchestra as musicians tune their instruments. When the conductor steps on stage, silence falls.

What is an orchestra?

An orchestra is a large group of musicians with instruments that play the classical music of Europe, Russia, and North America. The orchestra plays music written by a composer to make use of all the different instruments and their various sounds. When all the instruments play together, the music blends into one magnificent sound.

The Royal Philharmonic Orchestra

Who's who in an orchestra?

he modern orchestra may contain more than 100 instruments, divided into four sections, or families: string, brass, percussion, and woodwind.

The conductor in charge

ith so many instruments and musicians, the conductor's role is essential. He or she stands facing the orchestra, beating time with a baton and making sure that the orchestra stays in time, in tune, and that the different instruments start and stop playing at the right times. A good conductor controls the sound of the whole orchestra. His or her interpretations of the music bring out the excitement, drama, or gentleness of the composition and makes it all the more enjoyable for the listener.

Herbert von Karajan

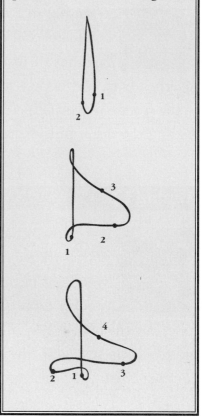

419

Take Your Seats

The string, woodwind, brass, and percussion sections each have their own special place in the orchestra and a unique part to play.

The string section contains violins, violas, cellos, and double basses.

Seating Plan

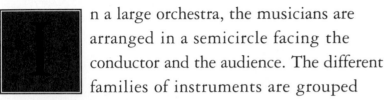

I n a large orchestra, the musicians are arranged in a semicircle facing the conductor and the audience. The different families of instruments are grouped together, with the loudest at the back and the quietest at the front. The principal violinist has the task of leading the other musicians.

The brass section contains French horns, trumpets, trombones, and tubas.

Tuning Up

A ll the instruments in an orchestra must play at the same pitch, otherwise they will sound out of tune. Heat and moisture can quickly cause an instrument to go out of tune, but the oboe is less affected than most. So, just before a concert begins, the oboe plays the note Middle A to which all the other instruments tune up.

The percussion section contains drums, cymbals, gongs, triangles, xylophones, and tambourines.

The woodwind section contains clarinets, oboes, flutes, and bassoons.

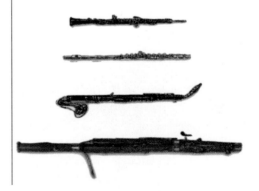

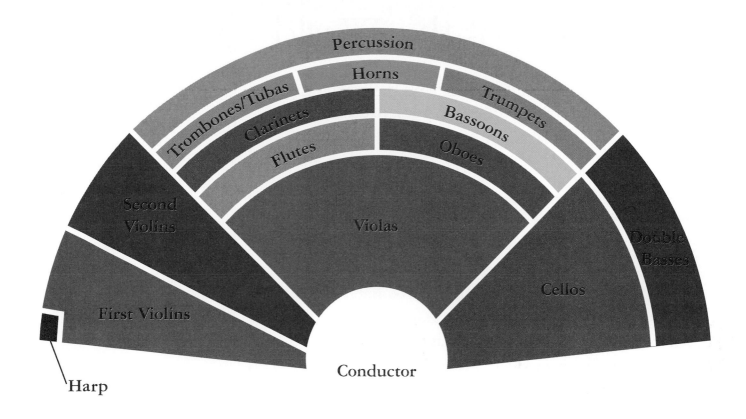

Percussion

Horns

Trombones/Tubas

Trumpets

Clarinets

Bassoons

Flutes

Oboes

Second
Violins

Violas

Double
Basses

Cellos

First Violins

Harp

Conductor

The London Symphony Orchestra

Orchestras of the World

The symphony orchestra originated in Europe and largely plays Western classical music. But groups of musicians have also played together for thousands of years in other parts of the world.

The gamelan sound

The gamelan is a type of orchestra found in Indonesia. The main instruments are percussion instruments, including gongs, chimes, drums, and xylophones, with some string and woodwind instruments. There may be as many as twenty to forty musicians. Each town or village has its own local gamelan. It often accompanies traditional dancing or shadow play performances. The musicians memorize their music, then improvise around certain set melodies.

A gamelan orchestra

Indian classical music

classical Indian group might consist of a *sitar* (a stringed instrument played like a guitar), *tablas* (drums), and a *sarangi* (a stringed instrument played with a bow, like a cello), or a *shahnai* (a woodwind instrument, like an oboe). The musicians do not play from a fixed score but improvise around patterns of notes, called *ragas*. There are hundreds of ragas designed for different times of the day and to create different moods. A raga is made up of five to seven notes, played in ascending or descending order.

South American music

lutes and pipes such as panpipes are often played in South American music, giving a soft, dreamy sound. More unusual stringed instruments, like the harp pictured below, are played by some South American Indians, such as these Quecha Indians. Mariachi bands, consisting of violins, guitars, trumpets, and a singer, are common in Mexico.

*South American
Quecha Indian players*

*Jazz trumpeter
Wynton Marsalis*

423

THINK ABOUT READING

Answer the questions in the story map.

SETTING

1. Where and when does the story take place?

CHARACTERS

2. Who are the main characters in the story?

BEGINNING

3. What is the grand sight that Alec points to as the story opens?

4. Why is Milo surprised once the concert begins?

5. What will happen if the orchestra doesn't play each day?

MIDDLE

6. What does Milo decide to do at 5:23 A.M.?

7. How do the musicians react to Milo's conducting?

ENDING

8. What happens when Chroma wakes up?

9. How do you think the orchestra responds to Chroma's conducting this time?

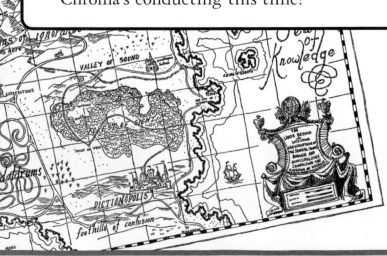

WRITE A FUND-RAISING LETTER

The conducter Chroma wants to raise money for his orchestra. Write a fund-raising letter for him. Your goal is to persuade the reader that the orchestra is doing the world a great service and deserves everyone's support. Be sure to list reasons why the musicians' playing is important. Don't forget to ask for a donation! Be sure to use a business letter format.

LITERATURE CIRCLE

Fantasies are fictional stories about people, events, or places that don't occur in real life. Discuss the elements of fantasy in *The Phantom Tollbooth,* and tell how this story differs from the article on orchestras. Then list some other fantasies you have read or have seen in films or on TV. Discuss why they fall into the fantasy category. Tell what qualities they share with *The Phantom Tollbooth.* Record your findings on a chart.

AUTHOR
NORTON JUSTER

Author Norton Juster is also an architect and college professor. He never intended to write a children's book when he began *The Phantom Tollbooth.* He wrote it for fun and relaxation while working on an architecture book. Juster never finished the book on architecture. However, his clever fantasy *The Phantom Tollbooth* went on to become not only a best-seller for young people, but also a movie in 1971 and an opera in 1995. Today *The Phantom Tollbooth* is considered a modern classic.

MORE BOOKS BY
NORTON JUSTER

- *The Dot and the Line*
- *Alberic the Wise*
- *Otter Nonsense*

PROJECT

How to
Give a Stage Presentation

It's your turn to be in the spotlight!

"**A**ll the world's a stage," wrote the famous playwright William Shakespeare. Though you may not be a performer, you'll probably be called "on stage" at some time in your life. You might have to make a speech or give an oral report. Here's an opportunity to give a stage presentation about something you know well or really care about. The format you choose for your presentation might be a monologue, a report, a speech, or a song.

Be expressive

Make eye contact

Smile

Wait for laughs

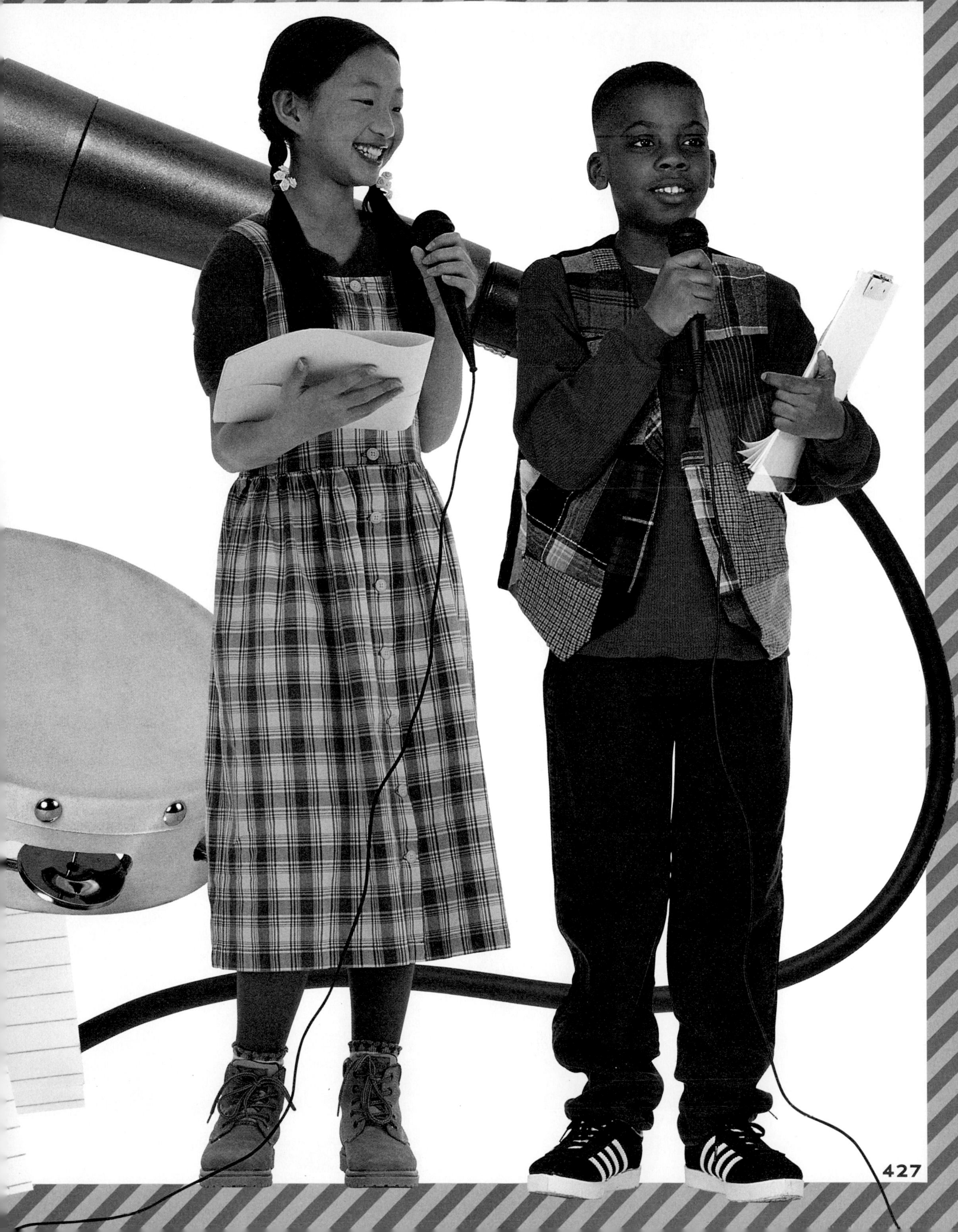

Choose Your Topic and Format

Begin by deciding what you want your presentation to be about. Aim for a presentation that's about five to ten minutes long. That can seem like a long time when you're on stage by yourself, so be sure the topic you pick is something you're interested in! You might want to focus on something that's happening in the news. Or you might choose to focus on a hobby, a person who inspires you, or something in which you consider yourself an expert.

Once you have picked your topic, think creatively about the best way to get your message across. For example, if your topic is a hot news story, you might deliver the information as if you were a newscaster.

If telling jokes is your hobby, you may want to organize a comedy routine. Here are some additional ideas for formats for your presentation. Can you think of any others?

- song
- oral report
- poem
- speech

TOOLS

- Paper and a pencil
- Props, costumes, and sound effects

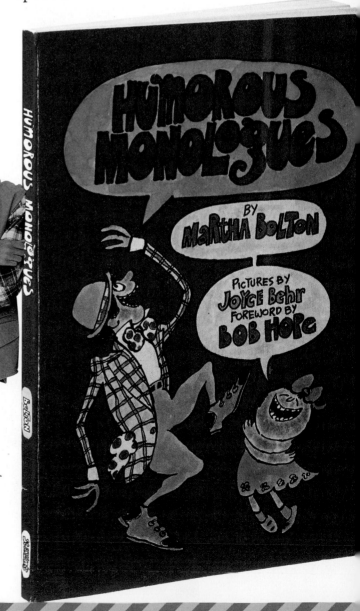

2 Write Your Script

Whatever your presentation is, you'll need to write a script for it. If you're creating your own monologue or comedy routine, or reading some of your own poems, you'll need to spend some time writing and organizing your material. If you're giving a report or a speech on a favorite topic, you'll need to write out what you'll say.

You might want to outline the main points you'll cover first and then fill in the details.

The Abraham Lincoln Joke Book

By
Beatrice Schenk de Regniers

Illustrations by
William Lahey Cummings

How Am I Doing?

Before you stage your presentation, take a few minutes to ask yourself these questions:

- Did I choose a topic that interests me and suits my audience?

- Do I know (or can I find out) 5–10 minutes worth of pertinent information about my topic?

- Have I chosen an appropriate format for my topic and audience?

Tip To choose the kind of presentation you want to do, list all your interests and hobbies and decide which one will be most entertaining for an audience.

3 Prepare Your Presentation

It takes more than a good script to give your presentation pizzazz. In the story-telling workshop, you learned how to make a presentation exciting. Think about using props, costumes, music, or visual aids to spice up your act. Mark up your script with any ideas you want to include.

Your presentation will be most successful if it's well-rehearsed. Have friends or family members observe a rehearsal. They can tell you whether you're speaking clearly and whether your props and other devices make sense to the audience. Refer to your script when you need to, but try to rely on it less the more you practice.

If You Are Using a Computer

Use the Sign format on your computer to make programs and banners for the performance. Illustrate them with clip-art or create your own drawings.

4 Stage Your Performance

Here are some suggestions for making your presentation a success.

- Monitor your voice. Speak loudly and clearly so that even the people in the back can hear you. To help your voice carry, keep your head up and face the audience.

- Use body language. Your gestures help to create drama and excitement! Move your face, hands, and body in ways that reinforce what you are saying.

- Organize your material so that the presentation goes smoothly.

- Finally, you might invite a parent or your school media specialist to videotape your presentation. You can watch the tape afterward and evaluate your performance.

CONGRATULATIONS

Now you know what it's like to share your interests with an audience. You'll use your creativity in many different situations.

José García
Drama Coach ▶

431

AMERICA'S

JOURNAL

AMERICA'S JOURNAL

THEME
Considering different points of view gives us a fuller understanding of history.

UNIT 5

Welcome to

LITERACY PLACE

Historical Museum

Considering different points of view gives us a fuller understanding of history.

Toliver's Secret

The country was counting on her!

BY
ESTHER
WOOD
BRADY

AWARD
WINNER

FROM TOLIVER'S SECRET

by Esther Wood Brady

illustrations by Paul Schmid

Ten-year-old Ellen Toliver knows that the American war for independence isn't an easy one. Her father has been killed in battle against the British, and her older brother Ezra is still away fighting for the Patriots. Ellen and her mother live in New York with her grandfather, a Patriot who fights against the British in his own way. He's about to carry an important message to an agent of General George Washington, when he falls and sprains his ankle. Now it's up to Ellen to deliver the message into safe hands.

"I will explain to you what this is all about," said Grandfather, "and then you can decide what to do, Ellen. I hear a lot of talk among the British officers in my shop. I hear a lot in the Tavern, too. I have information that must get to General Washington by tomorrow night at the latest. It must get there without fail. That's why I have hidden it in a loaf of bread. The bread won't attract attention, and it can be passed from one messenger to another until it gets to headquarters."

With a frown on her face, Mother jumped up from her chair and stood in front of him. "How could a message be that important, now?" she protested. "It is only two weeks until Christmas! And the officers are planning to stop the war for Christmas. I know they are."

Grandfather scowled at her. "And how could you know that, pray tell?"

"Why," said Mother, "people all over New York are having parties and balls for the officers. I hear that hundreds of fruitcakes have been made already—and thousands of candles. That's what I heard when I went to the candle shop."

Grandfather shook his head. His face, usually so pink cheeked and jolly, looked gray and drawn.

"And General Howe loves parties," Mother pressed on eagerly. "They all love parties. I know there won't be any fighting at Christmastime!"

Grandfather's eyes were grim. "Nevertheless, this message is very important! Our army has been defeated time and time again for months!" He pulled his foot from the pot of water and sat up. "Why," he exclaimed, "the British brought thirty thousand men— three times as many as Washington had!" He swung his leg over the side of the couch as if, in his eagerness to do something for Washington's army, he was ready to start.

"Whatever information we Patriots here in New York can send him about the British is important! The only way we can win is by using surprise and cunning and determination." He started to get up, but his foot touched the floor, and he groaned and fell back on the couch.

He looked at Ellen intently. "Can you understand what I have been telling you?"

"I think so."

Ellen could see that Grandfather was very serious about the need to send his message. She, too, had been worried about all the news of lost battles and retreats, especially since Ezra was with that army. She remembered how joyous everyone had been last July when they heard about the Declaration of Independence. There had been bonfires on the village green and singing and dancing in the streets. And then the British army came to New York and there had been three months of defeat.

"If you understand how important it is to take the message, Ellen, I'll tell you how it can be done. And then you are to decide."

Ellen listened and didn't say a word.

"You walk down to the docks near the Market-house and get on a farmer's boat—or an oysterman's. They come over early every morning and they go back to Elizabeth-town at eleven o'clock. Elizabeth is a very small town. When you get off the boat, you'll find the Jolly Fox Tavern without any trouble. My good friend Mr. Shannon runs the tavern, and you give the loaf of bread to him. That's all there is for you to do, Ellen. The Shannons will welcome you and take good care of you."

Sailing across the Bay didn't seem so hard. It was finding a boat here in New York and asking a stranger for a ride that worried her.

"How could I find the right boat to take me?" she asked. She didn't intend to go, but she thought she'd ask anyway.

"The docks are right near Front Street where we walked on Sunday afternoon. The farmers and the oystermen tie up their boats near the Market-house. They are friendly people and they often take passengers back to Elizabeth-town since the ferryboat stopped running. I'll give you money to pay."

"And how would I get home again—if I should decide to go?" she said in a very low voice.

"Oh, the Shannons will put you on a boat early in the morning. You'll be back here by ten o'clock."

"Does Mr. Shannon take the bread to General Washington?" she asked.

"No, he takes it to a courier who will ride part of the way. Then he'll give it to another courier who will ride through the night with it. And finally a third man will carry it to the General in Pennsylvania."

Ellen thought about the messengers riding alone through the countryside to carry the secret message. She wondered how it felt to be all alone among the British soldiers.

Mother interrupted. "It's too much to ask of her, Father. She's only ten."

Her father reached out and squeezed her hand. "Abby, dear," he said, "I know you are distressed because of all that has happened this fall. But don't make the child timid. We all have to learn to do things that seem hard at first. A child can't start too early to learn that."

Ellen knew her grandfather wouldn't send her if he thought she couldn't do it. Now that she thought it over she knew that if she walked carefully she could remember the way to Front Street. And she would have money to pay for the boat. She had liked sailing across the East River when she and Mother had taken the ferryboat from Brooklyn to New York last November. Perhaps it wouldn't be too hard. "But what would I do if I got lost?"

"If you lose your way, just speak up and ask someone for directions," said Grandfather.

"You're sure there is no one else to take it for you, Grandfather?"

"With this bad ankle I can't walk around New York to find one of my friends—and I wouldn't know where to send you or your mother to look. Besides, there isn't time. I need your help, Ellen."

Ellen was quiet for a long time.

"Very well," she said finally. "I'll do it—if you are really sure I can."

"I know you can, Ellen. And Abby," he said, "this is nothing too hard for a child of ten. The Shannons will take good care of her, you may be sure of that. In that chest in the kitchen are clothes that Ezra left here years ago. Go out and see what you find, Ellen."

Now that she had decided to go, Ellen ran quickly to the kitchen and poked around among the blankets and old clothes in the chest that sat near the fireplace. She was eager to see what was there. "Here's a striped cap," she exclaimed. "And here's that old blue jacket with the holes in the elbows. I remember these brass buttons." Grandfather had bought Ezra all new clothes when he had come to New York to visit several years ago.

Ellen put on a red knitted shirt that was too small and the blue wool jacket that was too big. The brass buttons made her think of Ezra's grin. She put on heavy gray stockings before she pulled up the short breeches. The leather breeches were so old and stiff they could almost stand alone. She kicked up her legs to make them soften up.

Not since she was a small child had she known what fun it was to kick her legs as high as she could. She tried to kick the skillet that hung beside the fireplace.

"These will be better for walking than petticoats," she said as she pranced about the kitchen. "Why can't girls wear these, too?"

"Ellen Toliver," said her mother primly. "It would be unseemly."

After trying on Ezra's boots, which were too big for her, she decided she would wear her own leather shoes to make walking easier. Certainly it would be easier to jump out of the way of horses and wheelbarrows and it would be better for climbing on the boat.

She ran into the shop to show her grandfather how she looked. For the first time since he fell on the ice, Grandfather laughed. "You look like a ragged little urchin all right," he said, "with those holes in your elbows. But all the better. No one will even notice you. And now we must cut your hair."

Mother picked up the scissors and stroked Ellen's long brown hair. "Couldn't we just tuck her hair under the cap?" she asked.

"No," said Ellen firmly. "I might forget and take it off! That would be dreadful. Besides, it might look bunchy beneath a cap." Better to have it short and not worry about it. She remembered her friend Lucinda who had short hair with a band of ribbon around her head. Lucinda looked very pretty with short hair. "Cut it off!" she said impatiently.

Grandfather smiled from his couch. "You'll do right well, Ellen," he said. "Tie a pigtail in back with a cord and then just snip off the part that is too long."

Ellen could feel her mother's hands tremble as she tied back the hair and snipped at the long pigtail.

"It will grow back," Ellen said to her. "How do I look?" Jumping up from the chair she stepped over the hair on the floor and stared at herself in the mirror.

"Why, I favor my father with my hair tied back!" she exclaimed. Her brown eyes were just like her father's eyes although not stern like his. Her face was thin like his, too. She stared at herself. Suddenly the person staring back at her didn't look like Ellen Toliver, and for a minute it frightened her to look so changed. Glancing sideways she could see her grandfather smiling his old cheerful smile.

Mother had given him the loaf of bread which he was wrapping in a blue kerchief and tying with a good strong knot.

"Where shall I hide the bread?" Ellen asked him.

"Don't hide it," he told her. "Don't think of hiding it. Just go along swinging this blue bundle as if it were nothing at all. There is only one thing to be careful about, Ellen. Be sure you give the bread to no one but Mr. Shannon."

His eyes grew as hard as they had been earlier that morning, when she surprised him in the kitchen. "No one but Mr. Shannon. He and I might hang if we were caught."

"Hang!" cried Ellen. "You mean on a gallows tree?"

Ellen's hands trembled so that she could hardly button the brass buttons on her jacket. No one had mentioned hanging before. If she had known her grandfather might hang she never would have agreed to do it. It wasn't fair. She gulped and at last the words came out. "I can't do it, Grandfather. I just can't. I'm too scared and I might make a mistake."

"You can do it, Ellen. Better than anyone else. No one in the world will suspect a loaf of bread in the hands of a child. If, perchance, someone found the message in the bread, just act surprised and say you don't know a thing about it!" He smiled at her to encourage her. "Just hang onto the bread good and tight until you see Mr. Shannon. That won't be hard to do, now will it?"

"But don't talk to any strangers, Ellie," Mother pleaded.

"Now, Abby. She has common sense."

"You're sure I won't make a mistake, Grandfather?"

"I can't see where you could go wrong, Ellen. The boatmen are kindly and they take people every day. And at the other end of the trip are my good friends the Shannons."

"Well, then," she said. "I think I am all ready now."

"Good!" cried Grandfather. "When you hand the bread to Mr. Shannon say this to him, 'I have brought you a present for your birthday.' He will understand what it means."

Mother slipped two corncakes into her pocket. "You'll get hungry before you get there, I'm sure." She was trying hard to sound cheerful. "I've always heard about Mistress Shannon's good potpies, and now you can eat one."

Grandfather slipped some coins into her pocket. Then he squeezed her hand until it hurt.

"God bless you, Ellen. I'm proud of you."

Mother pulled the red and white striped cap down around her ears and gave her a pair of mittens as well as a hug that almost smothered her. Then she stepped to the door and opened it. "I think you are a brave girl, Ellen."

Ellen stood at the top of the steps and looked up and down the street. She took a deep breath. Mother had said she was brave and Grandfather had said he was proud of her—well, she hoped they were right.

At first it felt strange to be walking down the same old street, looking like someone else. Ellen was sure people were watching her and wondering why she was dressed as a boy. What should she say if a woman walked up to her and asked, "Why is a girl wearing those clothes? It's not very seemly to show your legs." She'd pretend the woman had mistaken her for someone else.

But after a while, in Ezra's old breeches, her legs free of skirts and petticoats, she found it was fun to stomp along the cobblestones. She forgot what people might say. It was fun to dodge the oxcarts and the wheelbarrows and run against the wind with no cloak to hold her back. No one noticed her at all.

When she came to the pump corner she saw that Dicey and the two Brinkerhoff boys were having a snowball fight.

"That's a fair match," Ellen said to herself. She turned her head so Dicey could not see her. "Let them fight it out."

But she knew Dicey had seen her when she heard her call out, "Stop!" Ellen's heart almost stood still.

"New boy!" Dicey called. "What's your name?"

Why, Dicey didn't know her! It was just like being invisible. Dicey had looked at her and didn't know her.

Ellen peeped over her shoulder just in time to see Aaron Brinkerhoff push Dicey against a tree trunk and hold her there while Arnie gleefully scrubbed her face with handfuls of snow.

"Stop!" screamed Dicey. "Stop! Two against one ain't fair." She kicked and twisted away from them. Then, to Ellen's surprise, Dicey turned and ran away, crying like a bawling calf. Ellen stood and stared at her. For a moment she even felt sorry for her.

"Well, at least she didn't know me," Ellen said to herself. "I feel invisible."

"I'm invisible, I'm invisible," she kept saying as she ran happily down the street. Already she felt better about making the trip.

And then she felt a whack on her back that sent her spinning across the slippery cobblestones. The blue kerchief with her grandfather's loaf of bread flew from her hands.

Swift as hawks after a field mouse the two Brinkerhoff boys swooped down and snatched up her blue bundle.

"Try and get it! Try and get it!" Aaron called out. He held it out to her with an impudent grin on his face. When his brother Arnie grabbed for the bundle, Aaron snatched it away and ran. They played with it as if it were a ball, tossing it back and forth and daring her to chase them.

Ellen stood frozen with fear. What if the bread was torn apart. And the snuffbox fell out. And the British officers learned that Grandfather was a spy! It was too horrible to think of. Grandfather hanging on a gallows tree.

Her hands became fists as she thought how two laughing boys could put them all in such danger.

"Thieves!" she could hear herself shouting. "Stop those thieves!" She surprised herself by shouting those words in a loud strong voice. She surprised herself, too, by racing after the boys, dodging in and out of the crowds, tripping over children and ducking under the noses of dray horses.

"Stop those thieves!" she screamed. "They stole my bread!"

She ran up to two redcoats who stood on the steps of a bakeshop, eating hot little pies while they flirted with a group of kitchen maids.

"Please, sirs!" she gasped, "those thieves have stolen my bread!"

The soldiers shrugged and laughed. "Plenty of bread inside. The baker has just opened his ovens."

Now the boys were playing a game in front of a tailor's shop. They were tossing the blue bundle across his sign and hurling it between the wooden blades of a giant pair of scissors. Around them a crowd formed a circle to watch the fun.

"Give me my bread!" Ellen shouted as she leaped from one side to the other. She felt as nimble as a lamb without her long skirts and petticoats, but she never was quick enough to catch the bread.

Aaron mocked her. "Give the poor child his bread. He's starving!"

"Starving! Starving!" shrieked little Arnie. He held the bread out to her and then snatched it away when she jumped for it.

Two beggars watched with hungry eyes. Their bony fingers reached out to grab the bread. Even the public pig who ate scraps of garbage in the streets raced around them with greedy alert little eyes. The crowd laughed, but no one helped.

A little old woman who swept the steps of the tailor's shop with a broom of corn straw called out sharply. "What ails you Brinkerhoff boys? Always making trouble! Give the boy his loaf of bread!" She stepped down into the street and shook her broom at them. "Can't you see he's thin and hungry?"

Angrily she pushed her way through the crowd. Her back was so bent she was hardly as tall as Ellen, but she seemed to know what to do.

"Here," she said as she thrust her broom handle into Ellen's hands. "Here, trip them up. Bread is precious these days."

Ellen snatched the broomstick from the old woman. Without a moment's hesitation she raised it up and brought it down with a whack across Aaron's legs. Her eyes were blazing as she watched him duck out of her way. It made her feel good to hear him yell, "Stop," and see him dance away from her.

Arnie snatched the bundle from his brother's hands, and whirling it about his head, he grinned at her. "Try and get it!" he shrieked as he turned to push his way through the circle of people.

Ellen rushed after Arnie and whacked his legs, too. Her anger was so great she whacked at his legs until he fell sprawling on the ground.

Quick as a flash she scooped up the bundle, dropped her broom and looked for a way out of the circle.

"This way!" cried the little old woman gleefully. She held out her arms and made an opening for Ellen to get through. "Run like the wind, boy," she cried. "They'll be after you."

Ellen raced down the street. Her feet seemed to have wings. "Where to go? Where to hide?" she thought desperately as she looked over her shoulder and saw that the boys and the hungry beggars and even that awful public pig were after her.

Two boys might catch a girl who never had run on cobblestones before. But no one could catch a girl who held her grandfather's secret snuffbox in her arms.

"Stop him!" she could hear Arnie Brinkerhoff shout. "Stop the thief!"

The thief! Why, it was her loaf of bread. And why would they want it? It was just a game to them. No more important than a snowball.

She jumped over the low stone wall of a churchyard and raced across the flat gravestones. Looking back, she could see that she must have lost the beggars and the pig. Only the boys were following her. And a church warden who ran after her flapping his arms and shouting, "Be gone! Be gone!"

Over the wall she scrambled and into a street filled with haycarts going to the officers' stables. Under one cart and around another she darted. Farmers shook their pitchforks at her as she whirled past. "Don't alarm the horses!" they cried. But Ellen didn't hear them.

She had no idea where she was now as she raced around corners and down streets filled with rubble. Everywhere there were black walls of houses with roofs that had fallen in.

Gasping for breath she darted through a doorway of a broken-down house and crept into an old fireplace to hide. She was sure she had outrun the boys, but she couldn't stop the shaking of her knees. They jerked up and down like puppets on strings.

She sat down in the old ashes of the fireplace, tucked her arms around her knees and put her head on her arms. Her breath came in great sobs and blew the ashes up around her, covering her breeches with a fine dust.

"This must be the way rabbits feel—when the hounds chase them. If only I were back at home—I could crawl into bed and pull the covers over my head."

Those boys! Those horrible boys! To spoil everything at the beginning. It wasn't to have been such a long walk to Front Street. She had done it before with Grandfather.

"And now I don't know where I am," she wailed.

Grandfather had never brought her to the west side of town where the great fire burned block after block last September. It made him too sad to look at it, he said. Six hundred houses had been burned. And Trinity Church. It was lucky the whole city didn't burn up!

Slowly she began to collect her wits. Grandfather would have to find someone else to carry his message. She'd go home and tell him he had asked too much of her. She couldn't go out on the streets and roister about like a boy. She couldn't go sailing across the Bay to a place where she had never been and find a man she had never seen. That was asking too much of a ten-year-old girl. She'd go home and tell him he must find someone else.

She waited a long time to make sure the boys had not followed her. As she waited she grew calm and a strange happy feeling came over her.

She, Ellen Toliver, had fought two boys in front of a crowd of people. She not only had raced them and beaten them but she had saved her grandfather's message. The bread was here with the snuffbox still inside. She could hardly believe it.

As she sat quietly, a new feeling of confidence came to her. "Perhaps I can try to walk to the docks after all." She took a deep breath. "Perhaps I can go to Jersey after all. Grandfather said it wasn't hard. I can start over again from here, if I can find my way to Front Street."

Very carefully she crept out of the fireplace and looked around. There were tents where people must be living amidst the broken-down walls. But she saw no one around. Only stray cats that slunk away in the rubble.

"It must be getting near ten o'clock," she said to herself. There were no church bells to ring the hour, for the wardens had hidden the bells when the British came. She looked up at the hazy sun that struggled wanly in a gray sky. Grandfather always pointed out directions by the shadows the sun cast. "If the sun is on my left side—that must be the east. And the East River would be that way."

Very carefully she picked her way through the black rubble flecked with white snow. And at last she came to streets lined with fine houses and beech and sycamore trees. These streets looked familiar and the breeze had the salty fish smell of the river.

As she stepped quickly along she had a feeling the trip wouldn't be so bad after all.

NARRATIVE
POEM

from
From Sea to Shining Sea

Paul Revere's Ride

by

Henry Wadsworth
Longfellow

AWARD
WINNER

illustrations by Anita Lobel

Listen, my children, and you shall hear
Of the midnight ride of Paul Revere,
On the eighteenth of April, in Seventy-five;
Hardly a man is now alive
Who remembers that famous day and year.

He said to his friend, "If the British march
By land or sea from the town tonight,
Hang a lantern aloft in the belfry arch
Of the North Church tower as a signal light,—
One, if by land, and two, if by sea;
And I on the opposite shore will be,
Ready to ride and spread the alarm
Through every Middlesex village and farm,
For the country folk to be up and to arm."

Then he said, "Good night!" and with muffled oar
Silently rowed to the Charlestown shore,
Just as the moon rose over the bay,
Where swinging wide at her moorings lay
The *Somerset*, British man-of-war;
A phantom ship, with each mast and spar
Across the moon like a prison bar,
And a huge black hulk, that was magnified
By its own reflection in the tide.

Meanwhile, his friend, through alley and street,
Wanders and watches with eager ears,
Till in the silence around him he hears
The muster of men at the barrack door,
The sound of arms, and the tramp of feet,
And the measured tread of the grenadiers,
Marching down to their boats on the shore.

Then he climbed the tower of the Old North Church,
By the wooden stairs, with stealthy tread,
To the belfry-chamber overhead,
And startled the pigeons from their perch
On the somber rafters, that 'round him made
Masses and moving shapes of shade,—
By the trembling ladder, steep and tall,
To the highest window in the wall,
Where he paused to listen and look down
A moment on the roofs of the town,
And the moonlight flowing over all.

Beneath, in the churchyard, lay the dead,
In their night-encampment on the hill,
Wrapped in silence so deep and still
That he could hear, like a sentinel's tread,
The watchful night-wind, as it went
Creeping along from tent to tent,
And seeming to whisper, "All is well!"
A moment only he feels the spell
Of the place and the hour, and the secret dread
Of the lonely belfry and the dead;
For suddenly all his thoughts are bent
On a shadowy something far away,
Where the river widens to meet the bay,—
A line of black that bends and floats
On the rising tide, like a bridge of boats.

Meanwhile, impatient to mount and ride,
Booted and spurred, with a heavy stride
On the opposite shore walked Paul Revere.
Now he patted his horse's side,
Now gazed at the landscape far and near,

Then, impetuous, stamped the earth,
And turned and tightened his saddle-girth;
But mostly he watched with eager search
The belfry-tower of the Old North Church,
As it rose above the graves on the hill,
Lonely and spectral and somber and still.
And lo! as he looks, on the belfry's height
A glimmer, and then a gleam of light!
He springs to the saddle, the bridle he turns,
But lingers and gazes, till full on his sight
A second lamp in the belfry burns!

A hurry of hoofs in a village street,
A shape in the moonlight, a bulk in the dark,
And beneath, from the pebbles, in passing, a spark
Struck out by a steed flying fearless and fleet;
That was all! And yet, through the gloom and the light,
The fate of a nation was riding that night;
And the spark struck out by that steed in his flight,
Kindled the land into flame with its heat.
He has left the village and mounted the steep,
And beneath him, tranquil and broad and deep,
Is the Mystic, meeting the ocean tides;
And under the alders, that skirt its edge,
Now soft on the sand, now loud on the ledge,
Is heard the tramp of his steed as he rides.

It was twelve by the village clock
When he crossed the bridge into Medford town,
He heard the crowing of the cock,
And the barking of the farmer's dog,
And felt the damp of the river fog,
That rises after the sun goes down.

It was one by the village clock,
When he galloped into Lexington.
He saw the gilded weathercock
Swim in the moonlight as he passed,
And the meeting-house windows, blank and bare,
Gaze at him with a spectral glare,
As if they already stood aghast
At the bloody work they would look upon.

It was two by the village clock,
When he came to the bridge in Concord town.
He heard the bleating of the flock,
And the twitter of birds among the trees,
And felt the breath of the morning breeze
Blowing over the meadows brown.
And one was safe and asleep in his bed
Who at the bridge would be first to fall,
Who at the bridge would be lying dead,
Pierced by a British musket-ball.

You know the rest. In the books you have read,
How the British Regulars fired and fled,—
How the farmers gave them ball for ball,
From behind each fence and farmyard wall,
Chasing the redcoats down the lane,
Then crossing the fields to emerge again
Under the trees at the turn of the road,
And only pausing to fire and load.

So through the night rode Paul Revere;
And so through the night went his cry of alarm
To every Middlesex village and farm,—
A cry of defiance, and not of fear,
A voice in the darkness, a knock at the door,
And a word that shall echo forevermore!
For, borne on the night-wind of the Past,
Through all our history, to the last,
In the hour of darkness and peril and need,
The people will waken and listen to hear
The hurrying hoofbeats of that steed,
And the midnight message of Paul Revere.

THINK ABOUT READING

Answer the questions in the story map.

SETTING
1. Where and when does the story take place?

CHARACTERS
2. Who are the main characters in the story?

BEGINNING
3. What problem is presented at the beginning of the story?
4. What does Ellen have to do for her grandfather?

MIDDLE
5. How does Ellen prepare for her task?
6. What threatens the success of Ellen's mission?
7. How does Ellen get the loaf of bread back?

ENDING
8. How does Ellen feel when she thinks that she is lost?
9. What does Ellen finally decide to do? Why?

WRITE A DIALOGUE

Ellen Toliver's goal is to deliver a loaf of bread to Mr. Shannon in New Jersey. Write the conversation—or dialogue—that takes place between Ellen and Mr. Shannon when they first meet. As you write, think about what kind of person Ellen is, what her purpose is, and what she might say. How would Mr. Shannon respond to her? Be sure to use correct punctuation in your dialogue.

LITERATURE CIRCLE

Toliver's Secret takes place over two hundred years ago during the War of Independence. Although the characters are made up, the setting and the situation are real. Discuss how the author makes this fictional story seem possible. In what ways does she make the problems of American Patriots important to a modern reader? Then talk about the use of historical information and fictional details in the poem "Paul Revere's Ride." How does it compare to *Toliver's Secret*?

AUTHOR
ESTHER WOOD BRADY

Writing historical fiction was a natural choice for Esther Wood Brady. She grew up listening to her grandparents tell stories about their ancestors, who were early colonists. Brady once said: "Our attic has tin boxes crammed with letters from many generations.... The characters in my books are imaginary, but their times and life-styles seem very real to me." Esther Wood Brady began writing in 1936 and wrote many historical novels over the next four decades. She died in 1987.

MORE BOOKS BY
ESTHER WOOD BRADY

- *Great Sweeping Day*
- *The Toad on Capitol Hill*

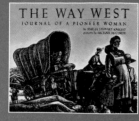

AWARD
WINNER

THE W

JOURNAL OF A PIONEER

462

AY WEST

WOMAN by AMELIA STEWART KNIGHT

pictures by MICHAEL MCCURDY

INTRODUCTION

This is the true story of Amelia Stewart Knight, her husband, and their seven children, who set out from Monroe County, Iowa, for the Oregon Territory in 1853. The boys were named Jefferson, Seneca, Plutarch, and Chatfield. The girls were Lucy, Frances, and Almira. The Knights started their journey in Iowa. Other families started in little towns along the Missouri River called jumping-off places because the travelers were leaving the United States and setting out through Indian Territory.

The overlanders traveled in big wagons pulled by yokes of six or eight oxen. Mrs. Knight cooked with "buffalo chips" over dusty fires. She rolled her pie dough on the wagon seat. If a family took their cows and dogs with them, the animals had to walk beside the wagons for more than a thousand miles.

A big wagon heavy with supplies could travel only ten or fifteen miles a day. It might take four to six months for a family to reach the Pacific coast. Only a few places existed on the long road where they could stop for repairs or more food. When the oxen got tired, or when the road got too rough, families lightened their loads by throwing away things they loved—rocking chairs, cradles, and even a piano might be left at the side of the road.

There were many rivers to cross on the long journey. But the people were ingenious; they painted the sides of their wagons with tar to keep water out. Then they lifted the wagon right off the flatbed and floated it across the river like a boat. They piled their belongings on the wagon bed and pushed that across the river like a raft. Indians helped the overlanders, warning them against quicksand, and trading salmon, deer meat, and moccasins for cloth and money.

When the overlanders came to the mountains, the work was different. The men pulled the wagons up to the mountaintops with winches and chains, and the women and children set rocks at the back wheels to keep the wagons from sliding down. Once they got to the top, the men tied strong rope around the wagons and pulled hard to keep them from smashing on the way down the other side.

Rain soaked through the canvas covers of the wagons, and people often became ill. Children were injured climbing on and off the moving wagons, and sometimes got lost when they strayed.

Mrs. Knight does not tell you until the very end that she is expecting another baby. You must remember her secret as you read.

LILLIAN SCHLISSEL

SATURDAY, APRIL 9, 1853. STARTED FROM HOME about eleven o'clock and traveled eight miles and camped in an old house; night cold and frosty.

MONDAY, APRIL 11, 1853. Jefferson and Lucy have the mumps. Poor cattle bawled all night.

THURSDAY, APRIL 14, 1853. Sixteen wagons all getting ready to cross the creek. Hurrah boys, all ready. Gee up Tip and Tyler, and away we go, the sun just rising.
(evening) The men have pitched the tent and are hunting something to make a fire to get supper.

SATURDAY, APRIL 16, 1853. Made our beds down in the tent in the wet and mud. Bed clothes nearly spoiled. Cold and cloudy this morning, and everybody out of humour. Seneca is half sick. Plutarch has broke his saddle girth. Husband is scolding and hurrying all hands and Almira says she wished she was home and I say ditto. "Home, Sweet Home."

THURSDAY, APRIL 21, 1853. Rained all night; is still raining. I have just counted seventeen wagons traveling ahead of us in the mud and water. No feed for our poor stock to be got at any price. Have to feed them flour and meal.

SATURDAY, APRIL 23, 1853. Still in camp. It rained hard all night, and blew a hurricane almost. All the tents were blown down, and some wagons capsized.... Dreary times, wet and muddy and crowded in the tent, cold and wet and uncomfortable in the wagon. No place for the poor children.

MONDAY, MAY 2, 1853. Pleasant evening. Threw away several jars, some wooden buckets, and all our pickles. Too unhandy to carry. Indians come to our camp every day, begging money and something to eat. Children are getting used to them.

SATURDAY, MAY 7, 1853. We have crossed a small creek, with a narrow Indian bridge across it. Paid the Indians seventy-five cents toll.

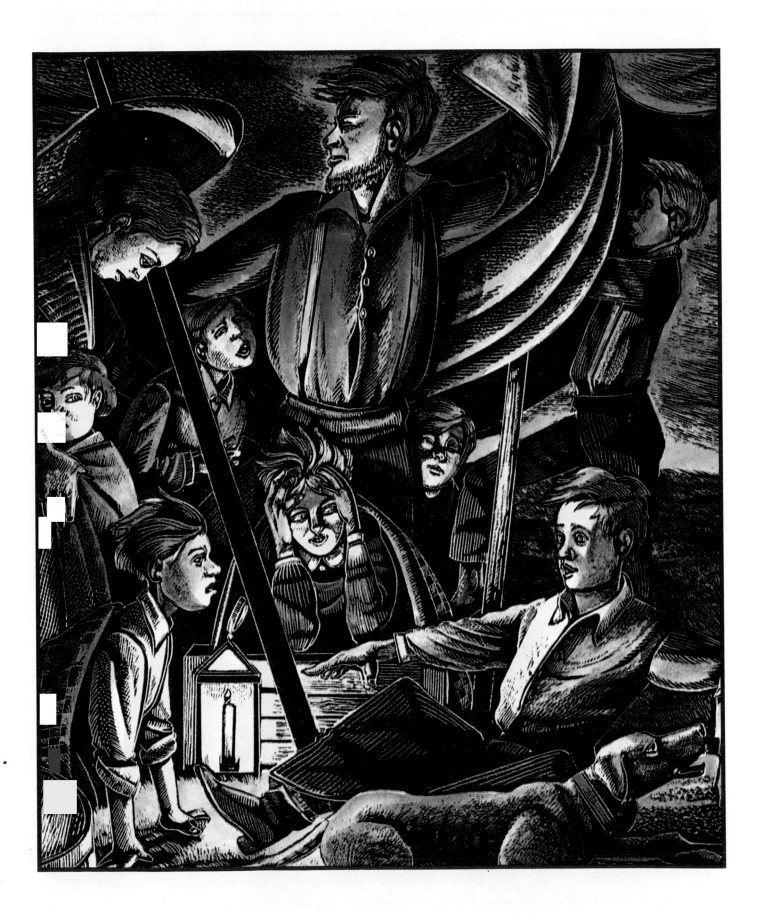

SUNDAY, MAY 8, 1853. There are three hundred or more wagons in sight and as far as the eye can reach, the land is covered, on each side of the river, with cattle and horses. There is no ferry here and the men will have to make one out of the tightest wagon bed. Everything must now be hauled out of the wagons, then the wagons must be all taken to pieces, and then by means of a strong rope stretched across the river, with a tight wagon bed attached to the middle of it, the rope must be long enough to pull from one side to the other, with men on each side of the river to pull it. In this way we have to cross everything a little at a time. Women and children last, and then swim the cattle and horses. There were three horses and some cattle drowned while crossing this place yesterday.

WEDNESDAY, MAY 11, 1853. It has been very dusty yesterday and today. The men all have their false eyes (goggles) on to keep the dust out.

FRIDAY, MAY 13, 1853. It is thundering and bids fair for rain. Crossed the river very early this morning before breakfast. Got breakfast over after a fashion. Sand all around ankle deep; wind blowing; no matter, hurry it over. Them that eat the most breakfast eat the most sand.

MONDAY, MAY 16, 1853. This afternoon it rained, hailed, and the wind was very high. Have been traveling all the afternoon in mud and water up to our hubs. Broke chains and stuck in the mud several times. The men and boys are all wet and muddy.

TUESDAY, MAY 17, 1853. I never saw such a storm. The wind was so high I thought it would tear the wagons to pieces. All had to crowd into the wagons and sleep in wet beds with their wet clothes on, without supper.

MONDAY, MAY 23, 1853. The road is covered with droves of cattle and wagons—no end to them.

TUESDAY, MAY 24, 1853. Husband went back a piece this morning in search of our dog, which he found with some rascals who were trying to keep him.

SATURDAY, MAY 28, 1853. Passed a lot of men skinning a buffalo. We got a mess and cooked some of it for supper. It was very good and tender. It is the first we have seen dead or alive.

TUESDAY, MAY 31, 1853. When we started this morning there were two large droves of cattle and about fifty wagons ahead of us, and we either had to stay poking behind them in the dust or hurry up and drive past them. It was no fool of a job to be mixed up with several hundred head of cattle, and only one road to travel in, and the drovers threatening to drive their cattle over you if you attempted to pass them. They even took out their pistols. Husband drove our team out of the road entirely, and the cattle seemed to understand it all, for they went into a trot most of the way. The rest of the boys followed with their teams and the rest of the stock. It was a rather rough ride to be sure, but was glad to get away from such a lawless set.... We left some swearing men behind us.

TUESDAY, JUNE 7, 1853. Just passed Fort Laramie and a large village of Sioux Indians. Numbers of them came around our wagons. Some of the women had moccasins and beads, which they wanted to trade for bread. I gave the women and children all the cakes I had baked. Husband traded a big Indian a lot of hard crackers for a pair of moccasins, [but when they] had eaten the crackers he wanted the moccasins back. We handed the moccasins to him in a hurry and drove away as soon as possible.

SATURDAY, JUNE 11, 1853. The last of the Black Hills we crossed this afternoon, over the roughest and most desolate piece of ground that was ever made (called by some the Devil's Crater). Not a drop of water, nor a spear of grass, nothing but barren hills.
—We reached Platte River about noon, and our cattle were so crazy for water that some of them plunged headlong into the river with their yokes on.

WEDNESDAY, JUNE 15, 1853. Passed Independence Rock this afternoon, and crossed Sweetwater River on a bridge. Paid three dollars a wagon and swam the stock across. The river is very high and swift. There are cattle and horses drowned there every day; there was one cow went under the bridge and was drowned, while we were crossing. The bridge is very rickety and must soon break down.

TUESDAY, JUNE 21, 1853. We have traveled over mountains close to banks of snow. Had plenty of snow water to drink. (Mr. Knight) brought me a large bucket of snow and one of our hands brought me a beautiful bunch of flowers which he said was growing close to the snow which was about six feet deep.

WEDNESDAY, JUNE 22, 1853. Very cold. Water froze over in the buckets; the boys have on their overcoats and mittens.

SUNDAY, JUNE 26, 1853. All hands come into camp tired and out of heart. Husband and myself sick. No feed for the stock. One ox lame. Camp on the bank of Big Sandy again.

MONDAY, JUNE 27, 1853. It is all hurry and bustle to get things in order. It's children milk the cows, all hands help yoke these cattle, the d– – –l's in them. Plutarch answers, "I can't, I must hold the tent up, it's blowing away." Hurrah boys. Who tied these horses? "Seneca, don't stand there with your hands in your pockets. Get your saddles and be ready."

WEDNESDAY, JUNE 29, 1853. The wagons are all crowded at the ferry waiting with impatience to cross. There are thirty or more to cross before us. Have to cross one at a time. Have to pay [the Indians] eight dollars for a wagon; one dollar for a horse or a cow. We swim all our stock.

SUNDAY, JULY 3, 1853. Two of our oxen are quite lame.

MONDAY, JULY 4, 1853. Chatfield has been sick all day with fever partly caused by mosquito bites.

THURSDAY, JULY 7, 1853. Our poor dog gave out with the heat so that he could not travel. The boys have gone back after him.

THURSDAY, JULY 14, 1853. It is dust from morning until night, with now and then a sprinkling of gnats and mosquitoes, and as far as the eye can reach there is nothing but a sandy desert, covered with wild sagebrush, dried up with the heat. I have ridden in the wagon and taken care of Chatfield till I got tired, then I got out and walked in the sand and through stinking sagebrush till I gave out.

SUNDAY, JULY 17, 1853. Travel over some rocky ground. Chat fell out of the wagon, but did not get hurt much.

FRIDAY, JULY 22, 1853. Here Chat had a very narrow escape from being run over. Just as we were all getting ready to start, Chatfield, the rascal, came around the forward wheel to get into the wagon, and at that moment the cattle started and he fell under the wagon. Somehow he kept from under the wheels, and escaped with only a good, or I should say, a bad scare. I never was so much frightened in my life.

SATURDAY, JULY 23, 1853. The empty wagons, cattle, and horses have to be taken further up the river and crossed by means of chains and ropes. The way we cross this branch is to climb down about six feet on the rocks, and then a wagon bed bottom will just reach across from rocks to rocks. It must then be fastened at each end with ropes or chains, so that you can cross on it, and then we climb up the rocks on the other side, and in this way everything has to be taken across. Some take their wagons to pieces and take them over in that way.

MONDAY, JULY 25, 1853. We have got on to a place in the road that is full of rattlesnakes.

THURSDAY, JULY 28, 1853. Have traveled twelve miles today and have camped in the prairie five or six miles from water. Chat is quite sick with scarlet fever.

FRIDAY, JULY 29, 1853. Chat is some better.

THURSDAY, AUGUST 4, 1853. Have seen a good many Indians and bought fish of them. They all seem peaceable and friendly.

FRIDAY, AUGUST 5, 1853. Tomorrow we will cross the Snake River. Our worst trouble at these large rivers is swimming the stock over. Often after swimming half the way over, the poor things will turn and come out again. At this place, however, there are Indians who swim the river from morning till night. There is many a drove of cattle that could not be got over without their help. By paying a small sum, they will take a horse by the bridle or halter and swim over with him. The rest of the horses all follow and the cattle will almost always follow the horses.

MONDAY, AUGUST 8, 1853. We left, unknowingly, our Lucy behind. Not a soul had missed her until we had gone some miles, when we stopped awhile to rest the cattle. Just then another train drove up behind with Lucy. She was terribly frightened and so were some more of us when we found out what a narrow escape she had run. She said she was sitting under the bank of the river when we started and did not know we were ready. And I supposed she was in Carl's wagon, as he always took charge of Frances and Lucy.... He supposed she was with me. It was a lesson to all of us.

FRIDAY, AUGUST 12, 1853. We were traveling slowly when one of our oxen dropped dead in the yoke. We unyoked and turned out the odd ox, and drove around the dead one.... I could hardly help shedding tears, and shame on the man who has no pity for the poor dumb brutes that have to travel and toil month after month on this desolate road.

WEDNESDAY, AUGUST 17, 1853. There are fifty or more wagons camped around us. Lucy and Almira have their feet and legs (covered with poison ivy).
—Bought some fresh salmon of the Indians this evening, which is quite a treat to us. It is the first we have seen.

WEDNESDAY, AUGUST 31, 1853. It is still raining this morning. The air cold and chilly. It blew so hard last night as to blow our buckets and pans from under the wagons, and this morning we found them scattered all over the valley.

THURSDAY, SEPTEMBER 1, 1853. After traveling eleven miles and ascending a long hill, we have encamped not far from the Columbia River and made a nice dinner of fried salmon. Quite a number of Indians were camped around us, for the purpose of selling salmon to the emigrants.

SATURDAY, SEPTEMBER 3, 1853. Here husband (being out of money) sold his sorrell mare (Fan) for a hundred and twenty-five dollars.

MONDAY, SEPTEMBER 5, 1853. Ascended a long steep hill this morning which was very hard on the cattle and also on myself, as I thought I never should get to the top.

FRIDAY, SEPTEMBER 9, 1853. There is a great deal of laurel growing here, which will poison the stock if they eat it. There is no end to the wagons, buggies, yokes, chains, etc., that are lying all along this road. Some splendid good wagons, just left standing, perhaps with the owners' names on them; and many are the poor horses, mules, oxen, cows, etc., that are lying dead in these mountains.

SATURDAY, SEPTEMBER 10, 1853. It would be useless for me to describe the awful road we have just passed over…. It is very rocky all the way, quite steep, winding, sideling, deep down, slippery and muddy…and this road is cut down so deep that at times the cattle and wagons are almost out of sight…the poor cattle all straining to hold back the heavy wagons on the slippery road.

TUESDAY, SEPTEMBER 13, 1853. We are in Oregon, with no home, except our wagons and tent.

SATURDAY, SEPTEMBER 17, 1853. A few days later my eighth child was born. We picked up and ferried across the Columbia River, utilizing skiff, canoes, and flatboat to get across, taking three days to complete. Husband traded two yoke of oxen for a half section of land with one half acre planted to potatoes, and a small log cabin and lean-to with no windows.

THIS IS THE JOURNEY'S END.

OREGON

Stories of rich farmland in Oregon gave many Easterners "Oregon Fever." The rugged trail that led them there was the longest of the great overland routes used in the westward expansion of the United States. Pioneers traveled the 2,000-mile trail one step at a time.

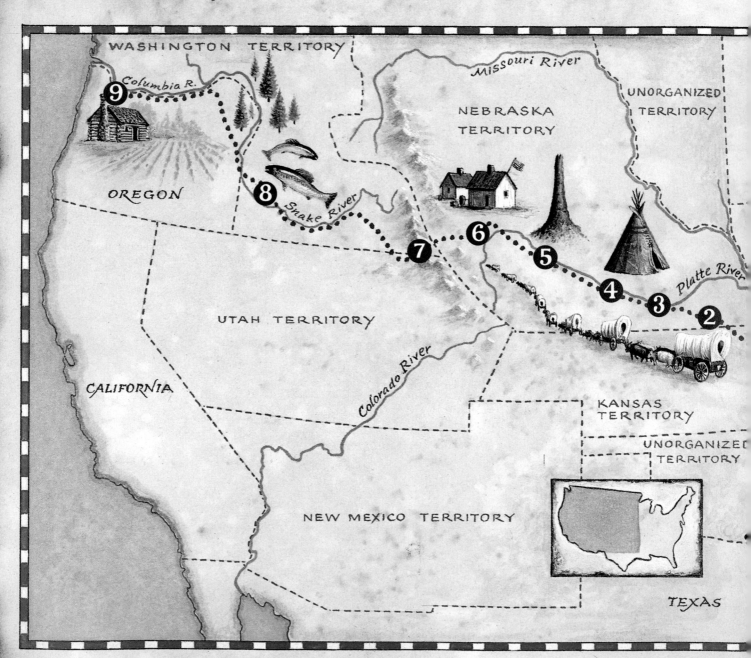

FEVER

❶ First Stop: Independence Hopeful settlers began following the trail to Oregon in 1841. More than 100 families gathered in Independence, Missouri, to start the six-month trek across the continent. Each spring, for the next 20 years, thousands of others followed.

❷ Wagons, Ho! The settlers joined together in wagon trains to cross the treeless plains. Wagon trains stretched for five miles and included three times more cattle and horses than people!

❸ Follow the Platte Nebraska's chief river, the Platte, was too shallow for navigation, but settlers were able to follow its banks upstream.

❹ Native Lands The land settlers crossed belonged to the Pawnee, Sioux, Arapaho, Cheyenne, and Crow. These Native Americans hoped the pioneers would pass through their land quickly.

❺ Chimney Rock When settlers reached this 500-foot column of rock in the Nebraska Territory, they knew they had traveled about 550 miles. (But they still had a long way to go!)

❻ Fort Laramie Fort Laramie was a trading post filled with useful goods such as flour, blankets, tools, rope, and water. After three months on the long trail, some people found it hard to leave.

❼ South Pass Crossing the Rocky Mountains through South Pass was one of the most difficult parts of the trek. Stubborn cattle, plus heavy wagons, had to be hauled through treacherous ravines.

❽ The Snake River By the fourth month, most wagon trains reached the Snake River. Its salmon-filled waters and surrounding green forests gave settlers renewed hope.

❾ Journey's End! For most settlers arriving in the 1840s and 1850s, the journey's end was the beautiful and fertile Willamette River Valley.

Map of the Oregon Trail, circa 1853

from I HAVE SPOKEN

I Love the Land

by

SATANTA, KIOWA CHIEF

In October 1867, a group of Native American chiefs, including Satanta, met with U.S. government officials at Medicine Lodge Creek in what is now Kansas. The purpose of the meeting was to negotiate treaties between native peoples and the government. This is the speech that Chief Satanta gave during the gathering.

I love the land and the buffalo and will not part with it. I want you to understand well what I say. Write it on paper.... I hear a great deal of good talk from the gentlemen, but they never do what they say. I don't want any of the medicine lodges [schools and churches] within the country. I want the children raised as I was....

I have heard that you intend to settle us on a reservation near the mountains. I don't want to settle. I love to roam over the prairies. There I feel free and happy, but when we settle down we grow pale and die. I have laid aside my lance, bow, and shield, and yet I feel safe in your presence. I have told you the truth. I have no little lies hid about me, but I don't know how it is with the commissioners. Are they as clear as I am? A long time ago this land belonged to our fathers; but when I go up the river I see camps of soldiers on its banks. These soldiers cut down my timber; they kill my buffalo; and when I see that, my heart feels like bursting; I feel sorry. I have spoken.

Satanta, Kiowa Chief 485

THINK ABOUT READING

Write your answers.

1. What is the Knight family's final destination? How long does it take them to get there?

2. How do you think Amelia Stewart Knight feels during the storm that she mentions on May 17?

3. If you were traveling with the Knights, which part of the journey would you find the most challenging? Why?

4. Do you think Michael McCurdy's illustrations are a good addition to the journal? Explain your answer.

5. What do Amelia Stewart Knight's journal and Satanta's speech have in common?

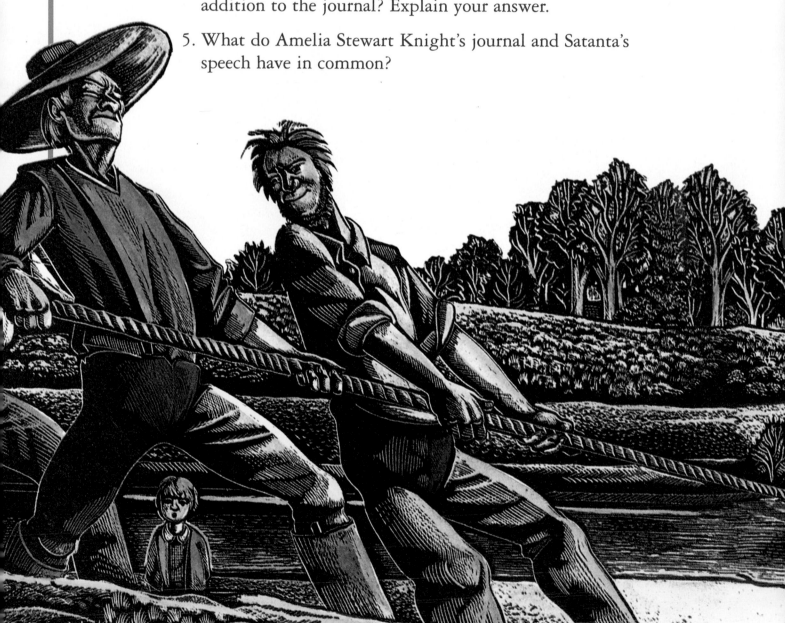

WRITE A PERSONAL NARRATIVE

Take the part of one of Amelia Stewart Knight's children. Write a personal narrative about one of the events that their mother describes in her journal. Describe what happens from the child's point of view, and tell how he or she feels. Use vivid verbs, and include as many details as possible in your writing. Be sure to use the personal pronouns *I, me, my, we, us,* and *our* as you relate the story.

LITERATURE CIRCLE

Crossing the western plains of the United States in a covered wagon required a special kind of person. Talk about the character traits that pioneers like Amelia Stewart Knight and her family displayed as they made their difficult journeys. Record your findings on a web about character traits. Then discuss which qualities were most important and tell why.

ILLUSTRATOR
MICHAEL MCCURDY

Award-winning illustrator Michael McCurdy creates his distinctive woodcuts and colored scratchboard illustrations in a big red barn in western Massachusetts. Although McCurdy has created art for classic works by Charles Dickens and Isaac Asimov, he takes a special interest in American history and has even illustrated Abraham Lincoln's "Gettysburg Address." McCurdy says, "For me—as with most book artists—inspiration comes from a text, from words."

MORE BOOKS ILLUSTRATED BY MICHAEL McCURDY

- *The Sailor's Alphabet* by Michael McCurdy
- *The Gettysburg Address* by Abraham Lincoln
- *Johnny Tremain* by Esther Forbes

WORKSHOP

How to Conduct an Oral History

This subject was interviewed about his college experiences during the Great Depression.

Questions such as "What did a dollar buy?" and "What did you do for fun?" are always interesting to investigate.

In some societies, history is passed down almost entirely through the spoken word. Collecting oral histories is one way that historians learn about the past.

What is an oral history? An oral history is the spoken recollections of one person. It presents that person's viewpoint and memories about a particular time or event.

Robert Gard

Professor of Drama, University of Wisconsin

I SET OUT for the University of Kansas on a September morning with $30 that I'd borrowed from my local bank. I had one suit and one necktie and one pair of shoes. My mother had spent several days putting together a couple of wooden cases of canned fruits and vegetables. My father, a country lawyer, had taken as a legal fee a 1915 Buick touring car. It was not in particularly good condition, but it was good enough to get me there. It fell to pieces and it never got back home anymore.

I had no idea how long the $30 would last, but it sure would have to go a long way because I had nothing else. The semester fee was $22, so that left me $8 to go. Fortunately, I got a job driving a car for the dean of the law school. That's how I got through the first year.

What a pleasure it was to get a pound of hamburger, which you could buy for about five cents, take it up to the Union Pacific Railroad tracks and have a cookout. And some excellent conversation. And maybe swim in the Kaw River. One friend of mine came to college equipped. He had an old Model T Ford Sedan, about a 1919 model. He had this thing fitted up as a house. He lived in it all year long. He cooked and slept and studied inside that Model T Sedan. How he managed I will never know. I once went there for dinner. He cooked a pretty good one on a little stove he had in this thing. He was a brilliant student. I don't know where he is now, but I shouldn't be surprised if he's the head of some big corporation. (Laughs.)

1 Choose a Topic

Decide on an event or a time period that you would like to know more about. Perhaps you are interested in the first moon landing, or maybe you're curious about the 1960s in general. Make sure the event or time is something that someone you know has experienced. For example, you can't record an oral history about the Civil War, which ended over 130 years ago.

Once you've chosen a time period, find a friend or family member who remembers it and would like to talk to you about it!

TOOLS

- paper and pencil

- cassette recorder or video camera (optional)

2 Prepare Questions

What do you want to know about the topic you've chosen? Make a list of the questions you'd like to have answered. Leave plenty of space after each question to jot down the answer. You may want to find out a few basic facts, such as how old your subject was during the event or era you're researching, where he or she lived, and what he or she felt was most exciting or important about the topic you chose.

3 Conduct an Interview

Record an oral history by conducting an interview with the person you've chosen. Get the ball rolling by asking the questions you prepared earlier. Be sure to write down (and ask!) any new questions you think of during the interview.

Some questions may prompt long, complicated answers. Don't worry about writing them down word for word. Make note of the main points and fill in the gaps when the interview is over.

Tips
- Ask your subject to show you school yearbooks, sports memorabilia, newspaper clippings, and photographs from the period.
- Tape the interview with a tape recorder.

4 Present Your Work

Write up the oral history you've collected using a question-and-answer format. Leave out questions and answers, or parts of answers, that you feel are uninteresting or unimportant.

Share the oral history with your class. Find out if any of your classmates collected an oral history on the same event or era you chose. Compare the two histories to find out how they are alike and how they are different.

If You Are Using a Computer ...

Draft your questions in the Journal format. After you complete your interview, write your oral history in the Newsletter format. Give it an attention-grabbing headline.

THINK
How are oral histories different from the stories you read in most history books?

Russell Freedman
Historian/Author ▶

F R O M

The House
of Dies Drear

AWARD
WINNER

By **VIRGINIA HAMILTON**

Illustrations by **KEAF HOLLIDAY**

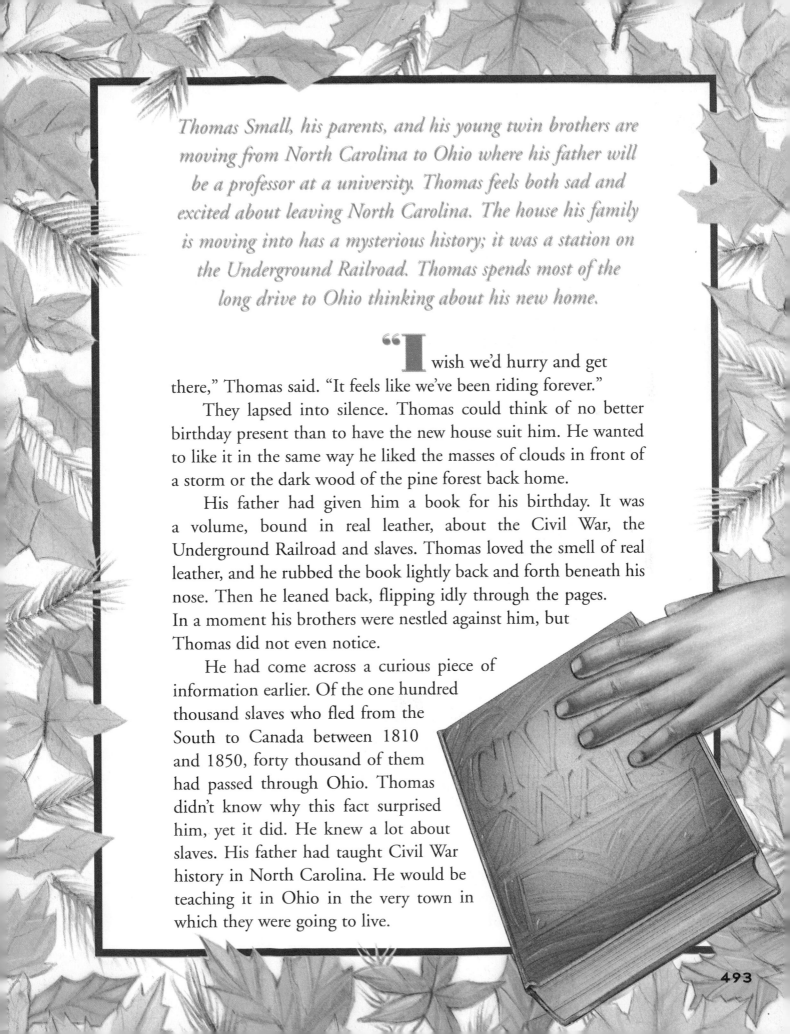

Thomas Small, his parents, and his young twin brothers are moving from North Carolina to Ohio where his father will be a professor at a university. Thomas feels both sad and excited about leaving North Carolina. The house his family is moving into has a mysterious history; it was a station on the Underground Railroad. Thomas spends most of the long drive to Ohio thinking about his new home.

"I wish we'd hurry and get there," Thomas said. "It feels like we've been riding forever."

They lapsed into silence. Thomas could think of no better birthday present than to have the new house suit him. He wanted to like it in the same way he liked the masses of clouds in front of a storm or the dark wood of the pine forest back home.

His father had given him a book for his birthday. It was a volume, bound in real leather, about the Civil War, the Underground Railroad and slaves. Thomas loved the smell of real leather, and he rubbed the book lightly back and forth beneath his nose. Then he leaned back, flipping idly through the pages. In a moment his brothers were nestled against him, but Thomas did not even notice.

He had come across a curious piece of information earlier. Of the one hundred thousand slaves who fled from the South to Canada between 1810 and 1850, forty thousand of them had passed through Ohio. Thomas didn't know why this fact surprised him, yet it did. He knew a lot about slaves. His father had taught Civil War history in North Carolina. He would be teaching it in Ohio in the very town in which they were going to live.

He had taught Thomas even more
history than Thomas cared to know.
Thomas knew that Elijah Anderson had been
the "superintendent" of the Underground
Railroad in Ohio and that he had finally died in
prison in Kentucky. He knew that in the space of
seven years, one thousand slaves had died in Kentucky.
But the fact that forty thousand escaping slaves had fled
through Ohio started him thinking.

Ohio will be my new home, he thought. A lot of those
slaves must have stayed in Ohio because Canada was farther
than they could have believed. Or they had liked Elijah
Anderson so much, they'd just stayed with him. Or maybe
once they saw the Ohio River, they thought it was the Jordan
and that the Promised Land lay on the other side.

The idea of exhausted slaves finding the Promised Land on
the banks of the Ohio River pleased Thomas. He'd never seen
the Ohio River, but he could clearly imagine freed slaves riding
horses up and down its slopes. He pictured the slaves living in
great communities as had the Iroquois, and they had brave
leaders like old Elijah Anderson.

"Papa…" Thomas said.

"Yes, Thomas," said Mr. Small.

"Do you ever wonder if any runaway slaves from North
Carolina went to Ohio?"

Mr. Small was startled by the question. He laughed and said,
"You've been reading the book I gave you. I'm glad, it's a good
book. I'm sure some slaves fled from North Carolina. They
escaped from all over the South, and it's likely that half of them
passed through Ohio on their way to Canada."

Thomas sank back into his seat, arranging his sprawling
brothers against him. He smoothed his hand over the book and
had half a mind to read it from cover to cover. He would wake the
twins and read it all to them. They loved for him to read aloud,
even though they couldn't understand very much.

No, thought Thomas. They are tired from being up late last night. They will only cry.

Thomas' brothers were named Billy and Buster and they knew all sorts of things. Once Thomas had taken up a cotton ball just to show them about it. They understood right away what it was. They had turned toward Great-grandmother Jeffers' house. She had a patch of cotton in her garden, and they must have seen her chopping it.

They loved pine, as Thomas did, although they couldn't whittle it. Thomas' papa said the boys probably never would be as good at whittling as he was. Thomas had a talent for wood sculpture, so his father said. There were always folks coming from distances offering Thomas money for what he had carved. But Thomas kept most of his carvings for himself. He had a whole box of figures tied up in the trailer attached to the car. He intended placing them on counters and mantles all over the new house.

Thomas could sit in front of his brothers, carving an image out of pine, and they would jump and roll all around him. When the carving was finished, the twin for whom it was made would grab it and crawl off with it. Thomas never need say, and never once were the twins wrong in knowing what carving was for which boy.

They were fine brothers, Thomas knew.

If the new house is haunted, he thought, the twins will tell me!

The sedan headed through the Pisgah National Forest in the Blue Ridge Mountains, and then out of North Carolina.

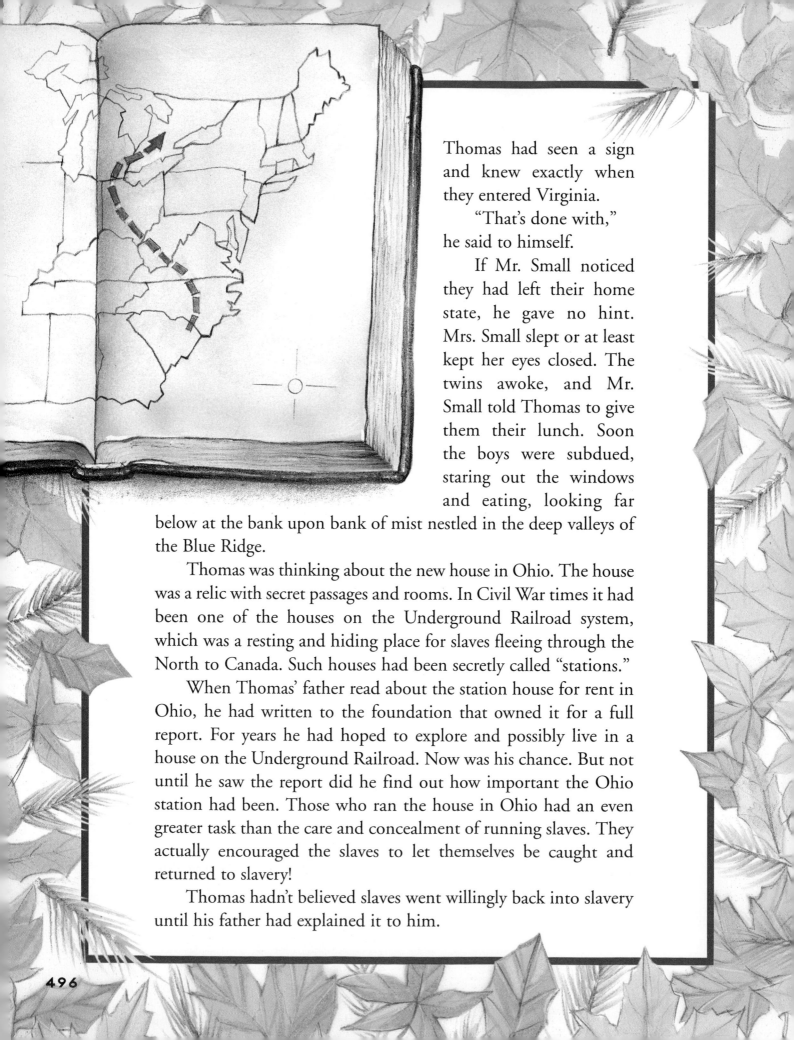

Thomas had seen a sign and knew exactly when they entered Virginia.

"That's done with," he said to himself.

If Mr. Small noticed they had left their home state, he gave no hint. Mrs. Small slept or at least kept her eyes closed. The twins awoke, and Mr. Small told Thomas to give them their lunch. Soon the boys were subdued, staring out the windows and eating, looking far below at the bank upon bank of mist nestled in the deep valleys of the Blue Ridge.

Thomas was thinking about the new house in Ohio. The house was a relic with secret passages and rooms. In Civil War times it had been one of the houses on the Underground Railroad system, which was a resting and hiding place for slaves fleeing through the North to Canada. Such houses had been secretly called "stations."

When Thomas' father read about the station house for rent in Ohio, he had written to the foundation that owned it for a full report. For years he had hoped to explore and possibly live in a house on the Underground Railroad. Now was his chance. But not until he saw the report did he find out how important the Ohio station had been. Those who ran the house in Ohio had an even greater task than the care and concealment of running slaves. They actually encouraged the slaves to let themselves be caught and returned to slavery!

Thomas hadn't believed slaves went willingly back into slavery until his father had explained it to him.

"If you'll recall your history, Thomas, you'll remember that the incredible history of the Underground Railroad actually began in Canada," his father had told him. Slaves who had reached Canada in the very early 1800s and established settlements there returned by the thousands to this country in order to free others. They came back for their families; they became secret "conductors" on the Underground Railroad system. And they returned to bondage hoping to free masses of slaves.

"But slaves continued to flee by whatever means," Mr. Small had said, "with or without help. Upon reaching the Railroad, they might hide in our house in Ohio, where they would rest for as little as a week. Some of them were given rather large sums of money and returned again to slavery."

"What would slaves need with money?" Thomas had wanted to know.

"Even a fleeing slave needs maneuvering money," his father had said. "He would need food and shelter and the best and safest way for him to get it was to buy it from freed Negroes."

"But the slaves connected with the house in Ohio were going back *into* slavery," Thomas had said.

"Yes," said Mr. Small. "And after they were caught and went back, they passed the hidden money on to other slaves, who would attempt to escape."

Still Thomas couldn't believe slaves could successfully hide money on themselves without having it found.

Some slaves did have their money found and taken away, his father said. It was dangerous work they were involved in. But others managed to return to bondage with the money still in their possession.

"Remember," his father had told him, "the slaves we're talking about weren't ordinary folks out for a peaceful stroll. Many had run for their lives for weeks from the Deep South. They had no idea how far they had to travel and they were armed with little more than the knowledge that moss grew only on the northern side of trees. Any who managed to get as far as Ohio and the Underground Railroad line had to be pretty brave and strong, and very clever. Most of them were young, with a wonderful, fierce desire to free themselves as well as others. It was the best of these who volunteered to return to slavery. They were hand-picked by Dies Drear himself, the abolitionist who built our house in Ohio. He alone conceived of the daring plan of returning numbers of slaves to the South with sizable amounts of money hidden on them."

"He must have been something!" Thomas had said.

"He was a New Englander," Mr. Small said, "so independent and eccentric, most Ohio abolitionists thought him crazy. He came from an enormously wealthy family of shipbuilders, and yet his house in Ohio was fairly modest. To give you an idea how odd he was," said Mr. Small, "his house was overflowing with fine antiques, which he neither took any interest in nor sold for profit. All the furniture remained in great piles, with just enough space to get through from room to room, until the house was plundered and Drear was killed.

"But when his plan to send slaves back to slavery worked," said Mr. Small, "there grew among freemen and slaves an enormous respect for him. You know, they never called him by his name, partly because they feared he might be caught, but also because they were in awe of him. They called him Selah. Selah, which is no more than a musical direction to raise the voice. And yet, Selah he was. *Selah*, a desperate, running slave might sigh, and the name— the man—gave him the strength to go on."

Selah. Freedom.

JACOB LAWRENCE

Harriet Tubman as a baby (detail)

PAINTING

Jacob Lawrence was born in Atlantic City, New Jersey, in 1917. He studied at the Harlem Art Workshop and the American Artists School in New York City. Today, he is one of America's best-known painters.

Lawrence has received many awards and honors during his long career. He served as Commissioner of the National Council of the Arts under President Carter and received the National Medal of Arts from President Bush. His work is represented in the National Gallery of Art, the Metropolitan Museum of Art, the Vatican Museum, and many other public collections.

Runaway slaves asleep in a barn

THE PAST

Harriet Tubman leads runaway slaves across the snows of the North.

The paintings shown on these pages first appeared in a picture-book biography called *Harriet and the Promised Land*. Lawrence wrote and illustrated the book to honor Harriet Tubman and her brave actions as a leader of the Underground Railroad.

Of the book, Lawrence says, "The United States is a great country. It is a great country because of people like John Brown, Frederick Douglass, Abraham Lincoln, Sojourner Truth, and Harriet Tubman.... American history has always been one of my favorite subjects. Given the opportunity to select a subject from American history, I chose to do a number of paintings in tribute to Harriet Tubman, a most remarkable woman...."

Slaves escape in a "chariot" driven by Harriet Tubman.

Harriet Tubman guides a group of escaped slaves through the woods.

Think About Reading

Write your answers.

1. What is special about the family's new house in Ohio?

2. Why do you think Mr. Small gave Thomas a book about the Civil War for his birthday?

3. If you were Thomas, how would you feel about living in the house of Dies Drear?

4. How does author Virginia Hamilton make the history of the Underground Railroad come alive?

5. Both Virginia Hamilton and Jacob Lawrence are interested in American history. Why do you think they chose heroes of the Underground Railroad as subjects for their work?

Write a Business Letter

Imagine that you are Mr. Small. Write a business letter to the foundation that owns the station house for the Underground Railroad. Tell the foundation that you are interested in renting the house and would like more information about it. Also include reasons why you think the foundation should rent the house to you and your family. Use a business-letter format, and remember to thank the foundation for its help.

Literature Circle

Author Virginia Hamilton and artist Jacob Lawrence present history through stories and paintings. What are some other formats that writers and artists use to preserve the past and teach others about it? List your ideas on a concept web. Discuss which presentations are most effective, and explain why.

AUTHOR

Virginia Hamilton

Virginia Hamilton has written many books based on her childhood in Yellow Springs, Ohio. Her grandfather, Grandpaw Levi Perry, was an escaped slave who found safety at an Underground Railroad station much like the one in *The House of Dies Drear.* Hamilton says, "*The House of Dies Drear* is one of my favorite books, I think, because it is so full of all the things I love: excitement, mystery, black history, the strong black family. In it I tried to pay back all those wonderful relatives who gave me so much in the past."

MORE BOOKS BY
Virginia Hamilton

- *The Mystery of Drear House*
- *Zeely*
- *M.C. Higgins, the Great*

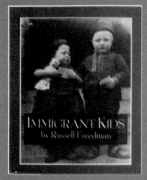

HISTORICAL
NONFICTION

AWARD
WINNER

At Home

from Immigrant Kids

by

Russell Freedman

Most turn-of-the-century immigrants settled in America's big cities. The immigrants needed jobs. The cities were growing fast and offered the best chances to find work. By 1910, three out of four people in New York City were immigrants and the children of immigrants. The same thing was true in Boston, Cleveland, Chicago, and Detroit.

Many immigrants could not speak English when they arrived. They knew little about American laws and customs. And so they clustered together, living in ethnic neighborhoods where they could mingle with their countrymen and speak their native languages. Almost every major city had its German and Irish neighborhoods, its Polish, Italian, Jewish, and Greek districts. People from the same village in Europe might wind up living as neighbors on the same street in America.

In most cities, immigrants moved into old, run-down neighborhoods. As newcomers, struggling to gain a foothold in America, they occupied the poorest and most congested districts. New York City absorbed more immigrants than any other city. Manhattan's Lower East Side, where so many immigrants settled, became one of the most densely populated places on earth.

Bargaining with a pushcart vendor

A walk through a crowded immigrant neighborhood was like a visit to the old country. The streets were noisy open-air markets. Pushcarts lined the pavements, offering fruit, vegetables, poultry, fish, eggs, soda water, and anything else you could think of—old coats for fifty cents, eyeglasses for thirty-five cents, hats for a quarter, ribbons for a penny. Peddlers hawked their wares in a dozen different dialects. Women wearing kerchiefs and shawls haggled for the best prices. Everyone except the kids seemed to be speaking a foreign language. Looking down upon these streets were the brick tenement buildings, where millions of immigrants began their lives in America.

Orchard Street on New York City's Lower East Side, 1898 (photo by Byron)

**Room in an immigrant family's tenement apartment, 1910
(photo by Jessie Tarbox Beals)**

Tenements were jammed with immigrants living in small,
cramped apartments. The family shown above used a single
makeshift room for cooking and eating, and as a bedroom for
the kids. The parents slept in a tiny bedroom to the rear.

A more prosperous family might have three rooms: a parlor (or living room); a kitchen; and a dark, windowless bedroom in between. The parlor often doubled as an extra bedroom, while the kitchen became the family's social center. In all tenements, the toilet (or water closet) was outside the apartment, in the hallway of the building. It was used by at least two families.

Family supper in a tenement kitchen (photo by Lewis Hine)

Community water faucet in a tenement hallway (photo by Lewis Hine)

In older tenements, the individual apartments had no running water. Tenants fetched their water from a community faucet in the hallway on each floor. And yet many immigrants had grown up in the old country carrying water from a well. To them, an inside faucet with running water seemed wonderful.

Leonard Covello has described his family's first American home and his mother's reaction to running water in the hallway:

> Our first home in America was a tenement flat near the East River at 112th Street. . . . The sunlight and fresh air of our mountain home in Lucania [southern Italy] were replaced by four walls and people over and under and on all sides of us, until it seemed that humanity from all corners of the world had congregated in this section of New York City. . . .
>
> The cobbled streets. The endless, monotonous rows of tenement buildings that shut out the sky. . . . The clanging of bells and the screeching of sirens as a fire broke out somewhere in the neighborhood. Dank hallways. Long flights of wooden stairs and the toilet in the hall. And the water, which to my mother was one of the great wonders of America—water with just the twist of a handle, and only a few paces from the kitchen. It took her a long time to get used to this luxury. . . .
>
> It was Carmelo Accurso who made ready the tenement flat and arranged the welcoming party with relatives and friends to greet us upon our arrival. During this celebration my mother sat dazed, unable to realize that at last the torment of the trip was over and that here was America. It was Mrs. Accurso who put her arm comfortingly about my mother's shoulder and led her away from the party and into the hall and showed her the water faucet. "Courage! You will get used to it here. See! Isn't it wonderful how that water comes out?"
>
> Through her tears my mother managed a smile.

In newer tenements, running water came from a convenient faucet above the kitchen sink. This sink was used to wash dishes, clothes, and kids. Water had to be heated on the kitchen stove. Since bathing was difficult at home, most immigrants went regularly to public bath houses.

Tenement apartments had no refrigeration, and supermarkets had not yet been invented. Kids were sent on daily errands to the baker, the fishmonger, the dairyman, or the produce stall. They would rush down rickety tenement stairs, a few pennies clutched tightly in their hands. Since there were no shopping bags or fancy wrappings either, they would carry the bread home in their arms, the herring in a big pan from mother's kitchen.

Carrying home the groceries (photo by Lewis Hine)

Some immigrants had big families. (photo by Augustus F. Sherman)

Many immigrants had to take in roomers or boarders to help pay the rent. Five or six people might sleep in one crowded room. Children were commonly tucked three and four to a bed. Privacy was unknown, and a room of one's own was a luxury beyond reach. When an immigrant family could occupy a three-room apartment without taking in boarders, they were considered a success.

On hot summer days, the stifling tenement rooms became unbearable. Whole families spilled out of their apartments, seeking relief up on the roof or down in the street, where there was some hope of catching a cooling breeze. Kids took over fire escapes and turned them into open-air clubhouses. They put up sleeping tents of sheets and bedspreads, and spent summer nights outside, as elevated trains roared past a few feet away.

Camping out on the fire escape, August, 1916

MENTOR

Russell Freedman

Historian/Author

History writers manage information about the past.

Russell Freedman is crazy about history. He studies it, he reads about it, and he has written many nonfiction books about United States history.

"History isn't just a bunch of dates and facts," Freedman says. "History is the stories of real people in real situations."

In his books, Russell Freedman brings those stories to life. How does he do it?

PROFILE

Name: Russell Freedman

Occupation: historian/author

Education: University of California at Berkeley

Favorite subjects in school: English and history

Favorite person from history: Abraham Lincoln

Favorite childhood books: *Treasure Island, Call It Courage*

Favorite library: the Donnell Library in New York City

Pet: Sybil, a white cat he rescued from the streets of New York

THE NATIONAL
COWBOY HALL OF FAME
AND WESTERN HERITAGE CENTER

RUSSELL FREEDMAN

QUESTIONS
for Russell Freedman

Here's how Russell Freedman uncovers the real stories about past events.

Q What are the steps you take when putting together a book?

A First, I research my subject. Then, I write a table of contents so that I have a clear idea of where to start and where I'm going. Next, I write five drafts of the book: a rough draft to get my ideas down, a second draft to organize the book, a third draft to cut unnecessary material, and fourth and fifth drafts to polish my writing.

Q What do you look for when you research?

A When I was researching *Cowboys of the Wild West*, for example, I relied on memoirs and diaries of cowboys. Librarians helped me find books on the subject that I hadn't read before. I also search for interesting and informative photos to illustrate my books.

Q Does your research take you to interesting places?

A Frequently. Right now, I'm writing a book about Crazy Horse, a Native American chief. I've already been to Montana, to the Little Big Horn National Monument, where Crazy Horse led a famous battle against U.S. troops. I've also traveled to his homeland in the Black Hills of South Dakota.

Q How do you choose the subjects of your biographies?

A It has to be somebody that I have a compelling interest in, and that I admire for some reason. The subject's life has to really mean something.

Q Have kids ever inspired you to write a book?

A Well, I never intended to research the Wright Brothers until so many kids asked me questions about them. That's when I decided to do a little probing. The rest is history.

Q How do you get readers interested in your topics?

A I focus on the details of the events or people I'm writing about so they seem as real as possible.

Q Is it difficult to find the real story about some events in history?

A Yes. The book I'm writing about Crazy Horse has been my toughest project yet. His life isn't well documented, and there are contradictory stories about how he lived.

Russell Freedman's Tips for History Detectives

1 Get interested. Never write about anything you don't care about.

2 Get current. Find the newest and most authoritative books on the subject.

3 Search for details. They'll give the reader a clearer sense of what you're writing about.

4 Be suspicious. Never have fewer than three different sources for the same event.

THE NEW COLOSSUS

by **Emma Lazarus**
illustrated by **Marcia Brown**

When the people of France gave the United States the Statue of Liberty to celebrate the centennial of the young nation, they gave a gift that has come to symbolize America the world over.

Not like the brazen giant of Greek fame,
With conquering limbs astride from land to land,
Here at our sea-washed, sunset gates shall stand
A mighty woman with a torch, whose flame
Is the imprisoned lightning, and her name
Mother of Exiles. From her beacon-hand
Glows world-wide welcome; her mild eyes command
The air-bridged harbor that twin cities frame.
"Keep ancient lands, your storied pomp!" cries she
With silent lips. "Give me your tired, your poor,
Your huddled masses yearning to breathe free,
The wretched refuse of your teeming shore.
Send these, the homeless, tempest-tost to me.
I lift my lamp beside the golden door!"

Think About Reading

Write your answers.

1. How would you describe the typical immigrant's home in New York City in the early 1900s?

2. What do you think daily life was like for immigrant children living on Manhattan's Lower East Side?

3. How was shopping for food in the early 1900s different from grocery shopping today?

4. What methods does Russell Freedman use to make "At Home" interesting to the reader?

5. Consider what Russell Freedman wrote in "At Home" and what he says in the interview. How do you think Freedman feels about the immigrants he describes?

Write a Photo-Exhibit Review

Imagine that the photographs in "At Home" are part of a photo exhibit about immigrant life in the early 1900s. Write a review of the exhibit. Briefly describe the exhibit's goal. Do the photos give a clear picture of life at that time? Are they good choices? Why? Conclude your review with a recommendation to attend or not attend the exhibit.

Literature Circle

Suppose the young immigrants in "At Home" could travel forward in time. Discuss their possible reactions to life today. What would they find most amazing? Consider their impressions of malls, transportation, and other modern conveniences. What questions might they ask you? Role-play conversations between young immigrants and you.

AUTHOR

Russell Freedman

Award-winning author Russell Freedman says that "a nonfiction writer is first and foremost a storyteller." The "story" that Freedman tells in *Immigrant Kids* is one that he can relate to personally. He got the idea for the book when he visited a photography exhibit about street kids in New York City. Freedman immediately thought of his own father who once played in New York's streets and was the son of immigrants. Russell Freedman has written over 40 nonfiction books for young people.

MORE BOOKS BY

Russell Freedman

- *Eleanor Roosevelt: A Life of Discovery*
- *Out of Darkness: The Story of Louis Braille*
- *Children of the Wild West*

How to
Prepare a Historical Account

Use multiple sources to tell about your favorite piece of history!

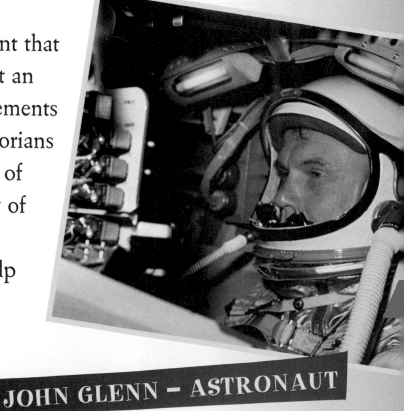

A historical account is a document that contains detailed information about an event, a time period, or the achievements of an important person. When historians prepare accounts, they include lots of well-researched facts from a variety of sources. They also find paintings, drawings, and photographs that help readers visualize what is being described. Preparing a historical account is a good way to bring history to life!

JOHN GLENN – ASTRONAUT

FIRST TO ORBIT THE EARTH

Research a Topic

How can you learn more about a past event? You can research it, of course! Choose a topic to research. The topic might be any historical event or era that interests you. It might even be a famous person who lived long ago!

TOOLS

- paper and pencil
- note cards
- folder
- research materials

Begin your research by gathering basic information about the topic you chose. Go to the library and look for books, encyclopedias, almanacs, and magazines that tell about your topic. Research your topic on the Internet. Check out your local video store— maybe there's a video you can use. Be sure to look for different accounts of the same event. Find as many different sources as possible. As you locate information, take notes and file them in a folder.

Tip Keep track of each source of information you use. Jot down the name or title of the source at the top of each note card or sheet of paper.

2 Personalize Your Research

Once you have collected enough information about your topic, think about ways to make your account unusual and exciting. For instance, eyewitnesses are great sources. Is there someone you can interview who has firsthand knowledge of your topic? If your event took place a long time ago, you might search for a collection of letters, journal entries, or oral histories from people who were alive at that time. Look for magazine photos or create visual aids to illustrate your account. Perhaps you could even visit a place related to your topic and get more information there.

Make an Outline

Many historical accounts are organized chronologically—in the order that events happened. Then the reader can understand how history unfolded. Start your outline with a heading that tells what happened first and when it happened. Beneath the heading, note the important details you've collected about that particular incident. Continue with the next major item and keep going until your outline is complete. The last item on your outline should be the most recent. Remember that an outline is a way to organize your information from your notes—you need not write out all your information as you will in your account.

How Am I Doing?

Before you prepare your historical account, take a minute to ask yourself these questions:

- Do I have all the information I need to write my account?

- Have I used many different sources of information?

- Have I located some unusual details?

- Have I outlined my account so that I know what to write?

4 Write Your Account

Now it's time to write your account. Try to make your topic sound exciting and fresh. Use your outline to help you write. Keep in mind that your account should be clear and interesting to read.

You might need to write several drafts before you are satisfied. Ask a classmate to read your first draft and make notes of anything he or she doesn't understand or wants to know more about. When you revise the draft, respond to your classmate's comments.

When you create your final draft, remember to include any visual aids you found. Put your historical account together in booklet form.

If You Are Using a Computer...

Publish your historical account using the Report format. Create a title page. Cite references using the Bibliography Maker.

5 Present Your Account

Have a History Day. Present your historical account to your classmates and listen to theirs. The accounts might be presented chronologically— starting with the earliest event and working up to the most recent. Look for ways that the accounts relate to one another. Did other students write about the same topic you chose? How are their accounts different from or similar to yours?

CONGRATULATIONS

You've discovered how to manage information about the past and bring a slice of history to life!

Russell Freedman
Historian/Author ▶

CITYSCAPES

CITYSCAPES

THEME

Cities depend on the strengths and skills of the people who live and work there.

UNIT 6

Welcome to

LITERACY PLACE

Urban Planner's Office

Cities depend on the strengths and skills of the people who live and work there.

537

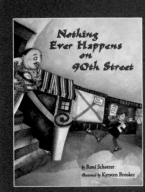

Nothing Ever Happens on 90th Street

by Roni Schotter

illustrated by Kyrsten Brooker

Eva unwrapped a cinnamon Danish, opened her notebook, and stared helplessly at the wide, white pages. "Write about what you know," her teacher, Mrs. DeMarco, had told her. So Eva sat high on the stoop and looked out over 90th Street waiting for something to happen. A horn honked. A radio rapped. A kid cried. The usual. "Nothing ever happens on 90th Street," Eva scribbled in her notebook.

A few doors down, Mr. Chang was arranging fish fillets in his newly opened Seafood Emporium. No one was buying, and his shop looked as empty and ignored as the tiny, boarded-up store next door to it. He nodded to a woman passing by and called hello to Eva.

Out of the door of Eva's building came Mr. Sims, the actor, carrying his enormous cat, Olivier. Mr. Sims was "on hiatus again," which meant out of work, in between shows, and so, every day, dressed in his finest, he embarked on a daily promenade with Olivier under his arm. "Writing?" he asked.

"Trying to," Eva answered, "but nothing ever happens on 90th Street!"

"You are mistaken, my dear," Mr. Sims said. "The whole world's a stage—even 90th Street—and each of us plays a part. Watch the stage, observe the players carefully, and don't neglect the details," he said, stroking Olivier. "Follow an old actor's advice and you will find you have plenty to write about."

"Thanks," Eva said, and fast as she could, using as many details as she could recall, Eva described Mr. Sims in her notebook—his felt fedora hat, his curly gray hair, his shiny button shoes. When she looked up, he was halfway down the street and Mr. Morley, the mousse maker, was at his window.

Just as he did every day, Mr. Morley set his chocolate pot and coffee urn out on his ledge with a sign. Mr. Morley dreamed of having a catering business where the fanciest people demanded his dessert. But the trouble was . . . Mr. Morley's mousse was missing something. No matter how he tried, his mousse never had much taste, and Mr. Morley never had many customers.

"Writing?" he asked.

"Um. Hmmm," Eva answered, chewing on her pencil.

"Try to find the poetry in your pudding," Mr. Morley said softly. "There's always a new way with old words."

"You're right," Eva said, wishing Mr. Morley would one day find the poetry in *his* pudding. Taking his advice, she tried to think up a new way to describe the look of Mr. Morley's mousse. Smooth and dark as midnight. Or maybe more like mink! Yes, that was it! Eva thought, writing in her notebook.

The door to the building slammed and a gust of wind sent dead leaves soaring and dipping like crazy kites. Alexis Leora nodded to Eva and stepped gracefully down the steps to do her warm-up exercises. Alexis was a dancer. When she wanted to, she could hold an extremely long leg straight up against her ear like a one-legged woman with three arms. But she couldn't smile. Eva decided it was because Alexis Leora was lonely.

"Writing?" Alexis Leora asked Eva.

"Yes," Eva answered.

Alexis Leora did six deep knee bends and then sighed. "Stretch," she said sadly. "Use your imagination. If your story doesn't go the way you want it to, you can always stretch the truth. You can ask, 'What if?' and make up a better story."

"You're right," Eva said, thinking "What if?" What if Alexis Leora met someone? Would she smile then? What would that look like? Eva closed her eyes and tried to picture it, but all she could picture was soup —Spanish soup—rich and brown and so spicy it seemed as if she could actually smell it.

She could! When Eva opened her eyes, Mrs. Martinez was standing beside her. She nodded to Alexis Leora as she handed Eva a bowl of soup. "Have some," she said. "Writers *need* soup. What's your story about?"

"Nothing much." Eva sighed. "Nothing ever happens on 90th Street."

"Add a little action," Mrs. Martinez said. "Like soup. A little this. A little that. And don't forget the spice. Mix it. Stir it. Make something happen. Surprise yourself!" She nodded again to Alexis Leora and went inside.

Eva put down her pencil and tasted Mrs. Martinez's wonderful, surprising soup. She thought about her story. It wasn't wonderful. It wasn't surprising. But what could she do? Nothing ever happened on 90th Street. How could she possibly "add a little action" and "make something happen"? Eva had no ideas. She was stuck!

Then Mrs. Friedman from up the block came wheeling Baby Joshua in his stroller. He was holding a bright red ball in two tiny, fat hands. "Bird!" he called out to a pigeon hunting for something to eat. "Bird. Hungry!"

"Pigeon," Mrs. Friedman told him.

Eva sighed and looked down at her half-eaten Danish, then at her notebook. She looked at Baby Joshua, then at the pigeon. She remembered Alexis Leora's words of advice. "What if?" Eva thought. Suddenly she had an idea.

What if she stood up, broke her Danish into dozens of tiny pieces, and scattered them wide and wild into the street? What would happen? Eva laughed to think of it. . . .

From lampposts and ledges dozens of pigeons swooped down to dine on Danish. Eva eagerly picked up her pencil and began to write again. "Bird!" Baby Joshua called out, pointing. "More bird!" he cried, panting. The bright red ball dropped out of his tiny, fat hands and bounced onto the sidewalk. "Bye, bye, ball!" Baby Joshua screamed.

The ball rolled off the curb, into the street, and straight into the path of a pizza delivery man on his bicycle!

Everyone gasped in horror. Alexis Leora paused in mid-plié and leaped to the rescue. She got there just as the pizza delivery man landed, right side up, at her feet. Alexis Leora looked down at the pizza man and he looked up at her. And then something almost unimaginable happened: Alexis Leora smiled! "Are y-y-you all right?" she asked, shyly. Her smile was sweet and bright. Her teeth were straight and white. (It was the first time Eva or anyone on 90th Street had seen them!)

"Yes," said the pizza man, smiling up at her. It was love at first sight. Pepperoni and peppers rained down on the happy couple. The pizza man pulled a pepper out of his hair as horns began to honk.

Eva added this to her notebook and wondered what could possibly happen next. . . .

A long, white limousine was honking its horn loudest of all. The limo driver rolled down his window. "Whad'ya wanna block traffic for?" he called out. The back door of the limo opened and out stepped a woman in sunglasses, wearing a turban and a coat the color of a taxi.

"There seems to be a problem, Henry," she said in a fake English accent. "There's some sort of accident here. Perhaps—"

"It's *Sondra!*" someone suddenly screamed, interrupting her. "Sondra! Can I have your autograph?" Mrs. Martinez called out.

"Sondra Saunderson!" Mr. Morley blushed.

Was Eva dreaming? There, in the middle of 90th Street, larger than life, stood Sondra Saunderson, star of stage, screen, and the sensational soap opera "One World To Live In."

"Darlings, what's happening here? I'm sure I . . . *Lar*-ry!" she called out suddenly, and stretched her arms toward Mr. Sims, who had just returned from his promenade. "It's been an age since we saw each other!"

Mr. Sims' cat, about to be crushed in an extravagant embrace, leaped out of Mr. Sims' arms to chase after Baby Joshua's ball.

"Olivier!" Mr. Sims called out. "Come back!"

Everyone raced into the street after the ball, but it was the limo driver who, in the right place at the right time, leaned into the gutter and picked it up.

With a flick of the wrist, he tossed the ball to Mrs. Friedman, who presented it to a drooling but grateful Baby Joshua.

"How's that for a throw?" the limo driver proudly asked the crowd.

No one, not even Baby Joshua, had a chance to answer. Olivier, frightened by so many people, raced past Eva, scrambled onto Mr. Morley's ledge, where he knocked over his coffee urn, spilling all the coffee into his mousse pot.

"Ruined!" Mr. Morley cried, wringing his hands.

At that, Olivier bounded to the top of a ginkgo tree, where he swayed dangerously like a heavy, white balloon.

"Now he'll *never* come down!" Mr. Sims lamented. "He's terribly stubborn."

"There, there, Larry," Sondra Saunderson comforted him. "I'm sure someone on 90th Street will have a solution."

Eva tried to imagine who that could possibly be. . . .

"I have one!" she heard Mr. Chang call out. Generously, he offered trout, fresh from his store, to Olivier.

High up in the tree, Olivier barely blinked.

"Raw trout?" Mr. Sims sighed. "My regrets, Mr. Chang. He won't eat it. He's a *gourmet* cat. I'm afraid I've spoiled him. Whatever will I do?"

"What if?" Eva asked herself for the second time that day, and suddenly she had another idea. A truly great one! She whispered it to Mr. Morley, Mrs. Martinez, and Mr. Chang.

"Brilliant!" Mr. Morley exclaimed. And with that he, Mrs. Martinez, and Mr. Chang, still clutching his trout, vanished into the building.

Eva righted Mr. Morley's coffee urn and stuck her finger into his ruined mousse, then into her mouth to determine the degree of damage.

"Mocha!" she called out in surprise. "Mr. Morley's mousse is mocha now and . . ." She paused, trying to find the perfect word. "*Magnificent!*" she announced to the assembled throng. And, giving the pot a stir, she dished out samples to all assembled.

"Delicious!" Alexis Leora said, spooning some into the pizza man's mouth.

"Poetry!" Sondra Saunderson pronounced.

Now on 90th Street, people who had never spoken to one another before were speaking at last. The pizza delivery man and the limo driver shook hands, and everyone tried to tempt Olivier down from his precarious perch.

And then . . . Mr. Morley appeared on the steps, followed by Mrs. Martinez and Mr. Chang. Mrs. Martinez carried a large pot of her surprising soup, while Mr. Morley carried a platter of Mr. Chang's trout, now surrounded by many tiny vegetables and cooked to perfection. With the addition of a cup of Mr. Morley's cat-created mocha mousse—it was a meal worthy of the finest culinary establishment.

"Do you smell that, Olivier?" Mr. Sims called, fanning the steam so it rose up the ginkgo tree.

Olivier took one deep sniff and bolted down the tree to dine!
Everyone on 90th Street sampled each course and everyone on
90th Street sighed with delight. "Superb!" "*Fantastico!*" "Yum!"

Eva smiled and glanced up from her notebook. For the third
time that day she asked herself, "What if?"

"Mr. Chang," she began, "you and Mr. Morley and Mrs.
Martinez are such great cooks. The boarded-up store next to your
Seafood Emporium, what if all of you used it for a restaurant?"

"A restaurant?" The three chefs looked at one another. "What
a wonderful idea," they said, shaking Eva's hand. "Everyone on 90th
Street could be our customers. You too, Sondra."

"Everyone but me," Mr. Sims said regretfully. "Just now, I'm between jobs and a bit low on cash."

"No longer!" Sondra called out. "You'll be on my show! I'll arrange it."

Mr. Sims kissed Sondra's hand, and everyone cheered.

"What an amazing day!" Mrs. Martinez said. "Who would believe it? If only someone had written it all down."

"I did," Eva announced, and she opened her notebook and began to read her story (the same story you're reading now) about how *nothing* ever happened on 90th Street.

"What a story!" Sondra exclaimed. "Full of detail. Dialogue. Suspense. A bit of poetry. A hint of romance. Even a happy ending. Why, you'd almost think some of it was made up!"

Eva smiled mysteriously. "Thanks," she said proudly. "But just wait. It'll be even better...after I rewrite it."

557

Open Window

The clock on my dresser
shows almost six but the
garbage truck is the alarm
as they empty cans along
our street and fling black
sacks of garbage into the
back of the open truck.

It is easy
to say
c l a n g
   b a n g.
It is easy
to hear
c r a s h
s m a s h.

The clock on my dresser
shows almost six but the
garbage truck is my alarm
this too early morning.
I can just see the first
sun shine on the back of
the truck as it moves
                down
                  the

                street.

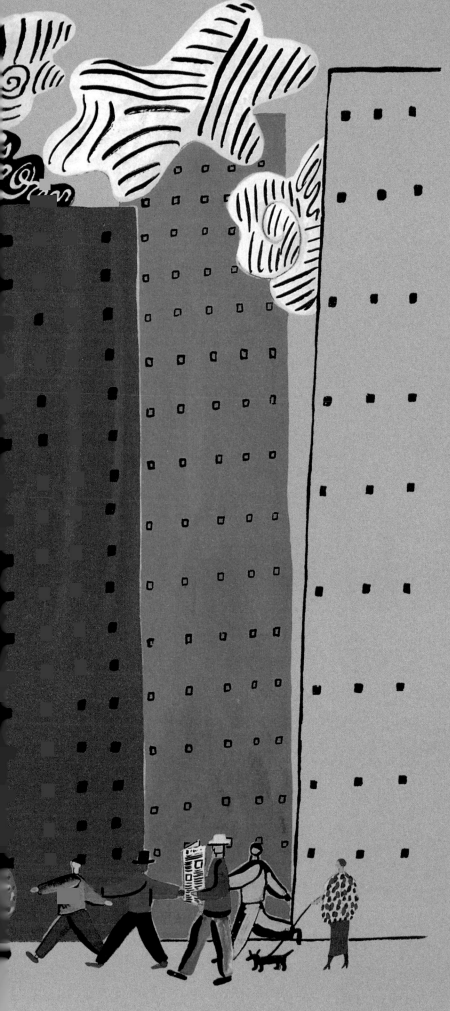

i Was Born Here in This City

but I still look up at   the
                  m a g i c
of tall buildings
pushing through the clouds.

One dry autumn afternoon
I lay down on the cool sidewalk in front of the downtown office tower. And all
the people had to walk
around me, because
I wouldn't stand
up until I had
seen the
clouds
move
over
the top
of that stone
giant, or the top
of that giant building
move through the clouds.

I was born here in this city
but I still look up at   the
                  m a g i c
of tall buildings
pushing through the clouds.

Street Music

This city:
the
always
noise
grinding
up from the
subways
under
ground:
slamming from bus tires
and taxi horns and engines
of cars and trucks in all
vocabularies
of
clash
flash
screeching
hot metal language
combinations:

as   planes
overhead
roar
an
o r c h e s t r a
of rolling drums
and battle blasts
assaulting
my ears
with
t h e
always
noise   of
this   city:

street   music.

Think About Reading

Answer the questions in the story map.

PROBLEM
1. As the story opens, what is Eva trying to do?

END   START

EVENTS

7. After everyone tastes the food, what does Eva suggest?

2. What happens when Eva scatters crumbs in the street?

6. How do the people of 90th Street get Olivier down from the tree?

3. What happens when the baby sees the pigeons?

5. What happens when Olivier jumps onto the ledge?

4. What happens when the pizza delivery man falls from his bike?

SOLUTION
8. What does Eva discover in her notebook at the end of the story?

Write a Thank-You Note

Take the part of Eva. Write a thank-you note to Alexis Leora for giving you the advice that helped you write your story. Be sure to mention why you are writing the note and tell how much you appreciate her help. Use the format of a friendly letter for your thank-you note.

Literature Circle

Author Roni Schotter and poet Arnold Adoff both write about cities. Compare the way these two writer's describe city life. What is the city in Schotter's story like? How does Adoff describe the city in his poems? Record your ideas on a chart. Then talk about which city—the one in Schotter's story or the one in Adoff's poems—you would rather visit. Tell why.

AUTHOR
Roni Schotter

Roni Schotter got the idea for *Nothing Ever Happens on 90th Street* from the many hours she used to spend sitting on a stoop in New York City. "What might happen," she asked herself, "if all my neighbors came out of their buildings at the same time and got to meet one another?" Roni Schotter loves to write, but she also knows exactly how it feels to face a blank sheet of paper. Asking "What if…?" helps her fill the page.

MORE BOOKS BY
Roni Schotter

- *Efan the Great*
- *Captain Snap and the Children of Vinegar Lane*
- *Dreamland*

NONFICTION

The Brooklyn

by **Elizabeth Mann**   illustrated by **Alan Witschonke**

In the winter of 1852, John Roebling and his 15-year-old son, Washington, were riding a Fulton Ferry boat across the East River from New York to Brooklyn. The day was bitterly cold. The ferry inched along, bumping against huge chunks of ice. The trip seemed to take forever. John paced up and down the deck.

"This ferry just isn't good enough, Washington!" he exclaimed. "There should be a bridge here."

Bridge

AWARD WINNER

FULTON FERRY PIER

NEW YORK

EAST RIVER

BROOKLYN

John Roebling was an engineer. His specialty was building bridges. As he looked across the East River, he could picture the bridge that he wanted there. He knew that it would be the most important one he would ever build.

For years after that, John tried to convince people that his plan for a bridge across the East River was a good one. Many liked the idea, especially those who lived in Brooklyn. They knew that as long as they had to depend on ferry boats to reach New York, Brooklyn would never become an important city. But most people thought it was impossible to bridge the wide and powerful river.

At that time, New York and Brooklyn were two different cities, separated by the East River. Today, New York and Brooklyn are part of one city called New York.

2. The towers hold up the main cables.

4. The main cables hold up the suspender cables.

3. The anchorages hold the ends of the main cables.

1. The foundations support the towers.

John knew it would be difficult. There were many problems to solve. The bridge would have to be strong enough to withstand the swift currents and powerful winds of the East River. It could not get in the way of the hundreds of boats that traveled on the river every day. It had to be so high that the masts of tall sailing ships could easily pass under it. And it had to be long. The East River was nearly half a mile wide at that point. But John also knew about

5. The suspender cables hold up the roadway.

6. The roadway.

John A. Roebling was born in 1806 in a small village in Germany. His father wanted him to work in his tobacco shop, but his mother encouraged him to study engineering. He became fascinated with bridges but was frustrated by the lack of opportunities to build them in Germany. He moved to America in 1831, where he became known as a brilliant engineer. He built bridges and canals all over the country. He also established a farming community and a successful cable making company. Although he did many things in his life, John Roebling will always be remembered as the designer of the Brooklyn Bridge.

a type of bridge that could solve all these problems. It was called a *suspension bridge.*

Every suspension bridge is different, but they all work in basically the same way. The roadway doesn't rest on supports. Instead it hangs in the air, suspended from thick cables. Only two towers are needed to hold up the cables, and they can be placed far apart to keep the river open for boat traffic.

John had already built three famous suspension bridges. This one across the East River would be the longest one he ever designed, but he was confident that it would work. Unfortunately, the people of New York and Brooklyn didn't agree with him. The idea was new to them, and they were afraid of it.

Then came the winter of 1867. It was so cold that the East River froze solid! Ferry boats were stuck in the thick ice. The only way to cross the river was on skates. People in Brooklyn couldn't get to their jobs in New York. They were desperate. At last they were willing to listen to John Roebling's plan.

Washington A. Roebling was born in Pennsylvania in 1837, the oldest of 7 children. Like his father, he studied engineering in college. He joined the Union Army during the Civil War and was promoted to Colonel. He fell in love with Emily, his commanding officer's sister. After the war, he married Emily and went to work as his father's assistant, building bridges.

In June of 1869, John Roebling finished the design for the bridge. He and Washington climbed out onto the end of the Fulton Ferry pier in Brooklyn to look over the place in the river where work would begin. He was so intent on what he was doing that he ignored the shrill whistle of an approaching ferry. Washington shouted a warning, but his father couldn't move fast enough. The boat slammed into the pier, crushing John's foot before he could jump out of the way. The injury became badly infected. He died a month later.

John's sudden death was a shock to everyone. Washington was especially sad. He was very close to his father and had shared his dream of a bridge across the East River. Now the dream was in danger, and he was the only one who could keep it alive. Although he was young and inexperienced, he decided he had to carry on the work his father had started. He accepted the job of Chief Engineer of the Brooklyn Bridge.

Washington began immediately. He had to build foundations under the water to support the bridge towers. If he built them on the muddy river bottom, they could slip, and the bridge would not be safe. He had to build them on a solid surface. He had to dig down through the mud to reach bedrock. To do this, he used enormous wooden boxes called caissons. The caissons sat on the river bottom and protected the workers inside them as they dug.

Washington had seen caissons used for small bridges in Europe, but the ones for the Brooklyn Bridge had to be much bigger. Imagine a building three stories tall and big enough to cover much of a city block. Imagine that the top two stories were made of solid wood, and that the building had no floor. That's what Washington's caissons looked like.

The Brooklyn caisson was built first, and the digging inside it went on for months. One evening a messenger raced to Washington's house. He pounded on the door with an urgent message: a fire had started deep inside the thick wooden roof of the caisson. If it continued to burn, the roof would weaken and the tower would crash through it. Washington hurried back to the bridge and stayed all night helping to put the fire out. No matter what they did, the high pressure air in the caisson just made the fire burn hotter. In desperation, Washington opened the doors in the top of the caisson and pumped it full of river water. Finally the fire was extinguished, but Washington collapsed and was carried to his home. He had suffered a severe attack of caisson disease.

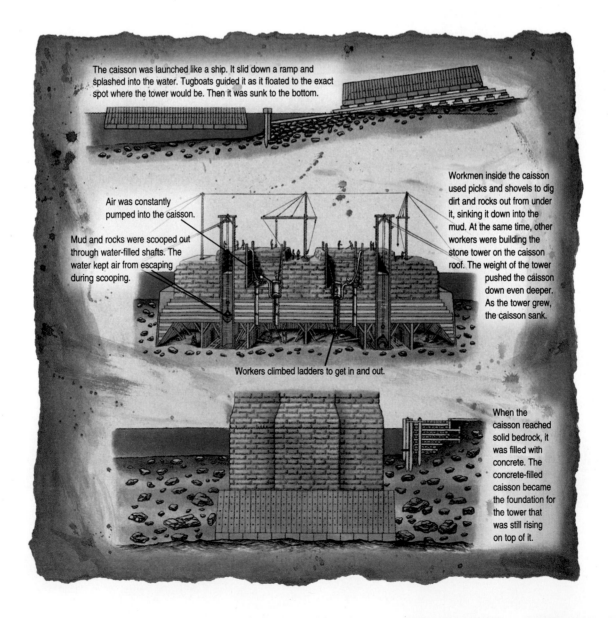

The caisson was launched like a ship. It slid down a ramp and splashed into the water. Tugboats guided it as it floated to the exact spot where the tower would be. Then it was sunk to the bottom.

Air was constantly pumped into the caisson.

Mud and rocks were scooped out through water-filled shafts. The water kept air from escaping during scooping.

Workmen inside the caisson used picks and shovels to dig dirt and rocks out from under it, sinking it down into the mud. At the same time, other workers were building the stone tower on the caisson roof. The weight of the tower pushed the caisson down even deeper. As the tower grew, the caisson sank.

Workers climbed ladders to get in and out.

When the caisson reached solid bedrock, it was filled with concrete. The concrete-filled caisson became the foundation for the tower that was still rising on top of it.

Caisson disease was a constant danger for Washington and his workers. The weight of the river water on a caisson was tremendous, and the air inside was under great pressure. Every day when their work was done, the men climbed from the high pressure beneath the river to the normal air pressure outside. They didn't know that their bodies needed time to adjust to the pressure change, and some became ill. Going to work was scary for the men because they didn't know why or when the mysterious pains and paralysis would strike. Many quit because of it. Nowadays we call it the bends—deep sea divers sometimes get it when they swim to the surface too quickly—and we know how to prevent it and cure it.

In 1871, the Brooklyn caisson reached solid bedrock at 44 1/2 feet below the river. The workmen climbed out for the last time, and the caisson was filled with concrete. The first foundation was finished.

On the New York side of the river, they were not so lucky. The caisson sank deeper and deeper below the river without reaching solid rock. Fifty feet. Many men were suffering from caisson disease. Sixty feet. Still no bedrock. Hundreds of workers quit. One man died of the disease, and then another. Washington was horrified. If the digging continued, more men would die. If he stopped the digging before the caisson rested on a solid surface, the tower might tip. He didn't want to risk workers' lives *or* the safety of the bridge. He had to make the most difficult decision of his life.

Washington worked day and night doing tests on the soil beneath the caisson. He discovered that it was hard-packed sand and gravel, a very solid surface. He concluded that it could support the bridge tower. The caisson was at 78 1/2 feet below the river when he gave the command,

"Stop digging!"

Hard-packed sand and gravel

Bedrock

One hundred men at a time worked in the hot, humid caissons. The pressurized air was difficult to breathe and candles gave only dim light. It was exhausting, dirty work. The pay was $2 a day.

Emily Warren was born in 1843 in Cold Spring, New York. She was known for her quick wit and common sense. After her marriage, she and Washington traveled through Europe to study new ways of building bridges. On that trip she gave birth to her only child, John Roebling II. He was born in Germany, right across the street from the house where his grandfather, John Roebling, had grown up.

Washington made the right decision. The tower has stood for more than a century. The foundation has not slipped.

Washington spent many hours in the caisson during this difficult time, and it made his disease even worse. Again he was rushed to his home, doubled over in terrible pain. This time the attack was so bad that he couldn't recover. He never returned to the bridge. From then on his only view of the construction was through binoculars from his bedroom window.

Work continued, thanks to Washington's wife Emily Roebling. She was his only contact with the world outside his sickroom. She carried his instructions to the men on the bridge and brought him progress reports. She talked with him about the work and became involved in making important decisions. In many ways, she took over for him. It would have been a challenge for anyone, but it was especially hard for Emily. At that time, women never worked on construction projects.

Emily was not an engineer, but she had learned a lot about suspension bridges from Washington and John. That knowledge, as well as her intelligence and calm manner, helped her to overcome the prejudice against her. She won the respect of all the workers. They realized how important she was to the building of the bridge.

The digging in the caissons had been carried out almost in secret. Only the workers really knew of the difficult and remarkable work that was done in those underwater rooms and of the terrible hardships they endured.

The construction of the towers was very different. Every day thousands of people watched in amazement from ferries and docks as three tall cranes, powered by noisy steam engines, hoisted each huge stone block high into the air and swung it into position.

Excitement mounted as the towers grew taller. Since most buildings then were less than 5 stories high, the 25-story towers must have seemed stupendous.

Once the towers were finished, the two anchorages were built. A giant tug of war is constantly happening in a suspension bridge. The heavy roadway pulls down on the main cables, but the anchorages hold them firmly and keep them from sagging. Each anchorage weighed 120,000,000 pounds. That's like having 12,000 large elephants hanging on to the main cables.

Next, thousands of thin steel wires were strung from Brooklyn to New York. It was called spinning cable. Bundles of wires were wrapped together to make four main cables. Each cable contained over 3,500 miles of steel wire, enough to stretch from Brooklyn to Los Angeles.

The wide, thin scaffoldings were called cradles. Workers stood on them during cable spinning to make sure each wire curved exactly the same.

278 steel wires were tied together into a bundle called a strand.

Each steel wire was about as thick as a pencil.

19 strands were wrapped together to make a main cable nearly 16 inches in diameter.

This was the first time that a bridge had been built with steel cables. Before that, iron cables, chains, or even rope had been used, and there had been disastrous results. Bridges had collapsed because of weak cables. Washington wanted to make sure that his bridge was not a disaster. He chose to use steel because it is stronger than iron. It was another wise decision. Since then, only steel has been used in bridge construction.

John Roebling started his wire rope company in a farm shed in 1841. By 1871, it was the largest one in the country. Most of the steel wire used in the Brooklyn Bridge came from the Roebling factories.

In August, 1876 hundreds of boats and thousands of people gathered to watch as Master Mechanic Frank Farrington glided from Brooklyn to Manhattan on a tiny swing attached to the first wire. He waved from his shaky seat and the crowd below cheered wildly. It was the first trip across the Brooklyn Bridge!

The elaborate construction project in the East River attracted even more attention while the cables were being spun. Even the most doubtful critics had to believe that the bridge would really be built. Newspapers and magazines in America and Europe wrote many articles about it. Politicians made speeches about it. The Brooklyn Bridge was the biggest show in town!

Cable work was done from small wooden perches that hung high above the East River. Sailors were often hired because they were used to working on the masts of tall sailing ships. They were able to hang on tight when the wind blew, and they weren't frightened when they looked down at the water far below. Not too frightened, anyway.

A wooden footbridge was built for the workers to use. Word of the fantastic views from it spread quickly, and tourists came from all over to walk out on it. Standing hundreds of feet above the deep, fast moving river on a swaying, narrow footbridge was a thrilling adventure for some. For others it was a little too exciting. People panicked, fainted, and had to be carried back down. The footbridge had to be closed to the public.

584

Although the men were skillful and very careful, accidents still happened. One of the most serious occurred when a strand broke loose. It whipped through the air, killing two men, injuring others, and narrowly missing a crowded ferry boat. Altogether, including John Roebling, 21 men died working on the Brooklyn Bridge.

The towers and anchorages were finished. The four main cables were in place. All that remained to be done was to hang the roadway from the main cables. Steel suspender cables were used for this. The suspenders were attached at the top to the main cables, and at the bottom to steel floor beams. Then the beams were bolted to each other to make a strong, stiff roadway floor. The roads, train tracks, and pedestrian walkway would all be built on this floor.

Washington strengthened the bridge even more by adding extra cables called diagonal stays. Diagonal stays had not been in his father's original plan, but Washington wanted to make sure that even heavy railroad trains could cross the Brooklyn Bridge safely. When it was finished, the bridge was six times stronger than it needed to be.

Safety and strength were not the only things that John Roebling thought about when he designed the Brooklyn Bridge. He believed the people of New York and Brooklyn deserved a bridge that was as beautiful as he could make it. The elegant high arches of the stone towers, the graceful swoop of the main cables, and the pattern created by the suspender cables and the diagonal stays made the bridge very lovely indeed. John even raised the walkway above the level of the road so pedestrians had a view of New York Harbor that was as breathtaking as the bridge itself.

The steel floor beams were attached to the ends of the suspender cables. The beams were bolted together and reinforced to stiffen the roadway so that it wouldn't move in the wind. The footbridge, where the two men are standing, was taken down when the bridge was finished.

Electric lamps, like the one at the left of the picture, lined the bridge. Electricity had never been used to light a bridge before. At night it looked quite magical.

On May 24, 1883, the Brooklyn Bridge was opened. Stores, businesses, and even the Brooklyn schools were closed for the day. People came from all over the country to be part of the opening ceremony. Washington Roebling peered through his binoculars as Chester A. Arthur, president of the United States, walked across the bridge from New York to meet Emily on the Brooklyn side.

That night, there was a great party in honor of the Roeblings' beautiful bridge. Hundreds of thousands of people cheered for over an hour as fireworks exploded from the towers. New York had never before had such a grand celebration!

Washington and Emily watched the fireworks from their bedroom window. After 14 years the long struggle was over. Their bridge was done.

Emily returned happily to a busy life away from the bridge. She gave large parties and traveled all around the United States and Europe. She went back to school and earned her law degree when she was 55 years old. For a woman living at that time it was a remarkable accomplishment.

For Emily Roebling it was not at all surprising.

Washington slowly recovered from his long illness. He worked in the family business, making steel wire for bridges all over the country. He lived quietly at home, playing music, collecting rocks and minerals, and writing long letters to his beloved son John. When he spoke of the Brooklyn Bridge, he said that it had been a time of great suffering for him. He died in 1926 at the age of 89.

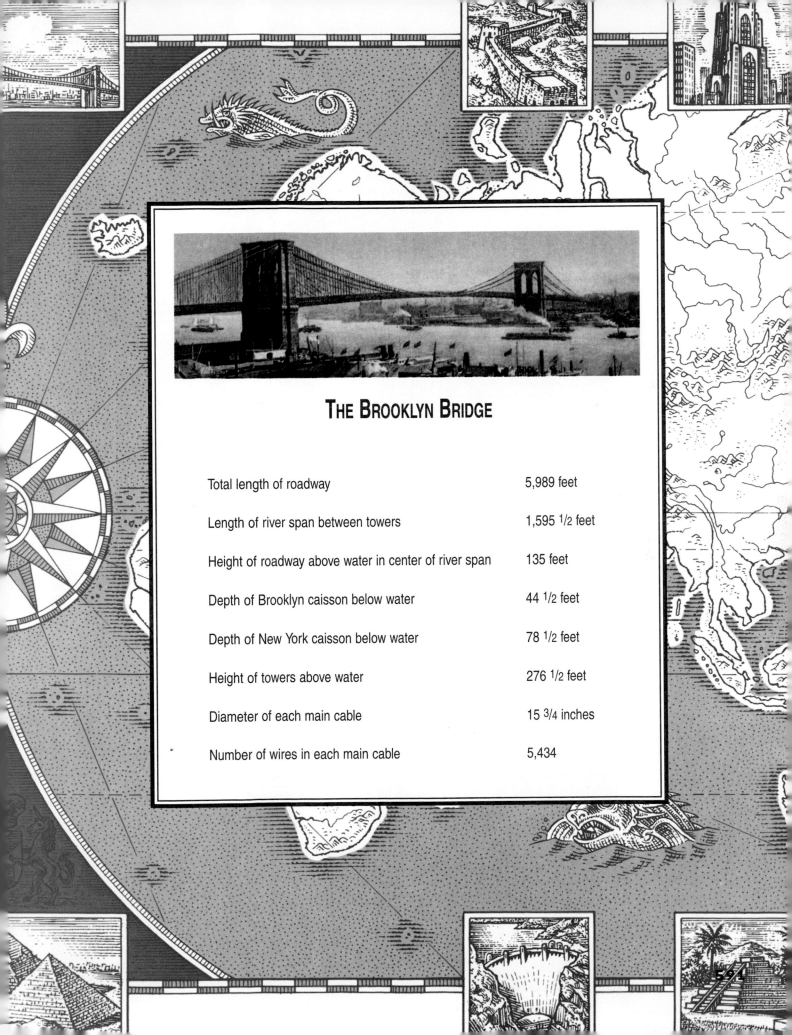

THE BROOKLYN BRIDGE

Total length of roadway	5,989 feet
Length of river span between towers	1,595 1/2 feet
Height of roadway above water in center of river span	135 feet
Depth of Brooklyn caisson below water	44 1/2 feet
Depth of New York caisson below water	78 1/2 feet
Height of towers above water	276 1/2 feet
Diameter of each main cable	15 3/4 inches
Number of wires in each main cable	5,434

from **Talking to Faith Ringgold**
by Faith Ringgold, Linda Freeman, and Nancy Roucher

Sonny's Quilt

Sonny's Quilt, 1986
by Faith Ringgold

The Brooklyn Bridge actually makes me think of quilts. Do you know why? Because it has the same kind of construction of squares and triangles. A quilt is put together in squares and triangles, and so are the towers of the bridge.

This piece is about the famous jazz musician Sonny Rollins, who also grew up in Harlem. He had this habit of practicing in strange places—on rooftops, fire escapes, and in this case a bridge!

—*Faith Ringgold*

Sonny Rollins, 1962

The Brooklyn Bridge

MENTOR

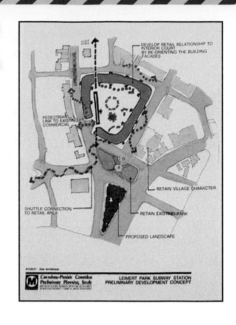

Karen Heit

Urban Planner

Urban planners plot the future of our cities.

The job of any urban planner is to think of ways to improve a city's future. In Los Angeles a better transportation system is needed. Each day millions of cars jam the city's freeways and pollute its air. The residents of Los Angeles hope to see an improved traffic situation in their future. That's where Karen Heit comes in. She's an urban planner specializing in public transportation.

PROFILE

Name: Karen Heit

Occupation: urban planner for the Los Angeles County Transportation Authority

Job title: Director, South Bay Area Team

Pets: two dogs, two turtles, a tadpole, and a tarantula

Favorite place to go in L.A.: the beach

Favorite way to get around L.A.: walking—until the subway system is completed!

QUESTIONS

for Karen Heit

Here's how urban planner Karen Heit gets L.A. moving.

Q What kind of transportation problems does Los Angeles have?

A For 20 years, L.A. has been known for having one of the worst traffic situations in the country. During an event like an L.A. Lakers basketball game, the highways become one big parking lot.

Q So what's the solution?

A It lies in expanding the rail system. We've got two lines running now, but we need to build many more.

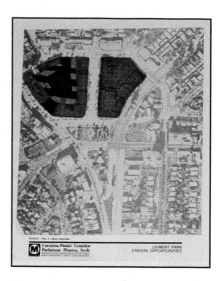

Q How do you plan the rail lines?

A First, my staff and I determine the best place to run the lines. We conduct surveys and talk with community members to come up with possible locations.

Q What happens next?

A I plot out routes for the lines on maps. It can take 12 to 13 years to complete a rail line! When the lines are up and

Q In your opinion, what quality helps an urban planner most?

A The number-one resource for urban planning is imagination. We have to be able to visualize a community springing back to life, then make it happen.

running, we continue to deal with the concerns of the people who live near them. We hold community meetings on a regular basis to get input from residents.

Q Will the rail lines help the community in other ways besides easing traffic?

A Absolutely. Our latest line will be built in a high-unemployment area. The line should attract new businesses and services, making the area a better place to live.

Karen Heit's Tips for Assessing and Responding

1 Survey community residents to find out what sorts of improvements they would most like to see in their community.

2 Interview local business owners and service persons to learn about the commercial needs of the area.

3 Meet with community members to get their feedback about changes in the community.

597

Think About Reading

Write your answers.

1. What were two of the main difficulties in building the Brooklyn Bridge?

2. How do you think Washington Roebling felt about his father? Give reasons for your answer.

3. If you could have worked on the Brooklyn Bridge, which job would you have chosen? Why?

4. What is the main theme of *The Brooklyn Bridge?* Explain your answer.

5. In what ways have John Roebling and Karen Heit tried to improve their cities?

Write a Newspaper Article

Picture yourself as a reporter, living at the time when the Brooklyn Bridge was built. You have just attended the opening ceremony for the bridge. Write an article for your newspaper about the event. Include background information about the bridge and tell why it is so important. Be sure to include *who, what, why, where, when,* and *how* in your article.

Literature Circle

Imagine a conversation between city planner, Karen Heit, and bridge designer, John Roebling. Discuss what they might talk about. What advice might Roebling give Heit about improving a modern city? How might Heit's modern-day experiences have helped John Roebling's project? If you could join the discussion, what suggestions would you offer?

AUTHOR
Elizabeth Mann

How many award-winning books were inspired by a class of second graders? *The Brooklyn Bridge* was. When author Elizabeth Mann was a teacher in a Brooklyn, New York, her students wanted to learn about their borough's most famous landmark. Mann couldn't find a book about the bridge to read to her class, so she wrote a "funky" version that she later revised for older readers. She says, "I'm interested in social studies, and I'm interested in stories." These interests have inspired Mann to write about other wonders of the world—an Egyptian pyramid, the Great Wall of China, and the Panama Canal.

MORE BOOKS BY
Elizabeth Mann

- *The Great Wall*
- *The Roman Colosseum*
- *The Panama Canal*

WORKSHOP

How to Create a Community Guide

In many cities and towns, municipal organizations publish guides that describe their communities. People who are interested in living or working in a particular place might consult a community guide to learn more about the area.

What is a community guide? A community guide is a pamphlet or brochure that answers important questions such as: Where will I live? How will I get to work? Where are schools and hospitals located? A community guide also tells about a town or city's special features — community events, things to do for fun, and nearby recreational areas.

Recent awards and honors received by the local public schools

—The Pittsburgh Public School district holds four Presidential Awards for Excellence.

—*The Christian Science Monitor* called Pittsburgh Public Schools one of America's "most successful" urban school districts.

—Pittsburgh Public Schools was ranked in the Top Six "progressive" U.S. urban school districts in a major Rand Corporation report.

—*Town and Country* named Pittsburgh's Allderdice High School among the Top Seven Urban High Schools nationwide.

—The U.S. Department of Education cited Schenley High School as a "School of Excellence."

—In 1990, the Clarissa Hug Award recognizing the International Teacher of the Year in Special Education went to a Pioneer School teacher in the Pittsburgh school district.

—*Newsweek* cited the district's Arts Propel program as the best arts education program in the world.

—In recent years, four Pittsburgh Public School teachers have been honored as Pennsylvania Teacher of the Year.

Names of the community's nine colleges and universities

Additional information of interest to local professionals

Public school. These are just a few of the accolades recently bestowed on Pittsburgh schools. A decade ago, parents of school-age children were leaving the City for wealthier suburban schools. Today, suburban residents are moving back because of the quality and diversity of the City's schools. For students K-12, Pittsburgh offers comprehensive programs in such subjects as creative and performing arts, international studies, geographic and life sciences, polytechnics, computer science, high technology, law and public service, and teaching as well as general academic programs at neighborhood schools. They also provide early childhood programs, day care, after school care, Head Start, a handicapped preschool and both half-day and full-day kindergartens. Innovative programs such as these have increased Pittsburgh's enrollment ... so much so that Pittsburgh Public Schools is one of the few school districts in Allegheny County that is reopening elementary schools.

Private school. Pittsburgh's private schools are highly regarded. The Independent Schools of Greater Pittsburgh include

nine schools within the City that offer intensive academic environments as well as racial, ethnic, religious and economic diversity. They are distinguished by small class sizes, which promote one-on-one teacher/student relationships conducive to learning. Financial assistance is available to help with tuition, which ranges from $6,000 to $10,000 per year, depending on the school. In addition, the Catholic Diocese operates 29 elementary and middle schools, and four secondary schools within Pittsburgh. They emphasize the religious principles of the Catholic tradition in addition to a progressive academic curriculum. Subsidized by parishioners, the cost of Catholic schooling in Pittsburgh is in the $2,000-a-year range.

Higher education. Pittsburghers derive enormous benefits through access to the nine colleges and uni-

versities within the City. They infuse the community with a wealth of academic and social opportunity—from the talent they recruit, to the resident students who volunteer in the community ... from the theatre, concerts, lectures and symposiums featuring universally known speakers and artists that they sponsor, to the credit and non-credit courses they teach. Pittsburgh's array of post-secondary technical schools, such as the Pittsburgh Art Institute and the Pittsburgh Culinary Institute, also offer unique educational opportunities. Whether you're interested in an M.B.A. or a Ph.D., or an elective course in speech writing or skydiving, sending your second grader to college computer camp, or becoming a world class chef, one of Pittsburgh's institutions of higher learning will meet your need.

Pittsburgh Colleges & Universities

Carlow College

Carnegie Mellon University

Chatham College

Community College of Allegheny County

Duquesne University

Pittsburgh Theological Seminary

Point Park College

Robert Morris College

University of Pittsburgh

Fortune has rated Pittsburgh the Eighth Best City for Business and the Fifth Largest Corporate Headquarters City. *Savvy* has named it the Third Most Livable City for Women; *Working Mother* has called it the Second Best City for Working Mothers. All told, Pittsburgh is a good place to grow professionally— for men and women.

Corporate diversity. Pittsburgh is headquarters to 12 *Fortune* 500 industrial companies, including *Fortune* 100 giants like Westinghouse Electric, H.J. Heinz, USX, Alcoa and PPG, and four *Fortune* 500 service firms. The skyline reflects this corporate prestige— seven skyrise office complexes have opened Downtown since 1980. Pittsburgh's economy is fueled today by health care, education, finance, light manufacturing and service businesses. High technology businesses are also flourishing— Pennsylvania ranks third in the U.S. behind California and Massachusetts in the number of high technology businesses, and

the Pittsburgh region home to 35 percent o state's high tech com nies. There are near companies and 65,0 employees in advanc technology in the Pi area. More than 170 research centers are in Pittsburgh, which of the highest concer tions of engineers, sc and technicians in the

Media. Pittsburgh among the Top 20 m markets in the U.S. eight television stati (including the count first public television WQED-TV) and 33 stations (including th nation's first, KDKA Both a morning and daily newspaper as an assortment of wel weekly and monthly cations catering to t ness, cultural and m ethnic communities Pittsburgh professio informed.

Networking. Two hundred ch of national fessional o zations, fr Toastm to the N

Information about the community's schools

Types of companies found in the community

Brainstorm

Research

First, choose the community you'd like to create a guide for—either your own or a neighboring city or town. You might also choose a community where you've lived in the past, or a city that you've often visited. Then, brainstorm a list of things about that community that you think people who are moving there would want to know about. Next, make a list of different subjects you want to cover in your guide, such as weather, transportation, schools, museums, businesses, neighborhoods, people, things to do, or any other subjects you think are important or interesting.

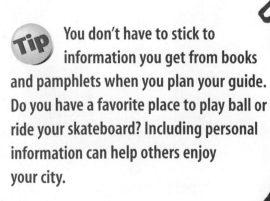

TOOLS

- paper and pencil
- colored pencils, crayons, or markers
- resource materials

Tip You don't have to stick to information you get from books and pamphlets when you plan your guide. Do you have a favorite place to play ball or ride your skateboard? Including personal information can help others enjoy your city.

Review the list of subjects you'd like to include in your guide. Then, decide what kind of information you want to present about each subject. For example, if you'd like to include museums in your guide, you can find out how many museums are in your community, their opening and closing times, current exhibits, and how many people visit each year. To find the information you need, you can check some or all of these sources: a book or Internet web site about the community, brochures from the Chamber of Commerce, a map of the city, or an almanac or encyclopedia.

ONE
TUCKER

A mouse was looking at Mario.

The mouse's name was Tucker, and he was sitting in the opening of an abandoned drain pipe in the subway station at Times Square. The drain pipe was his home. Back a few feet in the wall, it opened out into a pocket that Tucker had filled with the bits of paper and shreds of cloth he collected. And when he wasn't collecting, "scrounging" as he called it, or sleeping, he liked to sit at the opening of the drain pipe and watch the world go by—at least as much of the world as hurried through the Times Square subway station.

Tucker finished the last few crumbs of a cookie he was eating— a Lorna Doone shortbread he had found earlier in the evening— and licked off his whiskers. "Such a pity," he sighed.

Every Saturday night now for almost a year he had watched Mario tending his father's newsstand. On weekdays, of course, the boy had to get to bed early, but over the weekends Papa Bellini let him take his part in helping out with the family business. Far into the night Mario waited. Papa hoped that by staying open as late as possible his newsstand might get some of the business that would otherwise have gone to the larger stands. But there wasn't much business tonight.

"The poor kid might as well go home," murmured Tucker Mouse to himself. He looked around the station.

The bustle of the day had long since subsided, and even the nighttime crowds, returning from the theaters and movies, had vanished. Now and then a person or two would come down one of the many stairs that led from the street and dart through the station. But at this hour everyone was in a hurry to get to bed. On the lower level the trains were running much less often. There would be a long stretch of silence; then the mounting roar as a string of cars approached Times Square; then a pause while it let off old passengers and took on new ones; and finally the rush of sound as it disappeared up the dark tunnel. And the hush fell again. There was an emptiness in the air. The whole station seemed to be waiting for the crowds of people it needed.

Tucker Mouse looked back at Mario. He was sitting on a three legged stool behind the counter of the newsstand. In front of him all the magazines and newspapers were displayed as neatly as he knew how to make them. Papa Bellini had made the newsstand himself many years ago. The space inside was big enough for Mario, but Mama and Papa were cramped when they each took their turn. A shelf ran along one side, and on it were a little secondhand radio, a box of Kleenex (for Mama's hay fever), a box of kitchen matches (for lighting Papa's pipe), a cash register (for money—which there wasn't much of), and an alarm clock (for no good reason at all). The cash register had one drawer which was always open. It had gotten stuck once, with all the money the Bellinis had in the world inside it, so Papa decided it would be safer never to shut it again. When the stand was closed for the night, the money that was left there to start off the new day was perfectly safe, because Papa had also made a big wooden cover, with a lock, that fitted over the whole thing.

Mario had been listening to the radio. He switched it off. Way down the tracks he could see the lights of the shuttle train coming towards him. On the level of the station where the newsstand was, the only tracks were the ones on which the shuttle ran. That was a short train that went back and forth from Times Square to Grand Central, taking people from the subways on the east side of New York City over to the lines on the west. Mario knew most of the conductors on the shuttle. They all liked him and came over to talk between trips.

The train screeched to a stop beside the newsstand, blowing a gust of hot air in front of it. Only nine or ten people got out. Tucker watched anxiously to see if any of them stopped to buy a paper.

"All late papers!" shouted Mario as they hurried by. "Magazines!"

No one stopped. Hardly anyone even looked at him. Mario sank back on his stool. All evening long he had only sold fifteen papers and four magazines. In the drain pipe Tucker Mouse, who had been keeping count too, sighed and scratched his ear.

Mario's friend Paul, a conductor on the shuttle, came over to the stand. "Any luck?" he asked.

"No," said Mario. "Maybe on the next train."

"There's going to be less and less until morning," said Paul.

Mario rested his chin on the palm of his hand. "I can't understand it," he said. "It's Saturday night too. Even the Sunday papers aren't going."

Paul leaned up against the newsstand. "You're up awfully late tonight," he said.

"Well, I can sleep on Sundays," said Mario. "Besides, school's out now. Mama and Papa are picking me up on the way home. They went to visit some friends. Saturday's the only chance they have."

Over a loudspeaker came a voice saying, "Next train for Grand Central, track two."

"'Night, Mario," Paul said. He started off toward the shuttle. Then he stopped, reached in his pocket and flipped a half dollar over the counter. Mario caught the big coin. "I'll take a Sunday *Times*," Paul said, and picked up the newspaper.

"Hey wait!" Mario called after him. "It's only twenty-five cents. You've got a quarter coming."

But Paul was already in the car. The door slid closed. He smiled and waved through the window. With a lurch the train moved off, its lights glimmering away through the darkness.

Tucker Mouse smiled too. He liked Paul. In fact he liked anybody who was nice to Mario. But it was late now: time to crawl back to his comfortable niche in the wall and go to sleep. Even a mouse who lives in the subway station in Times Square has to sleep sometimes. And Tucker had a big day planned for tomorrow, collecting things for his home and snapping up bits of food that fell from the lunch counters all over the station. He was just about to turn into the drain pipe when he heard a very strange sound.

Now Tucker Mouse had heard almost all the sounds that can be heard in New York City. He had heard the rumble of subway trains and the shriek their iron wheels make when they go around a corner. From above, through the iron grills that open onto the streets, he had heard the thrumming of the rubber tires of automobiles, and the hooting of their horns and the howling of their brakes. And he had heard the babble of voices when the station was full of human beings, and the barking of the dogs that some of them had on leashes. Birds, the pigeons of New York, and cats, and even the high purring of airplanes above the city Tucker had heard. But in all his days, and on all his journeys through the greatest city in the world, Tucker had never heard a sound quite like this one.

TWO

Mario heard the sound too. He stood up and listened intently. The noise of the shuttle rattled off into silence. From the streets above came the quiet murmur of the late traffic. There was a noise of rustling nothingness in the station. Still Mario listened, straining to catch the mysterious sound. . . . And there it came again.

It was like a quick stroke across the strings of a violin, or like a harp that had been plucked suddenly. If a leaf in a green forest far from New York had fallen at midnight through the darkness into a thicket, it might have sounded like that.

Mario thought he knew what it was. The summer before he had gone to visit a friend who lived on Long Island. One afternoon, as the low sun reached long yellow fingers through the tall grass, he had stopped beside a meadow to listen to just such a noise. But there had been many of them then— a chorus. Now there was only one. Faintly it came again through the subway station.

Mario slipped out of the newsstand and stood waiting. The next time he heard the sound, he went toward it. It seemed to come from one corner, next to the stairs that led up to Forty-second Street. Softly Mario went toward the spot. For several minutes there was only the whispering silence. Whatever it was that was making the sound had heard him coming and was quiet. Silently Mario waited. Then he heard it again, rising from a pile of waste papers and soot that had blown against the concrete wall.

He went down and very gently began to lift off the papers. One by one he inspected them and laid them to one side. Down near the bottom the papers became dirtier and dirtier. Mario reached the floor. He began to feel with his hands through the dust and soot. And wedged in a crack under all the refuse, he found what he'd been looking for.

It was a little insect, about an inch long and covered with dirt. It had six legs, two long antennae on its head and what seemed to be a pair of wings folded on its back. Holding his discovery as carefully as his fingers could, Mario lifted the insect up and rested him in the palm of his hand.

"A cricket!" he exclaimed.

Keeping his cupped hand very steady, Mario walked back to the newsstand. The cricket didn't move. And he didn't make that little musical noise any more. He just lay perfectly still—as if he were sleeping, or frightened to death.

Mario pulled out a tissue of Kleenex and laid the cricket on it. Then he took another and started to dust him off. Ever so softly he tapped the hard black shell, and the antennae, and legs, and wings. Gradually the dirt that had collected on the insect fell away. His true color was still black, but now it had a bright, glossy sheen.

When Mario had cleaned off the cricket as much as he could, he hunted around the floor of the station for a matchbox. In a minute he'd found one and knocked out one end. Then he folded a sheet of Kleenex, tucked it in the box and put the cricket in. It made a perfect bed. The cricket seemed to like his new home. He moved around a few times and settled himself comfortably.

Mario sat for a time, just looking. He was so happy and excited that when anyone walked through the station, he forgot to shout "Newspapers!" and "Magazines!"

Then a thought occurred to him: perhaps the cricket was hungry. He rummaged through his jacket pocket and found a piece of a chocolate bar that had been left over from supper. Mario broke off one corner and held it out to the cricket on the end of his finger. Cautiously the insect lifted his head to the chocolate. He seemed to smell it a moment, then took a bit. A shiver of pleasure went over Mario as the cricket ate from his hand.

Mama and Papa Bellini came up the stairs from the lower level of the station. Mama was a short woman—a little stouter than she liked to admit—who wheezed and got a red face when she had to climb steps. Papa was tall and somewhat bent over, but he had a kindness that shone about him. There seemed always to be something smiling inside Papa. Mario was so busy feeding his cricket that he didn't see them when they came up to the newsstand.

"So?" said Mama, craning over the counter. "What now?"

"I found a cricket!" Mario exclaimed. He picked the insect up very gently between his thumb and forefinger and held him out for his parents to see.

Mama studied the little black creature carefully. "It's a bug," she pronounced finally. "Throw it away."

Mario's happiness fell in ruins. "No, Mama," he said anxiously. "It's a special kind of bug. Crickets are good luck."

"Good luck, ay?" Mama's voice had a way of sounding very dry when she didn't believe something. "Cricketers are good luck—so I suppose ants are better luck. And cockroaches are the best luck of all. Throw it away."

"Please, Mama, I want to keep him for a pet."

"No bugs are coming to my house," said Mama. "We've got enough already with the screens full of holes. He'll whistle to his friends—they'll come from all over—we'll have a houseful of cricketers."

"No we won't," said Mario in a low voice. "I'll fix the screens." But he knew it was no use arguing with Mama. When she made up her mind, you might as well try to reason with the Eighth Avenue subway.

"How was selling tonight?" asked Papa. He was a peaceful man and always tried to head off arguments. Changing the subject was something he did very well.

"Fifteen papers and four magazines," said Mario. "And Paul just bought a Sunday *Times*."

"No one took a *Musical America*, or anything else nice?" Papa was very proud that his newsstand carried all of what he called the "quality magazines."

"No," answered Mario.

"So you spend less time playing with cricketers, you'll sell more papers," said Mama.

"Oh now, now," Papa soothed her. "Mario couldn't help it if nobody buys."

"You can tell the temperature with crickets too," said Mario. "You count the number of chirps in a minute, divide by four and add forty. They're very intelligent."

"Who needs a cricketer-thermometer?" said Mama. "It's coming on summer, it's New York—it's hot. And how do you know so much about cricketers. Are you one?"

"Jimmy Lebovski told me last summer," said Mario.

"Then give it to the expert Jimmy Lebovski," said Mama. "Bugs carry germs. He doesn't come in the house."

Mario looked down at his new friend in the palm of his hand. Just for once he had been really happy. The cricket seemed to know that something was wrong. He jumped onto the shelf and crept into the matchbox.

"He could keep it here in the newsstand," suggested Papa.

Mario jumped at that idea. "Yes, and then he wouldn't have to come home. I could feed him here, and leave him here, and you'd never have to see him," he said to Mama. "And when you took the stand, I'd bring him with me."

Mama paused. "Cricketer," she said scornfully. "What do we want with a cricketer?"

"What do we want with a newsstand?" said Papa. "We got it—let's keep it." There was something resigned, but nice, about Papa.

"You said I could have a dog," said Mario, "but I never got him. And I never got a cat, or a bird, or anything. I wanted this cricket for my pet."

"He's yours then," said Papa. And when Papa spoke in a certain quiet tone—that was all there was to it. Even Mama didn't dare disagree.

She took a deep breath. "Oh well—" she sighed. And Mario knew it would be all right. Mama's saying "oh well" was her way of giving in. "But only on trial he stays. At the first sign of the cricketer friends, or if we come down with peculiar diseases—out he goes!"

"Yes, Mama, anything you say," said Mario.

"Come on, Mario," Papa said. "Help me close up."

Mario held the matchbox up to his eye. He was sure the cricket looked much happier, now that he could stay. "Goodnight," he said. "I'll be back in the morning."

"Talking to it yet!" said Mama. "I've got a cricketer for a son."

Papa took one side of the cover to the newsstand, Mario the other, and together they fitted it on. Papa locked it down. As they were going downstairs to the trains, Mario looked back over his shoulder. He could almost feel the cricket, snugged away in his matchbox bed, in the darkness.

THREE

CHESTER

Tucker Mouse had been watching the Bellinis and listening to what they said. Next to scrounging, eavesdropping on human beings was what he enjoyed most. That was one of the reasons he lived in the Times Square subway station. As soon as the family disappeared, he darted out across the floor and scooted up to the newsstand. At one side the boards had separated and there was a wide space he could jump through. He'd been in a few times before—just exploring. For a moment he stood under the three legged stool, letting his eyes get used to the darkness. Then he jumped up on it.

"Psst!" he whispered. "Hey you up there—are you awake?"

There was no answer.

"Psst! Psst! Hey!" Tucker whispered again, louder this time.

From the shelf above came a scuffling, like little feet feeling their way to the edge. "Who is that going 'psst'?" said a voice.

"It's me," said Tucker. "Down here on the stool."

A black head, with two shiny black eyes, peered down at him. "Who are you?"

"A mouse," said Tucker, "Who are *you*?"

"I'm Chester Cricket," said the cricket. He had a high, musical voice. Everything he said seemed to be spoken to an unheard melody.

"My name's Tucker," said Tucker Mouse. "Can I come up?"

"I guess so," said Chester Cricket. "This isn't my house anyway."

Tucker jumped up beside the cricket and looked him all over. "A cricket," he said admiringly. "So you're a cricket. I never saw one before."

"I've seen mice before," the cricket said. "I knew quite a few back in Connecticut."

"Is that where you're from?" asked Tucker.

"Yes," said Chester. "I guess I'll never see it again," he added wistfully.

"How did you get to New York?" asked Tucker Mouse.

"It's a long story," sighed the cricket.

"Tell me," said Tucker, settling back on his haunches. He loved to hear stories. It was almost as much fun as eavesdropping—if the story was true.

"Well it must have been two—no, three days ago," Chester Cricket began. "I was sitting on top of my stump, just enjoying the weather and thinking how nice it was that summer had started. I live inside an old tree stump, next to a willow tree, and I often go up to the roof to look around. And I'd been practicing jumping that day too. On the other side of the stump from the willow tree there's a brook that runs past, and I'd been jumping back and forth across it to get my legs in condition for the summer. I do a lot of jumping, you know."

"Me too," said Tucker Mouse. "Especially around the rush hour."

"And I had just finished jumping when I smelled something," Chester went on, "liverwurst, which I love."

"You like liverwurst?" Tucker broke in. "Wait! Wait! Just wait!"

In one leap, he sprang down all the way from the shelf to the floor and dashed over to his drain pipe. Chester shook his head as he watched him go. He thought Tucker was a very excitable person—even for a mouse.

Inside the drain pipe, Tucker's nest was a jumble of papers, scraps of cloth, buttons, lost jewelry, small change, and everything else that can be picked up in a subway station. Tucker tossed things left and right in a wild search. Neatness was not one of the things he aimed at in life. At last he discovered what he was looking for: a big piece of liverwurst he had found earlier that evening. It was meant to be for breakfast tomorrow, but he decided that meeting his first cricket was a special occasion. Holding the liverwurst between his teeth, he whisked back to the newsstand.

"Look!" he said proudly, dropping the meat in front of Chester Cricket. "Liverwurst! You continue the story—we'll enjoy a snack too."

"That's very nice of you," said Chester. He was touched that a mouse he had known only a few minutes would share his food with him. "I had a little chocolate before, but besides that, nothing for three days."

"Eat! Eat!" said Tucker. He bit the liverwurst into two pieces and gave Chester the bigger one. "So you smelled the liverwurst—then what happened?"

"I hopped down from the stump and went off toward the smell," said Chester.

"Very logical," said Tucker Mouse, munching with his cheeks full. "Exactly what I would have done."

"It was coming from a picnic basket," said Chester. "A couple of tuffets away from my stump the meadow begins, and there was a whole bunch of people having a picnic. They had hard boiled eggs, and cold roast chicken, and roast beef, and a whole lot of other things besides the liverwurst sandwiches, which I smelled."

Tucker Mouse moaned with pleasure at the thought of all that food.

"They were having such a good time laughing and singing songs that they didn't notice me when I jumped into the picnic basket," continued Chester. "I was sure they wouldn't mind if I had just a taste."

"Naturally not," said Tucker Mouse sympathetically. "Why mind? Plenty for all. Who could blame you?"

"Now I have to admit," Chester went on, "I had more than a taste. As a matter of fact, I ate so much that I couldn't keep my eyes open—what with being tired from the jumping and everything. And I fell asleep right there in the picnic basket. The first thing I knew, somebody had put a bag on top of me that had the last of the roast beef sandwiches in it. I couldn't move!"

"Imagine!" Tucker exclaimed. "Trapped under roast beef sandwiches! Well, there are worse fates."

"At first I wasn't too frightened," said Chester. "After all, I thought, they probably come from New Canaan or some other nearby town. They'll have to unpack the basket sooner or later. Little did I know!" He shook his head and sighed. "I could feel the basket being carried into a car and riding somewhere and then being lifted down. That must have been the railroad station. Then I went up again and there was a rattling and roaring sound, the way a train makes. By this time I was pretty scared. I knew every minute was taking me further away from my stump, but there wasn't anything I could do. I was getting awfully cramped too, under those roast beef sandwiches."

"Didn't you try to eat your way out?" asked Tucker.

"I didn't have any room," said Chester. "But every now and then the train would give a lurch and I managed to free myself a little. We traveled on and on, and then the train stopped. I didn't have any idea where we were, but as soon as the basket was carried off, I could tell from the noise it must be New York."

"You never were here before?" Tucker asked.

"Goodness no!" said Chester. "But I've heard about it. There was a swallow I used to know who told about flying over New York every spring and fall on her way to the North and back. But what would I be doing here?" He shifted uneasily from one set of legs to another. "I'm a country cricket."

"Don't worry," said Tucker Mouse. "I'll feed you liverwurst. You'll be all right. Go on with the story."

"It's almost over," said Chester. "The people got off one train and walked a ways and got on another—even noisier than the first."

"Must have been the subway," said Tucker.

"I guess so," Chester Cricket said. "You can imagine how scared I was. I didn't know *where* I was going! For all I knew they could have been heading for Texas, although I don't guess many people from Texas come all the way to Connecticut for a picnic."

"It could happen," said Tucker, nodding his head.

"Anyway I worked furiously to get loose. And finally I made it. When they got off the second train, I took a flying leap and landed in a pile of dirt over in the corner of this place where we are."

"Such an introduction to New York," said Tucker, "to land in a pile of dirt in the Times Square subway station. Tsk, tsk, tsk."

"And here I am," Chester concluded forlornly. "I've been lying over there for three days not knowing what to do. At last I got so nervous I began to chirp."

"That was the sound!" interrupted Tucker Mouse. "I heard it, but I didn't know what it was."

"Yes, that was me," said Chester. "Usually I don't chirp until later on in the summer—but my goodness, I had to do *something*!"

The cricket had been sitting next to the edge of the shelf. For some reason—perhaps it was a faint noise, like padded feet tiptoeing across the floor—he happened to look down. A shadowy form that had been crouching silently below in the darkness made a spring and landed right next to Tucker and Chester.

"Watch out!" Chester shouted, "A cat!" He dove headfirst into the matchbox.

FOUR
HARRY CAT

Chester buried his head in the Kleenex. He didn't want to see his new friend, Tucker Mouse, get killed. Back in Connecticut he had sometimes watched the one-sided fights of cats and mice in the meadow, and unless the mice were near their holes, the fights always ended in the same way. But this cat had been upon them too quickly: Tucker couldn't have escaped.

There wasn't a sound. Chester lifted his head and very cautiously looked behind him. The cat—a huge tiger cat with gray-green and black stripes along his body—was sitting on his hind legs, switching his tail around his forepaws. And directly between those forepaws, in the very jaws of his enemy, sat Tucker Mouse. He was watching Chester curiously. The cricket began to make frantic signs that the mouse should look up and see what was looming over him.

Very casually Tucker raised his head. The cat looked straight down on him. "Oh him," said Tucker, chucking the cat under the chin with his right front paw, "he's my best friend. Come out from the matchbox."

Chester crept out, looking first at one, then the other.

"Chester, meet Harry Cat," said Tucker. "Harry, this is Chester. He's a cricket."

"I'm very pleased to make your acquaintance," said Harry Cat in a silky voice.

"Hello," said Chester. He was sort of ashamed because of all the fuss he'd made. "I wasn't scared for myself. But I thought cats and mice were enemies."

"In the country, maybe," said Tucker. "But in New York we gave up those old habits long ago. Harry is my oldest friend. He lives with me over in the drain pipe. So how was scrounging tonight, Harry?"

"Not so good," said Harry Cat. "I was over in the ash cans on the East Side, but those rich people don't throw out as much garbage as they should."

"Chester, make that noise again for Harry," said Tucker Mouse.

Chester lifted the black wings that were carefully folded across his back and with a quick, expert stroke drew the top one over the bottom. A "thrumm" echoed through the station.

"Lovely—very lovely," said the cat. "This cricket has talent."

"I thought it was singing," said Tucker. "But you do it like playing a violin, with one wing on the other?"

"Yes," said Chester. "These wings aren't much good for flying, but I prefer music anyhow." He made three rapid chirps.

Tucker Mouse and Harry Cat smiled at each other. "It makes me want to purr to hear it," said Harry.

"Some people say a cricket goes 'chee chee chee,'" explained Chester. "And others say, 'treet treet treet,' but we crickets don't think it sounds like either one of those."

"It sounds to me as if you were going 'crik crik crik,'" said Harry.

"Maybe that's why they called him a 'cricket,'" said Tucker.

They all laughed. Tucker had a squeaky laugh that sounded as if he were hiccuping. Chester was feeling much happier now. The future did not seem nearly as gloomy as it had over in the pile of dirt in the corner.

"Are you going to stay a while in New York?" asked Tucker.

"I guess I'll have to," said Chester. "I don't know how to get home."

"Well, we could always take you to Grand Central Station and put you on a train going back to Connecticut," said Tucker. "But why don't you give the city a try. Meet new people—see new things. Mario likes you very much."

"Yes, but his mother doesn't," said Chester. "She thinks I carry germs."

"Germs!" said Tucker scornfully. "She wouldn't know a germ if one gave her a black eye. Pay no attention."

"Too bad you couldn't have found more successful friends," said Harry Cat. "I fear for the future of this newsstand."

"It's true," echoed Tucker sadly. "They're going broke fast." He jumped up on a pile of magazines and read off the names in the half light that slanted through the cracks in the wooden cover. "*Art News—Musical America.* Who would read them but a few long-hairs?"

"I don't understand the way you talk," said Chester. Back in the meadow he had listened to bullfrogs, and woodchucks, and rabbits, even a few snakes, but he had never heard anyone speak like Tucker Mouse. "What is a long-hair?"

Tucker scratched his head and thought a moment. "A long-hair is an extra refined person," he said. "You take an Afghan Hound—that's a long-hair."

"Do Afghan Hounds read *Musical America*?" asked the cricket.

"They would if they could," said Tucker.

Chester shook his head. "I'm afraid I won't get along in New York," he said.

"Oh sure you will!" squeaked Tucker Mouse. "Harry, suppose we take Chester up and show him Times Square. Would you like that, Chester?"

"I guess so," said Chester, although he was really a little leery of venturing out into New York City.

The three of them jumped down to the floor. The crack in the side of the newsstand was just wide enough for Harry to get through. As they crossed the station floor, Tucker pointed out the local sights of interest, such as the Nedick's lunch counter—Tucker spent a lot of time around there— and the Loft's candy store. Then they came to the drain pipe. Chester had to make short little hops to keep from hitting his head as they went up. There seemed to be hundreds of

twistings and turnings, and many other pipes that opened off the main route, but Tucker Mouse knew his way perfectly— even in the dark. At last Chester saw light above them. One more hop brought him out onto the sidewalk. And there he gasped, holding his breath and crouching against the cement.

They were standing at one corner of the Times building, which is at the south end of Times Square. Above the cricket, towers that seemed like mountains of light rose up into the night sky. Even this late the neon signs were still blazing. Reds, blues, greens, and yellows flashed down on him. And the air was full of the roar of traffic and the hum of human beings. It was as if Times Square were a kind of shell, with colors and noises breaking in great waves inside it. Chester's heart hurt him and he closed his eyes. The sight was too terrible and beautiful for a cricket who up to now had measured high things by the height of his willow tree and sounds by the burble of a running brook.

"How do you like it?" asked Tucker Mouse.

"Well—it's—it's quite something," Chester stuttered.

"You should see it New Year's Eve," said Harry Cat. Gradually Chester's eyes got used to the lights. He looked up. And way far above them, above New York, and above the whole world, he made out a star that he knew was a star he used to look at back in Connecticut. When they had gone down to the station and Chester was in the matchbox again, he thought about that star. It made him feel better to think that there was one familiar thing, twinkling above him, amidst so much that was new and strange. ■

One Batty

This story shows what can happen when a whole city gets in a *bat* mood.

It started with a bridge in Austin, Texas. About 10 years ago, the old Congress Avenue Bridge was rebuilt. The new bridge had lots of tiny nooks that were perfect places for bats to roost in.

Soon, hundreds of thousands of pregnant Mexican free-tailed bats moved in. After the babies were born, the bats numbered more than one million.

That worried people in Austin. Newspapers ran scary stories about the bats, saying they brought rabies and other problems. Many people wanted the government to get rid of the bats.

ONE BATTY GROUP

Then a group called Bat Conservation International (BCI) came to the rescue. How? They turned to children for help.

People from BCI talked with Austin schoolchildren about bats. They explained that the bats roost in the bridge by day. But then in the evening, they fly out to eat lots of pesky insects— up to 30,000 pounds (13,500 kg) every night.

Bridge!

The children told their families about the bats. BCI also talked to state officials and news people.

Pretty soon, the whole city was talking about how important bats are. People started gathering at the Congress Avenue Bridge every evening to see the bats fly out (**above**). What a show!

Now, hundreds of tourists come each night during the warm months to see the bats (**right**). The visitors travel from all over the world. And they spend their money in town. So bats are good for Austin in many ways!

LEARN ABOUT BATS— AND PASS IT ON

Dr. Merlin Tuttle, the head of BCI, wants more people to learn about bats (**left**). He teaches children and adults about the animals every chance he gets.

"Enjoy bats and tell others about them," he says to the kids. "The more people know about bats, the more they'll care about them."

Now *that's* a bat attitude!

BAT INTERPRETER ON SITE

THINK ABOUT READING

Write your answers.

1. How does Chester Cricket get to New York City?

2. What kind of person do you think Mario is?

3. If you were Mario, how would you feel if you found the cricket in the subway? Explain your answer.

4. Do you think Chester Cricket will enjoy living in New York City? Why or why not?

5. Both *The Cricket in Times Square* and "One Batty Bridge!" are about animals in the city. How are these two selections different?

WRITE AN AUTOBIOGRAPHICAL SKETCH

Take the part of Chester Cricket and write a short autobiography that will accompany a job resume. Describe yourself, where you have lived, your talents and interests, and what your goals are. Make yourself sound interesting to a prospective employer.

LITERATURE CIRCLE

George Selden's *The Cricket in Times Square* is a classic animal fantasy. Talk about the qualities that the animal characters in the story have. How are they different from real animals? Then list other animal fantasies and discuss how the characters are similar to or different from those in *The Cricket in Times Square*. Record your ideas on a concept web.

AUTHOR
GEORGE SELDEN

Like Chester Cricket, George Selden was born in Connecticut and grew up there. Many years later, Selden was in the Times Square subway station in New York City when he heard the unexpected sound of a cricket. It reminded Selden of his childhood home in Connecticut, and right away a story came to mind about a cricket who, like him, found itself in the busy city but was homesick for the country.

MORE BOOKS BY

GEORGE SELDEN

- *Harry Kitten and Tucker Mouse*
- *Tucker's Countryside*
- *Chester Cricket's New Home*

FROM

The City by the Bay

A MAGICAL JOURNEY AROUND SAN FRANCISCO

By **TRICIA BROWN**
and **THE JUNIOR LEAGUE OF SAN FRANCISCO**
Illustrated by **ELISA KLEVEN**

For centuries, perhaps millennia, San
Francisco and its Bay were known
only by native peoples who lived in
small communities throughout Central
California. Typically, each community had
its own distinct language. As a result,
there was never a common name used
for the population as a whole.

When the Spanish arrived, they called the
natives *costeros,* or "coast people." Later,
the English-speaking settlers referred to
them as *Costanoans.* Today, descendants
of the early natives generally call
themselves *Ohlones.*

In the late 16th century, explorers from
around the globe began sailing the waters
surrounding the San Francisco peninsula.
Since that time, San Francisco's population
has been made up of an ever-changing
mosaic of cultures.

Chinatown

Gung Hay Fat Choy! That means "Happy New Year!" in Chinese. New Year's is a special time in this neighborhood, the largest Chinese community in the western hemisphere. People wish one another good luck and happiness, and children receive *lai-see*—small red envelopes filled with money.

The holiday is celebrated in January or February, depending on the cycle of the moon. Each year is named after one of the twelve animals in the Chinese zodiac. There are many parades and ceremonies. Lots of firecrackers are set off to scare away evil spirits and bring good fortune.

Chinatown is colorful all year round. Walk down Grant Avenue, with its street lights that look like lanterns and street signs written in Chinese. Look at the fresh vegetables and fruits overflowing out to the sidewalk from the grocery stores. Smell the aromas coming from all the different restaurants. Is it time for *dim sum*, a Chinese lunch?

The Cable Cars and Lombard Street

Before 1922, the famous crooked block of Lombard Street was straight, and so steep that it could not be traveled by carts or wagons. The only way for people to get up and down the hill was on foot. After the invention of the automobile, the city added eight turns so that cars would be able to travel the street as well. Today, tourists wait in line to drive down this twisting street.

Visitors can also view Lombard Street from the cable car that runs along Hyde Street. Andrew Hallidie introduced the cable car to San Francisco in 1873 because he felt sorry for the horses pulling wagons up the steep hills. People laughed at his idea at first, but he didn't give up. Today, San Francisco's cable cars are a National Historic Landmark.

644

The Golden Gate Bridge

Looking from the Marin Headlands to San Francisco on clear evenings, you can watch the twinkling lights of the city, the Golden Gate Bridge, and the San Francisco–Oakland Bay Bridge. On other nights, when the fog rolls in, you can hear the foghorns, and feel the cool fog as it wraps around the Golden Gate Bridge like a blanket.

Although the name of this bridge is the Golden Gate, the paint used to cover it is actually "International Orange." The bridge is named after the strait at the bay's entrance—the Golden Gate.

Some people believed that a bridge could never be built across the Golden Gate, but a group of determined engineers found a way. Built in 1937, the bridge spans a length of 6,450 feet—that's longer than twenty football fields! The tallest tower is 746 feet high—as tall as a 70-story building. The amount of wire used for the main cable is enough to wrap three times around the earth.

The Palace of Fine Arts

Although it was originally intended as a temporary exhibit for the 1915 Panama-Pacific Exhibition, the Palace of Fine Arts was so well-loved that it was later rebuilt to become a permanent part of San Francisco's skyline. The beauty of this graceful palace is reflected in a natural lagoon, which is bordered by lawns and trees. The sight is especially stunning at night when the palace is spectacularly lighted. It's a wonderful place to take a stroll, to have a picnic, or to feed the swans and ducks.

The palace is a majestic domed rotunda, with six supporting columns, that is as tall as an eighteen-story building. The angel sculptures inside the rotunda are twenty feet tall. If you want to get an idea of how big that is, you can go into the neighboring Exploratorium and stand next to one of the original angels from the 1915 exhibition!

Lighthouses, foghorns, and buoys guide ships as they navigate San Francisco Bay. Mariners identify the different foghorns by the length and frequency of their "blasts" and the length of the pauses between blasts.

There are eleven islands within San Francisco's city limits: Angel Island, Yerba Buena, Alcatraz, Treasure Island, and the Farallones (a group of seven islands outside the Golden Gate).

The Bay Bridge's deepest pier drops 242 feet into the water. Its tallest tower (from bedrock, below the Bay, to the very top) measures nearly 550 feet, making it taller than the largest of the Egyptian pyramids.

San Francisco Bay is not really a bay at all—it's an estuary. (A bay is filled with ocean water. An estuary is filled with a combination of salt water and fresh water.) It is the largest estuary on the west coast of the United States, and has one of the most diverse populations of marine life in the world.

Sutro Tower, San Francisco's tallest structure, transmits television and radio signals from the top of Mt. Sutro.

In 1850, when sourdough bread was delivered to San Franciscans, loaves were placed on spikes outside the doors so that animals could not reach them. Sourdough bread is unique to San Francisco—the wild yeast that is used to make it rise won't grow anywhere else!

San Francisco has more than 3,000 restaurants.

The Bay Bridge is actually made up of four bridges: two suspension bridges on the San Francisco side, and a cantilever bridge and a truss bridge on the Oakland side. The two pairs of bridges are connected by a tunnel through Yerba Buena Island.

City by the Bay...

"BART" stands for Bay Area Rapid Transit, the computer-operated, electric-rail train system that connects San Francisco with the East Bay and the Peninsula.

BART's Transbay Tube is 3.6 miles long and rests on the Bay floor, 135 feet beneath the surface of the water. It is made up of 57 giant steel and concrete sections.

Chocolate was not the first product to be manufactured at Ghirardelli Square—it was originally the site of the Pioneer Woolen Mill, which produced uniforms and blankets for the Union Army during the Civil War.

The San Francisco Ballet is the oldest ballet company in America. Founded in 1933, it was the first American ballet company to perform "Nutcracker" and "Swan Lake."

Cable cars are pulled along by underground cables that are constantly moving. A gripman pulls a lever that grips the cable through a slot in the street. When the gripman lets go, a brakeman stops the cable car with wheel and track brakes. The gripman and brakeman ring bells to tell each other when to brake (stop) or grip (go).

San Francisco's firefighters locate emergency water reserves by looking for circles on the streets. 151 intersections have large circles of bricks set into the pavement—each marks a reserve tank holding about 75,000 gallons of water.

Abandoned sailing ships from the Gold Rush days lie buried beneath the streets of San Francisco. The ships were covered by landfill during the city's early days of expansion.

Cities at a Glance

According to the 1990 census, over half the U.S. population lives in cities. Cities around the country have to make sure they can accommodate the growing number of new citizens. This chart shows how two cities from each region of the country meet the needs of their residents.

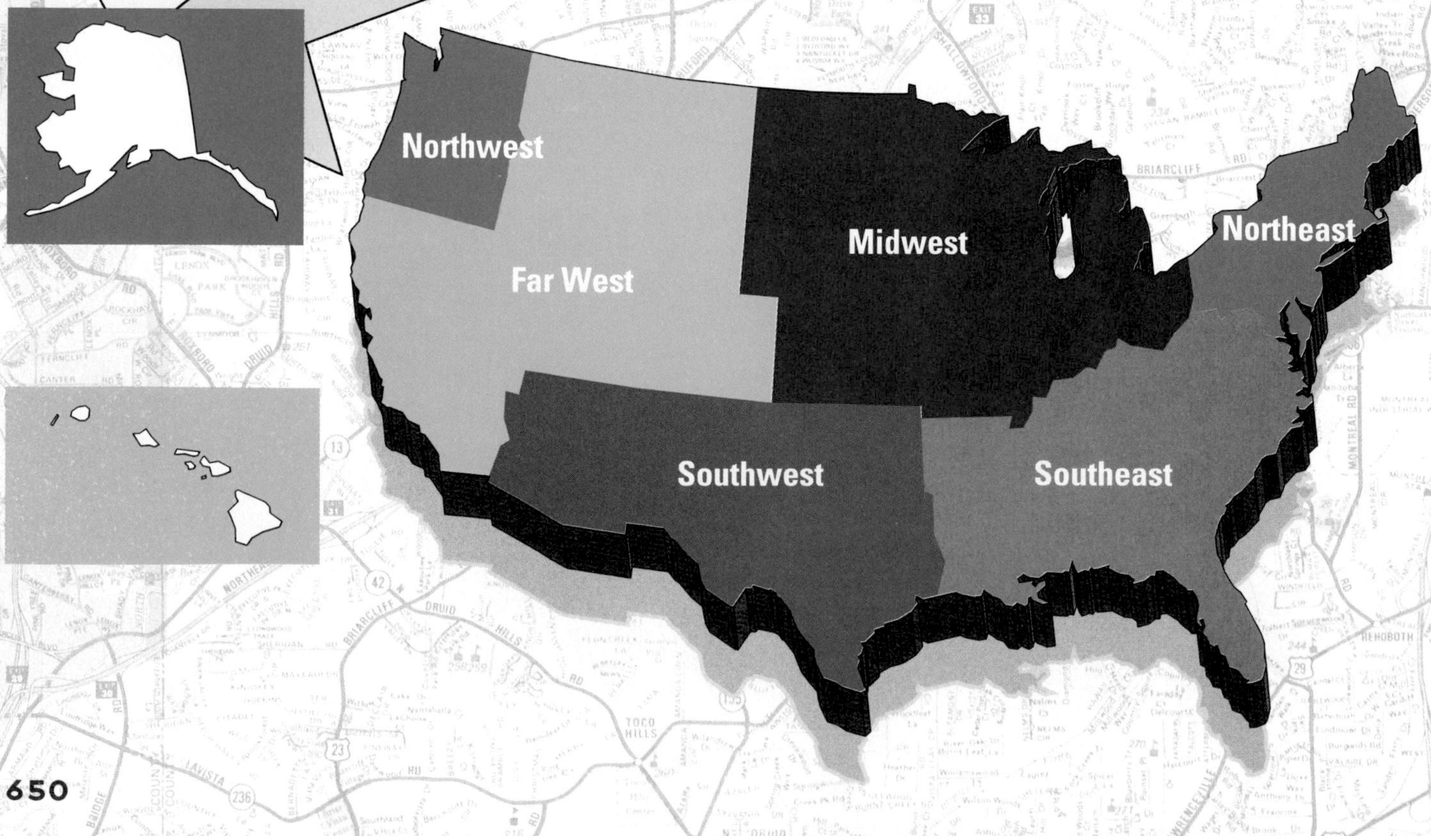

Northwest

Far West

Midwest

Northeast

Southwest

Southeast

| | NORTHEAST | | SOUTHEAST | |
	NEW YORK	PHILADELPHIA	JACKSONVILLE	MEMPHIS
POPULATION	7,323,000	1,600,000	672,971	610,000
GETTING AROUND	Three subway systems run 230 miles in the city.	Trains connect the city to its suburbs.	Mass transit takes a back seat to cars here.	The city bus and the Main Street Trolley
FAVORITE SPORTS TEAM	Basketball's Knicks and baseball's Yankees	Baseball's Phillies	The Jacksonville Jaguars football team	The Memphis State University Tigers basketball team
MOST RECOGNIZABLE FEATURE	The Statue of Liberty	The Liberty Bell	Jacksonville Landing, a horseshoe-shaped marketplace	The Pyramid, a multipurpose arena that seats 22,500 spectators
LARGEST NEWSPAPER	*The New York Times*: circulation over 1,000,000	*The Philadelphia Inquirer*: circulation over 400,000	*The Florida Times-Union*: circulation over 150,000	*The Commercial Appeal*: circulation over 200,000
CITY HELPERS	Teenagers in the City Volunteer Corps help with city events and services.	Action AIDS helps people with the HIV virus.	Volunteer Jacksonville serves the city's many needs.	The Metropolitan Inter-Faith Association uses 3,000 volunteers.
WHERE TO VISIT	The Empire State Building	The Liberty Bell	Twenty miles of white, sandy beaches	Graceland, the home of Elvis Presley
MAJOR INDUSTRIES	Manufacturing, trade, and finance	Banking, insurance, healthcare, and education	Banking and insurance	Education, transportation, and communication
WHERE IT IS	New York	Pennsylvania	Florida	Tennessee

	MIDWEST		NORTHWEST	
	CHICAGO	**DETROIT**	**SEATTLE**	**PORTLAND**
POPULATION	2,783,726	1,028,000	516,000	437,319
GETTING AROUND	Bus and rail systems make 1.8 million trips daily.	A car is a must in the motor city, but the elevated People Mover provides public transportation downtown.	The Washington State Ferry System is the largest in the U.S.A.	The MAX (Metropolitan Area Express) — a light-rail system
FAVORITE SPORTS TEAM	The Bulls basketball team, baseball's Cubs and White Sox, and football's Bears	Baseball's Tigers and Hockey's Detroit Red Wings	Basketball's Supersonics and football's Seahawks	Basketball's Portland Trail Blazers
MOST RECOGNIZABLE FEATURE	The Sears Tower, one of the tallest buildings in the world	The Renaissance Center, one of the tallest hotels in North America	The Space Needle, a tower with a revolving restaurant on top	The beautiful snow-capped peaks of Mt. Hood
LARGEST NEWSPAPER	*The Chicago Tribune:* circulation over 600,000	*The Detroit Free Press:* circulation over 500,000	*The Seattle Times:* circulation over 200,000	*The Oregonian:* circulation over 300,000
CITY HELPERS	The Children's Home and Aid Society of Illinois helps children and teenagers.	The Detroit Grand Prix Association volunteers at the huge annual auto race.	Patrons of Northwest Civic Cultural and Charitable Organizations raise money for the arts.	The Royal Rosarians pitch in for Portland's famous annual Rose Festival.
WHERE TO VISIT	The Lincoln Park Zoo	The Motown Museum	Pike Place Market, where merchants throw fish to customers	The Oregon Museum of Science and Industry
MAJOR INDUSTRIES	The service industry (workers who do things for others)	Automobile manufacturing and related industries	Aerospace and computer software	Timber and manufacturing
WHERE IT IS	Illinois	Michigan	Washington	Oregon

| | SOUTHWEST | | FAR WEST | |
	HOUSTON	DALLAS	LOS ANGELES	SAN FRANCISCO
POPULATION	1,600,000	1,006,877	3,485,398	724,000
GETTING AROUND	Because Houston is spread out over many miles, the most popular form of transit is the car.	DART— Dallas Area Rapid Transit	The recently built metro system provides another way to travel to downtown LA.	Cable cars provide a picturesque way to get from here to there.
FAVORITE SPORTS TEAM	Basketball's Rockets and football's Oilers	Football's Dallas Cowboys	Basketball's Lakers and baseball's Dodgers compete for fans.	Football's Forty-Niners
MOST RECOGNIZABLE FEATURE	The Astrodome, the first domed stadium ever built	Reunion Tower, a tall, skinny building with a big ball on top	The Hollywood sign sits high in the Hollywood Hills. HOLLYWOOD	The Golden Gate Bridge
LARGEST NEWSPAPER	*The Houston Chronicle:* circulation over 400,000	*The Dallas Morning News:* circulation over 500,000	*Los Angeles Times:* circulation over 1,000,000	*The San Francisco Chronicle:* circulation over 500,000
CITY HELPERS	The Green Houston organization supplies fresh produce for soup kitchens.	Big Brothers/Big Sisters pairs adults with kids from single-parent families.	The Tree People plant and maintain city trees.	The St. Anthony Foundation serves San Francisco's inner city.
WHERE TO VISIT	Astroworld amusement park and Galveston Island	Pioneer Plaza, a downtown park that commemorates Old West cattle drives	Beverly Hills and Universal Studios	Oceanfront Fisherman's Wharf and Pier 39
MAJOR INDUSTRIES	Oil and gas	Financial services — banks, investing, etc.	Entertainment, finance, and tourism	Tourism and business services
WHERE IT IS	Texas	Texas	California	California

FUTURE

What will cities look like in fifty, a hundred, or even a thousand years? Students around the country answer that question when they enter a special contest.

Held each year as part of National Engineers Week, the Future City Competition™ challenges seventh and eighth graders to design the perfect urban environment—a future city. That's not all the students do! They also have to solve some of the BIG problems that cities of the future will undoubtedly face—pollution, traffic jams, crime, crowding, and even energy shortages.

How do they do it? Small teams of students under the expert guidance of a teacher and an engineer mentor use their knowledge of math, science, and social studies to design and engineer the best possible cities of tomorrow. Over a four-month period, each team spends hundreds of hours—after school, on weekends, and during holiday breaks—perfecting their plan for a future metropolis.

This computer-generated model shows Aquapolis, an underwater city that covers about ten square miles and is located in the warm waters off the Gulf of Mexico.

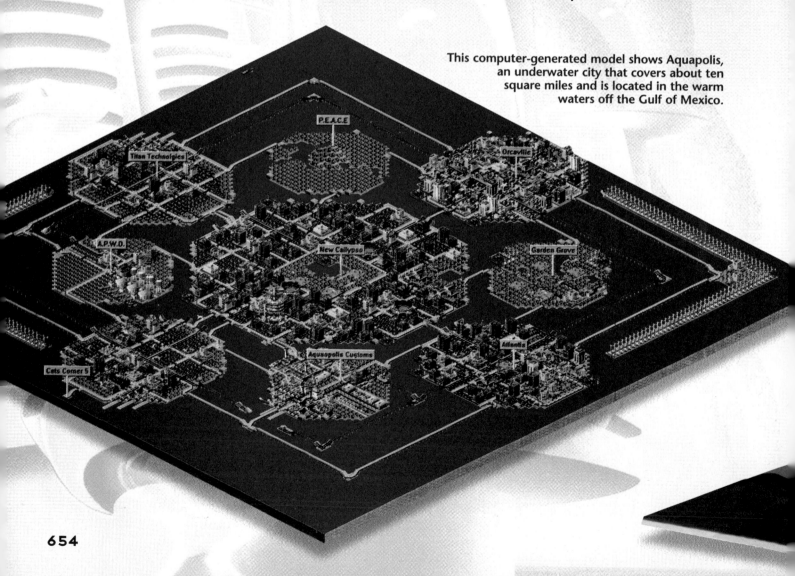

CITIES

Here's how students create a future city.

First, the young urban planners create a computer model of their imaginary metropolis using the software game *SimCity 2000*™. Many teams choose unusual locations—underwater sites, the moon, or even another planet. As the students work on their computer-generated design, they plan for a power source, water and sewer systems, roads, industrial parks, and commercial and residential zones.

Next, the team brings the cybercity to life by building a three-dimensional model of one specific part of the computer design. With a budget of $100, students use mostly recyclable materials—everything from bottle caps, glass jars, and egg cartons to Ping-Pong balls and computer disks.

Finally, each team writes a 500-word essay about their city of the future. They identify a specific problem, such as transportation, food production, or pollution, and explain how they used creative engineering to solve it.

In Brooklyn, New York, students from J.H.S. 113 created this 3-D model of their future city, Metropolis. Like all 3-D models for the Future City Competition™, Metropolis is built to scale and contains a moving part.

A team member from St. Francis of Assisi School in Tonawanda, New York, works on the 3-D model of Lakeland, a future city of about 121,000 residents. The completed model is shown below.

What do future cities look like? Turn the page and take a peek. Some are out of this world!

These student are riding the wave of the future with the 3-D model of their underwater city, Aquapolis.

Each of the nine sections of Aquapolis has an inner sphere and an outer sphere. The outer sphere absorbs the immense water pressure.

AQUAPOLIS

Which future city is wet and wonderful? For student designers from Bellevue, Nebraska, the answer is "Aquapolis." This unique underwater city is made up of nine connecting spheres that are linked by a pneumatic tube transport system and conveyor sidewalks. Aquapolis can be reached from the surface by taking a sea shuttle to the Aquapolis hydroport.

What do the residents do in this unusual underwater environment? Many work or study at the Cousteau Institute of Oceanography, while others work in futuristic industries including electronics, new technologies, and marine products. When they aren't working, residents relax and watch the sea life swim by. In Aquapolis, every home has an ocean view!

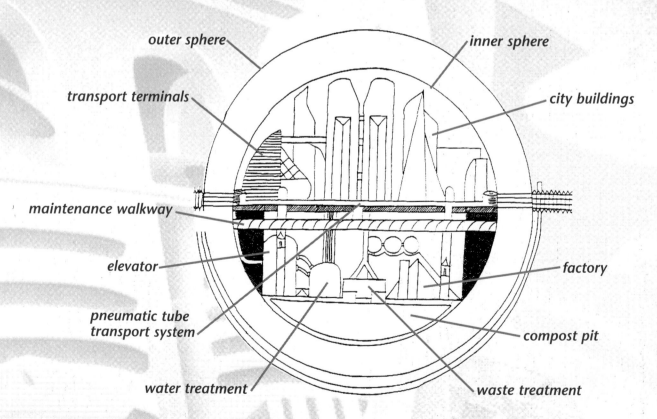

outer sphere

inner sphere

transport terminals

city buildings

maintenance walkway

elevator

factory

pneumatic tube transport system

compost pit

water treatment

waste treatment

This hand-drawn diagram shows the Aquapolis Public Works District where garbage and waste for the whole city are processed.

The Mountainside Middle School team from Scottsdale, Arizona, won second place at the national finals with their high-tech future city, Griffon.

This team from Central School in Glencoe, Illinois, won first place with their future city, Seolforis, at the national finals held in Washington, D.C.

GRIFFON

The student designers of Griffon worked hard to create this perfect metropolis located on the Pacific Coast. First, they imagined a city, much like Phoenix, Arizona. Then they figured out a way to limit urban pollution. The city's environmentally friendly energy sources include ocean-current turbines and wave-motion pumps. Energy is also generated by solar and wind power and fusion.

Griffon's greatest innovation is its Holonet system, which was engineered to replace the Internet, telephones, and televisions. Free to all residents, it can be accessed by a computer, a wristwatch device, or a headset. On the Holonet, Griffon residents can get information, take classes, and even order all kinds of goods.

In the Griffon 3-D model, you can see the tubes that are part of the city's Holonet system. Goods ordered on the Holonet are sent to the nearest bus station through vacuum tubes like the ones used in drive-up banks.

SEOLFORIS

Seolforis is far out—in outer space that is. The Seolforis team created this unusual city of the future on an imaginary ice-covered planet—a very cool place to live. Residents use lasers to extract silver ore from the ice. Student designer Adam Patinkin says, "The greatest challenge was balancing the atmosphere so the ice wouldn't melt."

Another challenge was food production, but the team solved that problem too. Since there is no soil on Seolforis, farmers grow fruit and vegetables in hydroponics plantations using only water and special nutrients.

This future city is a fun place to live. Residents can play baseball on climate-controlled Koufax Field and watch 3-D holographic movies at the holo-theater. Even getting around on Seolforis is a blast. Everyone 14 or older drives an "icemobile," which is similar to a snowmobile but runs on battery-powered jets.

A Bright Future

Thanks to the Future City Competition™, students all over the country learn how to make cities better places to live through creativity, ingenuity, and technology. With young people like these around, there's no doubt about it—cities have a bright future!

Think About Reading

Write your answers.

1. Which of San Francisco's special features are highlighted in *The City by the Bay*?

2. How do you think San Francisco residents feel about their city? Why?

3. If you could visit one site in San Francisco, which one would you choose? Explain your answer.

4. How do you feel about the illustrations for *The City by the Bay*? Do you think they complement the descriptions? Why or why not?

5. What extra information about San Francisco do you find in "Cities at a Glance"?

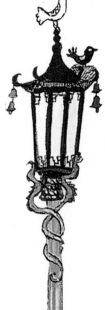

POWELL & HYDE Sts.

SAN FRANCISCO MUNICIPAL RAILWAY

Write an E-Mail Request

Find out more facts about one of the cities in "Cities at a Glance." Write an E-mail message to that city's chamber of commerce, asking for information. Be specific about what you would like to know, such as upcoming sports events or museum exhibits, places to stay, or other interesting sites to visit. Be sure to write the name of the chamber of commerce at the top of your E-mail message, and include a short sentence or phrase that tells what your message is about.

Literature Circle

Discuss the special features that make San Francisco famous. Which ones would you duplicate if you were creating a city? Which features would you change? Then talk about the metropolises presented in "Future Cities." Tell which one you like best and explain why. List your ideas on a graphic organizer such as a chart.

AUTHOR
Tricia Brown

Tricia Brown has traveled throughout Latin America and Southeast Asia, but she is always happy to return home to San Francisco. She is well-known for the photo essays she has written about young people in different California neighborhoods. *The City by the Bay* is special to her because she wrote it to assist people in her hometown. Brown donates her earnings from this book to organizations that help children in San Francisco.

MORE BOOKS BY
Tricia Brown

- *Chinese New Year*
- *Hello, Amigos!*
- *Lee Ann: The Story of a Vietnamese-American Girl*

How to

Make an Action Plan

Work to get something changed in your community.

Making an action plan is one way to bring about community improvement. An action plan is a written proposal, stating what the writer wants to do, why he or she wants to do it, and how it can be done. The proposal should also include evidence that supports the writer's position. This evidence can be photos, articles, and surveys. Together, the proposal and the evidence make up an action plan.

Dear mayor:

I would like a baseball field built in the space

BOSTON ST.

BLEACHERS

BLEACHERS

BLEACHERS

WHITFIELD ST.

nother ch

on the floor at all for
of a close playoff v
in the

FAIR

ST

GT

FAIR

ST

ST

ER

RIVER

ST

HELWIN
LA

FARM
VIEW DR

MILE
COURSE

RIVER

NORTH

CHERRY ST

WATER

STATE

STATE
ST INTERSTATE

CHURCH
ST

HUDSON

MILL
POND

YORK
RD

LONG

POST RD

RD

NUT PLAINS

STATE
RD WEST

X-58

HILL

SAW

HUBBARD
RD

CIR

WOODRUFF

OXBOW LN

77

CT

GRIS

FOOT CT

Choose and Support an Issue

What is one thing in your community you want to change? Check out local news reports to see what other people think your community needs. Pick an issue you feel strongly about, but not one that's too big to tackle. Perhaps you feel that your neighborhood needs a dog run where dogs can exercise safely or that your community needs a new public softball diamond. You may want to survey classmates to find an issue that seems important. Then write a short proposal telling about your idea.

Once you choose an issue, collect evidence to support your idea. Start a file of newspaper clippings. As you collect information, take notes. Support for your position can come from many sources. Talk to people you know. They may be willing to sign a petition or write letters in support of your idea. Local or national newspapers, TV stations, and radio shows may have covered your issue.

TOOLS

- paper and pen
- markers, crayons, or pencils
- folder with pockets
- camera (optional)

2 Making a Plan

Any good action plan includes ideas for how the plan might work. For example, if you think your community needs a public dog run, you might find out how much land must be set aside for it. You might research available public areas. You may want to include information about how much the project is likely to cost the community.

Decide what information you need to explain how your idea could work. Then, research that information.

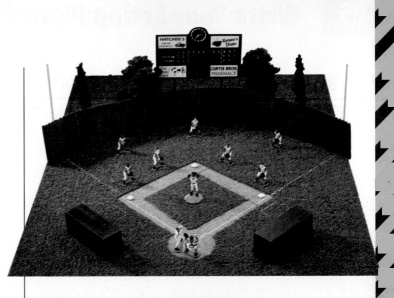

How Am I Doing?

Before you begin your action plan, take a minute to ask yourself these questions:

● Can you state the idea for your action plan briefly and clearly?

● Do you have at least three pieces of evidence that support your idea?

● Have you collected enough information to explain how the idea could work?

Tips Here are some useful sources of information for researching your plan:
- school or public library
- city hall
- chamber of commerce

Write Your Action Plan

Write a proposal for action. Begin by briefly stating what it is that you want to build or change. Continue the proposal by giving at least three reasons explaining why your idea is a sound one. Finally, explain how the idea might be put into action. Be sure to list the evidence you have collected to support your idea and to show how it could work. Reread your proposal to be sure that it is clear and complete. Draft a brief letter about your proposal that you can include, if you decide to send it to your mayor or community leader.

If You Are Using a Computer . . .

Draft your action proposal using the Report format. Then write the letter for your proposal in the Letter format. Create your own stationery by choosing from the selection of letterheads.

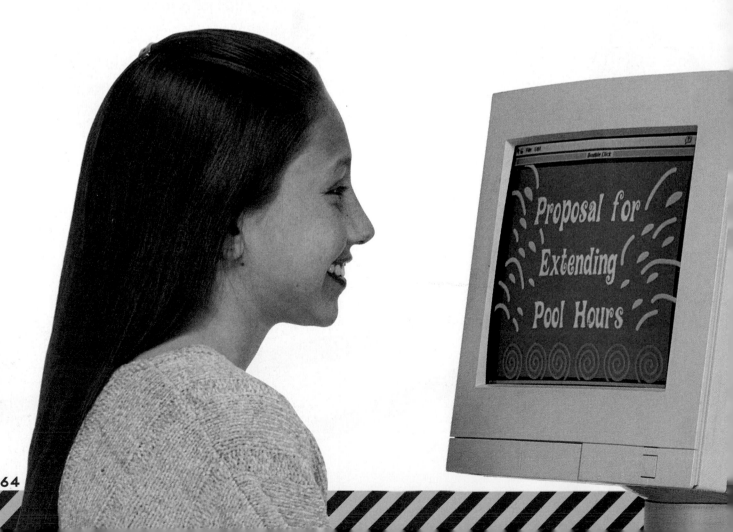

4 Present Your Action Plan

Now it's time to put your action plan together. Put your proposal in the left-hand pocket of your folder. Gather together all of the evidence you have collected. Put the evidence in the right-hand side of the folder. Are you going to mail your action plan to the mayor or a community leader? Include the letter you wrote stating your idea and explaining that you have included an action plan to describe the idea. Put everything in a mailing envelope and address it clearly and neatly. Include a self-addressed, stamped envelope so the material can be returned to you. Remember to keep a copy of the letter and evidence for yourself. You might want to put your copy of the action plan on display in your classroom.

CONGRATULATIONS

Now you know what an urban planner does. Next time you're in a city, think about all the planning that's needed to make things run.

Karen Heit
Urban Planner ▶

You will find all your vocabulary words in alphabetical order in the Glossary. Look at the sample entry below to see how to use it.

This is the **entry word** you look up. It is divided into syllables.

This part tells you how to **pronounce** the entry word. It uses the marks in the pronunciation key.

ex·plain·ing (ik splān´ ing) *verb*
Showing the meaning of something. The teacher was *explaining* how to take the test.
▲ explain

This tells you what **part of speech** the entry word is.

Look here to find the **meaning** of the word. There also may be a sentence that tells more about the word or that shows how the word is used.

This is **another form** of the entry word.

a	add	o͝o	took	ə =	
ā	ace	o͞o	pool	a in *above*	
â	care	u	up	e in *sicken*	
ä	palm	û	burn	i in *possible*	
e	end	yo͞o	fuse	o in *melon*	
ē	equal	oi	oil	u in *circus*	
i	it	ou	pout		
ī	ice	ng	ring		
o	odd	th	thin		
ō	open	ŧh	this		
ô	order	zh	vision		

The **pronunciation key** will help you figure out how to pronounce the entry word.

ab·duct (ab dukt´) *verb*
To carry off by force;
to kidnap.

ab·o·li·tion·ist
(ab´ ə lish´ ə nist) *noun*
A person who worked
to end slavery in the United
States.

adze (adz) *noun*
A tool with a sharp, curved
blade for trimming and
shaping wood.

aer·i·al
(âr´ ē əl) *adjective*
Done in the air. *Aerial*
photographs are often taken
from airplanes.

am·bush
(am´ bŏŏsh) *verb*
To attack from a hiding
place.

an·thro·pol·o·gists
(an´ thrə pol´ ə jists) *noun*
Scientists who study the
origins, development,
communities, and
customs of people.
▲ anthropologist

WORD HISTORY

Anthropologist comes
from the Greek words
anthropos, meaning
"human," and *logy*,
meaning "the study
of." An anthropologist
is one who studies
human beings.

ap·plause
(ə plôz´) *noun*
The act of showing appreciation
for something by hand
clapping. The audience's
loud *applause* filled the
theater when the play was
finished.

ar·chae·ol·o·gists
(är´ kē ol´ ə jists) *noun*
Scientists who study ancient
times and peoples.
Archaeologists search for
and examine the artifacts
left behind by ancient
peoples in order to learn
about life in the past.
▲ archaeologist

archaeologist

audience

au•di•ence
(ô´ dē əns) *noun*
The people who watch a play, speech, movie or other public performance.

a•vi•a•tion
(ā´ vē ā´ shən) *noun*
The science of building and flying aircraft. Airline pilots work in the field of *aviation*.

> **WORD HISTORY**
>
> The word **aviation** comes from the Latin word *avis*, which means "bird."

back•ground
(bak´ ground´) *noun*
A person's origin, education, and experience. You have the perfect qualifications and *background* to qualify for the job.

bal•lads
(bal´ ədz) *noun*
Songs or poems that tell stories. ▲ **ballad**

bass (bās) *noun*
A large stringed instrument that makes a low sound. My friend plays *bass* in the orchestra.

ba•ton
(bə ton´) *noun*
A short, thin stick used by a conductor to beat time for an orchestra. The conductor waved her *baton* during the symphony.

bear•ing
(bâr ing´) *noun* The direction or relative position of something. Rescuers found the sinking ship when the captain radioed its *bearing*.

bi•zarre
(bi zär´) *adjective*
Very odd, strange; hard to believe.

baton

bloodhound

blood•hound
(blud´ hound´) *noun*
A large dog with very long
ears and loose skin that is
known for its keen sense
of smell. Also a slang term
that means "detective."

bond•age
(bon´ dij) *noun* Slavery.

ca•ble car
(kā´ bəl kär´) *noun*
A railroad car pulled
along the rails by an
underground cable.

ca•bles
(kā´ bəlz) *noun*
Thick wires or ropes.
Heavy objects can be
suspended from *cables*.
▲ cable

can•yon
(kan´ yən) *noun*
A deep, narrow river valley
with steep walls.

canyon

ca•per (kā´ pər) *noun*
A criminal act or plan,
especially a robbery.

WORD HISTORY

The word **caper** comes
from an old Irish word
that meant "sheep."
Over time, *caper* came
to mean "sprightly,
prancing movements"—
like the ones a lamb
might make. Finally,
caper became a slang
term for an illegal act,
such as a robbery.

car•go (kär´ gō) *noun*
The load of goods carried
by a ship, airplane, or truck.

caulked (kôkt) *verb*
Made seams watertight
or airtight by applying
a sealing substance.
▲ caulk

cable car

a	add	o͞o	took	ə =
ā	ace	o͞o	pool	a in *above*
â	care	u	up	e in *sicken*
ä	palm	û	burn	i in *possible*
e	end	yo͞o	fuse	o in *melon*
ē	equal	oi	oil	u in *circus*
i	it	ou	pout	
ī	ice	ng	ring	
o	odd	th	thin	
ō	open	ŧh	this	
ô	order	zh	vision	

cavern

cav•ern (kav´ ərn) *noun*
A large cave. The fearless explorers entered the damp, dark *cavern*.

ce•leb•ri•ty
(sə leb´ ri tē) *noun*
A famous person. A movie star is a *celebrity*.

cham•pi•on•ships
(cham´ pē ən ships´) *noun*
The final games in a series that determine who wins. Our team won the state hockey *championships*.
▲ championship

Civ•il War
(siv´ əl wôr´) *noun*
The war between the North and the South in the United States, 1861–1865.

com•pe•ti•tion
(kom´ pi tish´ ən) *noun*
A rivalry in which several contestants are trying to win the same thing. He won the race despite tough *competition* from other runners.

con•cen•tra•tion
(kon´ sən trā´ shən) *noun*
The ability to focus one's thoughts and attention on something. A person with good *concentration* is not easily distracted.

concentration

con·duc·tor
(kən´ duk´ tər) *noun*
Before the Civil War, a person who led fugitive slaves to freedom in the northern United States or Canada using the escape system called the Underground Railroad.

con·fi·dence
(kon´ fi dəns) *noun*
A powerful belief or trust in oneself or someone else. I have *confidence* that I will do a good job.

crater

cra·ter **(krā´ tər)** *noun*
A large hole in the ground caused by an explosion or by the impact of a heavy object. A fallen meteorite formed that *crater*.

crim·i·nal
(krim´ ə nl) *noun*
Someone who breaks the law. The *criminal* was arrested by the police.

cu·li·nar·y
(kyoo´ lə ner´ ē or kul´ ə ner´ ē)
adjective Having to do with cooking or the kitchen. Restaurants are *culinary* establishments.

cun·ning
(kun´ ing) *noun*
Clever or sly ways of getting what one wants or escaping one's enemies. The mouse used *cunning* to trick the hungry cat.

dank **(dangk)** *adjective*
Unpleasantly damp or humid.

de·but
(dā byoo´ or dā´ byoo)
noun A first public appearance by a performer.

a	add	oo	took	ə =
ā	ace	oo	pool	a in *above*
â	care	u	up	e in *sicken*
ä	palm	û	burn	i in *possible*
e	end	yoo	fuse	o in *melon*
ē	equal	oi	oil	u in *circus*
i	it	ou	pout	
ī	ice	ng	ring	
o	odd	th	thin	
ō	open	th	this	
ô	order	zh	vision	

DETOUR

ded·i·ca·tion
(ded´ i kā´ shən) *noun*
A ceremony that marks
the opening of a building
or monument.

depth (depth) *noun*
Deepness, or a measurement
of deepness. The river has
a *depth* of twenty feet.

des·ti·na·tion
(des´ tə nā´ shən) *noun*
The place to which
someone travels. Our
destination is the state
capital.

de·ter·mi·na·tion
(di tûr´ mə nā´ shən) *noun*
Persistence; the ability to
work steadily toward a
goal until it is achieved.
The runner's *determination*
to do well helped her win
the marathon.

de·tour
(dē´ toor or di toor´)
noun A route taken when
the direct route is closed.
Dad took the *detour* onto
a dirt road when the
highway was being
repaved.

dra·mat·i·cal·ly
(drə ma´ tik lē´) *adverb*
Vividly; in an exciting or
suspenseful way. ▲ **dramatic**

dream (drēm) *noun*
A succession of thoughts,
feelings, or experiences
that pass through the
mind during sleep.

droves (drōvz´) *noun*
Large herds of animals,
such as cows or sheep, that
are moved together from
place to place. ▲ **drove**

Thesaurus
droves
flocks
herds
packs
swarms

dug·out (dug´ out´)
noun A place where
baseball players sit
during a game when
they are not on the field.
Dugouts are usually built
below ground at the side
of a baseball field.

ech•oed

(ek´ ōd) *verb*
Repeated or sent back
the sound of. The sound
of thunder *echoed* off the
canyon's high walls.
▲ echo

em•i•grants

(em´ i grənts) *noun*
People who leave one part
of a country and settle in
another part of it.
▲ emigrant

eth•nic

(eth´ nik) *adjective*
Of or relating to a group
of people who have the
same national origins,
language, and culture.

ex•am•ines

(ig zam´ inz) *verb*
Looks carefully at
something. The dentist
examines my teeth once
a year. ▲ examine

Thesaurus
examines
inspects
scrutinizes
studies

ex•ca•vat•ing

(eks´ kə vāt´ ing) *verb*
Uncovering by digging.
The archaeologists are
carefully *excavating* the
buried building with
small shovels. ▲ excavate

examines

emigrants

a	add	o͝o	took	ə =
ā	ace	o͞o	pool	a in *above*
â	care	u	up	e in *sicken*
ä	palm	û	burn	i in *possible*
e	end	yo͞o	fuse	o in *melon*
ē	equal	oi	oil	u in *circus*
i	it	ou	pout	
ī	ice	ng	ring	
o	odd	th	thin	
ō	open	ᵺ	this	
ô	order	zh	vision	

explaining

fear·less
(fēr´ lis) *adjective*
Brave; unafraid.

fil·lets (fi lāz´) *noun*
Pieces of meat or fish with
the bones removed.
▲ fillet

fillets

ex·hil·a·rat·ed
(ig zil´ ə rā´ tid)
adjective Very excited and
thrilled. I was *exhilarated*
when I hit a home run.

ex·plain·ing
(ik splān´ ing) *verb*
Showing the meaning of
something. The teacher
was *explaining* how to take
the test. ▲ explain

foul (foul) *noun*
A baseball hit out of
bounds by a batter;
not a fair ball.

Thesaurus
exhilarated
elated
euphoric
excited

Thesaurus
explaining
clarifying
defining
illustrating

foun·da·tion
(foun dā´ shən) *noun*
A solid structure on which
something is built. Our
house is built on a solid
foundation of bricks
and concrete.

fas·ci·nat·ed
(fas´ ə nāt´ əd) *adjective*
Very interested.

924

exhilarated

gey•ser (gī´ zər) *noun*
A hole in the ground through which hot water and steam shoot up in bursts. Old Faithful is a *geyser* in Yellowstone National Park.

geyser

WORD HISTORY

The word **geyser** comes from *Geysir*, the name of a hot spring in Iceland. *Geysir* comes from the Icelandic word *geysa*, which means "to gush."

horizon

gour•met (go͞or mā´) *adjective*
Having to do with or liking fancy foods. The *gourmet* chef made a tasty dish.

ground•ers (groun´ dərz) *noun*
Baseballs that roll or bounce along the ground when hit; also called ground balls.
▲ grounder

hang•ar (hang´ ər) *noun*
A shelter in which aircraft are stored and repaired. The airplane was kept in a *hangar*.

hi•jack•ing (hī´ jak´ ing) *verb*
Seizing by threat or force, often for ransom, and taking to a place that is not the original destination.
▲ hijack

hom•ers (hō´ mərz) *noun*
Hits in baseball that allow batters to go around all the bases and score a run; also called home runs.
▲ homer

ho•ri•zon (hə rī´ zən) *noun*
The line where the sky and the earth or sea seem to meet. At sunset, the sun sinks below the *horizon*.

a	add	o͝o	took	ə =
ā	ace	o͞o	pool	a in *above*
â	care	u	up	e in *sicken*
ä	palm	û	burn	i in *possible*
e	end	yo͞o	fuse	o in *melon*
ē	equal	oi	oil	u in *circus*
i	it	ou	pout	
ī	ice	ng	ring	
o	odd	th	thin	
ō	open	ᴛh	this	
ô	order	zh	vision	

hull
(hul) *noun*
Hollow, lower part of a ship's frame.

i·den·ti·ty
(ī den´ ti tē) *noun*
Who a person is. I don't know the *identity* of my secret pal.

im·mi·grants
(im´ i grənts) *noun*
People who come to a new country to live.
▲ immigrant

WORD HISTORY

Immigrant is based on the word *migrate*, which comes from a Latin word meaning "to move from one place to another."

---

im·pressed
(im prest´) *verb*
Positively influenced or affected. Having a strong, positive opinion about someone or something. ▲ impress

in·ci·dent
(in´ si dənt) *noun*
A distinct event or occurence. I heard a story about a funny *incident* that happened at school.

Thesaurus
incident
episode
event
occurrence

in·ning (in´ ing) *noun*
A part of a baseball game in which each team is at bat once and in the field once. There are usually nine innings in a baseball game. During an inning, each team has a chance to score until three outs are made against it.

in·spired (in spīrd´) *verb*
Caused or influenced someone to do something. The coach *inspired* her team to win the game.
▲ inspire

in·stru·ments
(in´ strə mənts) *noun*
Objects used to make music. Saxophones and clarinets are wind *instruments*. ▲ instrument

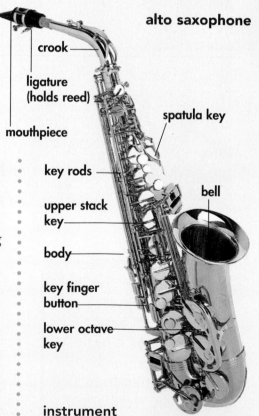

alto saxophone

crook

ligature
(holds reed)

mouthpiece

spatula key

key rods

upper stack key

bell

body

key finger button

lower octave key

instrument

in•tent•ly
(in tent´ lē) *adverb*
With sharply focused attention. The cat *intently* watched the birds in the tree above. ▲ intent

in•ter•cept
(in´ tər sept´) *verb*
To stop or cut off the movement of something or someone. The spy may *intercept* that letter before it reaches its destination.

in•ter•na•tion•al date•line
(in´ tər nash´ ə nl dāt´ līn´) *noun* A theoretical line on the map at about the 180th meridian. The regions to the east of this line are counted as one day earlier in time than the regions to the west of it.

keel (kēl) *noun* A central piece that runs the length of a ship's bottom and plays an important role in holding together the ship.

land•mark
(land´ märk) *noun*
A building or place designated as important to a city's history; an easily seen object, such as a building, tree, or statue, that helps one to find or recognize a place.

landmark

lime•light (līm´ līt) *noun*
The center of public attention.

a	add	o͝o	took	ə =	
ā	ace	o͞o	pool	a in *above*	
â	care	u	up	e in *sicken*	
ä	palm	û	burn	i in *possible*	
e	end	yo͞o	fuse	o in *melon*	
ē	equal	oi	oil	u in *circus*	
i	it	ou	pout		
ī	ice	ng	ring		
o	odd	th	thin		
ō	open	th	this		
ô	order	zh	vision		

loud•speak•er
(loud´ spē´ kər) *noun*
A machine that turns electrical signals into sounds loud enough to be heard in a large area. The announcer's voice boomed over the *loudspeaker*.

maiden voy•age
(mād´ n voi´ ij) *noun*
A ship's first journey.

make•shift
(māk´ shift´) *adjective*
Used as a temporary replacement for the usual item. The kitchen table served as a *makeshift* ironing board.

me•mo•ri•al
(mə môr´ ē əl) *noun*
Something that reminds people of a person or event; a monument.

memorial

mem •o•ry (mem´ ə rē)
noun An event or something that is remembered; a recollection.

mixed-me•di•a
(mikst´ mē´ dē ə)
adjective Combining more than one artistic medium in a single work. Max used paint and chalk in his *mixed-media* mural.

mixed-media

mo•cha (mō´ kə) *noun*
A flavoring that blends chocolate with coffee. My favorite yogurt flavor is *mocha*.

mon•u•ment
(mon´ yə mənt) *noun*
A structure that commemorates a person or event.

monument

WORD HISTORY

The word **monument** is from the Latin word *monumentum* meaning "to remind."

mousse

mousse (mo͞os) *noun*
A cold, fluffy dessert made with egg whites or whipped cream and gelatin. Mousse looks like pudding but is lighter in texture.

WORD STUDY

The words **mousse** and *moose* have the same pronunciation. However, you don't want to get them mixed up. A mousse is a dessert and a moose is a large member of the deer family.

mused (myo͞ozd) *verb*
Said in a deeply thoughtful way. "It was a lovely day," *mused* the thoughtful teacher. ▲ muse

nav•i•ga•tor
(nav´ i gā tər) *noun*
A crew member on an aircraft who plots the course using maps, compasses, and so on. The *navigator* plotted the plane's course.

WORD HISTORY

The word **navigator** is based on the Latin word *navis*, which means "ship."

Na•zi (nät´ sē) *noun*
A member of the National Socialist German Workers' Party which controlled Germany from 1933 to 1945.

news•stand
(no͞oz´ stand´ or nyo͞oz´ stand´) *noun*
A place where newspapers and magazines are sold. I bought a comic book at the *newsstand*.

oc•cu•pa•tion forces
(ok´yə pā´ shən fôrs´ iz)
noun Military forces that control a foreign territory.

out•field•er
(out´ fēl´ dər) *noun*
A baseball player who plays in the area beyond the diamond.

outfielder

a	add	o͝o	took	ə =
ā	ace	o͞o	pool	a in *above*
â	care	u	up	e in *sicken*
ä	palm	û	burn	i in *possible*
e	end	yo͞o	fuse	o in *melon*
ē	equal	oi	oil	u in *circus*
i	it	ou	pout	
ī	ice	ng	ring	
o	odd	th	thin	
ō	open	th	this	
ô	order	zh	vision	

pan·to·mime
(pan´ tə mīm´) *noun*
A performance in which a story is told through movement and gestures, not words.

WORD HISTORY
The word **pantomime** comes from two Greek words, *panto*, meaning "all," and *mimos*, meaning "imitator." Panto + mime = someone who can imitate anything.

pas·tels (pa stelz´)
noun Chalky crayons used in drawing. Elena drew a portrait with *pastels*.
▲ pastel

pastels

Pa·tri·ot
(pā´ trē ət) *noun*
A person who supported and fought for the independence of the Thirteen Colonies during the War for Independence.

Patriot

per·cus·sion
(pər kush´ ən) *noun*
Musical instruments played by being hit or shaken. The *percussion* was louder than the horns.

WORD HISTORY
The word **percussion** is based on the Latin word *percutere*, which means "to strike hard" or "to beat."

per·plex·ing
(pər pleks´ ing) *adjective*
Puzzling. The police struggled to solve the *perplexing* mystery.
▲ perplex

Thesaurus
perplexing
bewildering
confusing
puzzling

per·se·cut·ing
(pər´ si kyo͞ot´ ing) *verb*
Treating someone in an unjustifiably cruel or harsh way, often because of religion or race.
▲ persecute

percussion instrument

per·spec·tive
(pər spek´ tiv) *noun*
A way of looking at
something; a viewpoint.
After working for a week,
I viewed work from a
new *perspective*.

pre·serv·ing
(pri zûrv´ ing) *verb*
Maintaining or keeping in
existence. We are *preserving*
our photos in a special
album. ▲ preserve

rec·ol·lec·tions
(rek´ ə lek´ shənz) *noun*
Memories. Grandpa's
recollections of his
childhood are happy.
▲ recollection

plateau

Thesaurus
recollections
memories
remembrances
reminiscences

pla·teau
(pla tō´) *noun*
An area of high, flat land.

po·di·um
(pō´ dē əm) *noun*
A raised platform on
which an orchestra
conductor stands. The
conductor stepped down
from the *podium* after
the concert.

ra·tioned
(rash´ ənd *or* rā´ shənd)
adjective A limited amount
of food and other goods a
person is allowed. During
the war, oil was *rationed*.

re·hears·al
(ri hûr´ səl) *noun*
A practice run of a
performance, speech, play,
or other public program.

Thesaurus
rationed
apportioned
distributed
parceled out

WORD HISTORY

The word **podium**
comes from the Greek
word *podion*, which
means "a small foot."
A podium gives a
conductor "a footup,"
or a boost in height.

a	add	o͞o	took	ə =
ā	ace	o͞o	pool	a in *above*
â	care	u	up	e in *sicken*
ä	palm	û	burn	i in *possible*
e	end	yo͞o	fuse	o in *melon*
ē	equal	oi	oil	u in *circus*
i	it	ou	pout	
ī	ice	ng	ring	
o	odd	th	thin	
ō	open	th	this	
ô	order	zh	vision	

re·lo·ca·tion
(rē′ lō kā′ shən) noun
The process of moving people from their homes to another place.

rep·u·ta·tion
(rep′ yə tā′ shən) noun
The worth or character of a person, as judged by others. Ann's *reputation* as a joker is due to her funny stories.

rick·e·ty
(rik′ i tē) adjective
Weak and shaky.

ro·tun·da
(rō tun′ də) noun
A round building or a large circular room, especially one with a dome. The large *rotunda* in the historic building was my favorite room.

rum·ble (rum′ bəl) noun
A low, rolling noise like the sound of thunder. We heard the *rumble* of trucks on the highway.

sagebrush

sage·brush
(sāj′ brush′) noun
A grayish-green bush or shrub with white or yellow flowers that grows on the dry plains in the western United States and smells like the herb sage.

scaf·fold·ing
(skaf′ əl ding) noun
The planks and ropes or poles on which workers stand to work above ground on a structure. Painters of tall buildings often stand on *scaffolding*.

ship·wright
(ship′ rīt′) noun
A person who works in shipbuilding and repair.

shut·tle (shut′ l) noun
A bus, a train, or an aircraft that travels frequently between two places. The air *shuttle* makes flights between Austin and Dallas every hour.

sight-seeing

sight-see·ing
(sīt´ sē´ ing) *noun*
Traveling for pleasure to
see interesting places.
They spent the day
sight-seeing at the
historic sites in Texas.

sky·line (skī´ līn´)
noun The outline of
buildings or other objects
seen against the sky from
a distance. The Empire
State Building is part of
New York City's *skyline*.

span (span) *noun*
The distance between two
points. The *span* of the
Brooklyn Bridge is the
distance between
Manhattan and Brooklyn.

spell·bound
(spel´ bound´) *adjective*
Fascinated by something.
She was *spellbound* by the
story her uncle told.

spic·y (spī´ sē)
adjective Seasoned
with substances having
strong, distinctive tastes.
Spicy food is not bland.

Thesaurus
spicy
piquant
zesty
hot

sta·di·um
(stā´ dē əm) *noun*
A sports arena; a large
structure, usually oval or
horseshoe-shaped, containing
rows of seats where people
sit to watch sporting
events. Wrigley Field is
a famous baseball *stadium*
in Chicago.

sta·tion
(stā´ shən) *noun*
1. A resting place for slaves
on the Underground
Railroad. 2. A regular
stopping place along a route.

a	add	o͝o	took	ə =	
ā	ace	o͞o	pool		a in *above*
â	care	u	up		e in *sicken*
ä	palm	û	burn		i in *possible*
e	end	yo͞o	fuse		o in *melon*
ē	equal	oi	oil		u in *circus*
i	it	ou	pout		
ī	ice	ng	ring		
o	odd	th	thin		
ō	open	ŧh	this		
ô	order	zh	vision		

skyline

stock (stok) *noun*
All of the animals raised on a farm or ranch; livestock. Because of the storm, we herded the *stock* into the barn.

stock

sub·way
(sub´ wā´) *noun* A system of electric trains that runs underground in a city. Many workers ride the *subway* to their jobs in the city.

WORD STUDY

The prefix *sub-* often means "under," "beneath," or "below." A **subway** runs underground, a *submarine* travels beneath the water's surface, and a *subnormal* temperature is below normal.

su·per·in·tend·ent
(soop´ ər in ten´ dənt) *noun* 1. A person in charge of part of the Underground Railroad. 2. The person who is in charge of a building, organization, or project.

subway

suspension bridge

sus·pen·sion bridge
(sə spen´ shən brij´) *noun* A bridge held up by large cables or chains that are strung between a series of towers.

FACT FILE

The longest **suspension bridge** in the world is the Akashi-Kaiko bridge in Japan, which spans 6,496 feet!

sym•bol•iz•ing
(sim′ bə līz′ ing) *verb*
Standing for or representing
something else. A lion,
symbolizing bravery, is
painted on the shield.
▲ symbolize

Thesaurus
symbolizing
exemplifying
representing
signifying

sym•pho•ny
or•ches•tra
(sim′ fə nē ôr′ kə strə)
noun A large group of
musicians who play
classical music together.
The *symphony orchestra* will
perform a concert in a
big hall downtown.

ten•e•ment
(ten′ ə mənt) *noun*
A run-down and crowded
apartment building in
a poor section of a city.

ter•ri•to•ry
(ter′ i tôr′ ē) *noun*
A part of the United States
not admitted as a state.
The island of Guam is
a *territory* of the United
States.

FACT FILE

Hawaii was a **territory**
of the United States
from 1900 to 1959. In
1959 Hawaii became a
state.

tour•ists (toor′ ists)
noun People who travel
and visit places for
pleasure. Many *tourists*
visit the national parks
every year. ▲ tourist

trans•mis•sion
(trans mish′ ən or
tranz mish′ en) *noun*
A message sent out
by radio or television
signals from one person
or place to another. The
control tower received the
pilot's radio *transmission*.

tri•umph (trī′ əmf)
noun A great victory
or achievement. Being
elected president is
a great *triumph*.

symphony orchestra

a	add	o͝o	took	ə =
ā	ace	o͞o	pool	a in *above*
â	care	u	up	e in *sicken*
ä	palm	û	burn	i in *possible*
e	end	yo͞o	fuse	o in *melon*
ē	equal	oi	oil	u in *circus*
i	it	ou	pout	
ī	ice	ng	ring	
o	odd	th	thin	
ō	open	th	this	
ô	order	zh	vision	

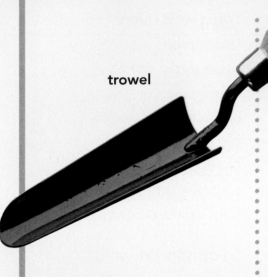

trowel

trow•el
(trou´ əl) *noun*
A hand tool with a small curved blade that is used for digging.

un•bear•a•ble
(un bâr´ ə bəl) *adjective*
Intolerable; too unpleasant or distasteful to tolerate.

Un•der•ground Rail•road
(un´ dər ground´ rāl´ rōd´) *noun*
A system set up before the Civil War to help runaway slaves escape to the northern United States, to Canada, and to other places of safety.

u•nique
(yōō nēk´) *adjective*
Existing only in a certain area. That type of cactus is *unique* to the desert.

val•ley (val´ ē) *noun*
An area of low ground between two hills, usually containing a river. The mountains towered above the rich river *valley*.

viv•id (viv´ id) *adjective*
Sharp and clear. I have *vivid* memories of our trip to the seashore.

FACT FILE

Death Valley, a deep desert **valley** in California and Nevada, is the lowest point in the western hemisphere. It is also the hottest place in North America. Its name dates back to 1849, when pioneers almost died trying to cross it.

valley

yoke

yoke (yōk) *noun*
A wooden frame that fits over a work animal's neck and is used to hitch the animal to a cart.

vi•sion (vizh´ ən) *noun*
The sense of sight. Her *vision* is good because she can see for long distances.

winch•es (winch´ iz)
noun Machines that use a chain or rope to pull or lift things. It took two *winches* to tow the car out of the mud. ▲ winch

winch

a	add	o͞o	took	ə =
ā	ace	o͞o	pool	a in *above*
â	care	u	up	e in *sicken*
ä	palm	û	burn	i in *possible*
e	end	yo͞o	fuse	o in *melon*
ē	equal	oi	oil	u in *circus*
i	it	ou	pout	
ī	ice	ng	ring	
o	odd	th	thin	
ō	open	ŧh	this	
ô	order	zh	vision	

INDEX

Colored page numbers refer to biographical information.

Acknowledgments

Grateful acknowledgment is made to the following sources for permission to reprint from previously published material. The publisher has made diligent efforts to trace the ownership of all copyrighted material in this volume and believes that all necessary permissions have been secured. If any errors or omissions have inadvertently been made, proper corrections will gladly be made in future editions.

Unit 3 *Voyagers* Table of Contents: Illustration from WILMA UNLIMITED: HOW WILMA RUDOLPH BECAME THE WORLD'S FASTEST WOMAN by Kathleen Krull. Illustration copyright © 1996 by David Diaz. Reprinted by permission of Harcourt Brace & Company.

Unit 4 *In the Spotlight* Table of Contents: Illustration from THE PHANTOM TOLLBOOTH by Norton Juster. Illustration copyright © 1961 and renewed © 1989 by Jules Feiffer. Used by permission of Random House, Inc.

Unit 6 *Cityscapes* Table of Contents: Illustration from STREET MUSIC: CITY POEMS by Arnold Adoff. Illustration copyright © 1996 by Karen Barbour. Used by permission of HarperCollins Publishers.

Unit 1 *Making a Difference*
"Fox Song" from FOX SONG by Joseph Bruchac, illustrations by Paul Morin. Copyright © 1993 by Joseph Bruchac, text. Copyright © 1993 by Paul Morin, illustrations. Used by permission of Philomel Books, a division of Penguin Putnam Inc.

"Like Father, Like Son: The Griffeys" from THE MACMILLAN BOOK OF BASEBALL STORIES by Terry Egan, Stan Friedmann, and Mike Levine. Copyright © 1992 Terry Egan, Stan Friedmann, and Mike Levine. Reprinted with the permission of Simon & Schuster Books for Young Readers, an imprint of Simon & Schuster Children's Publishing Division.

"Who's on First?" by Bud Abbott & Lou Costello. Edited and abridged by Amy L. Cohn. Reprinted by permission of Abbott & Costello Enterprises, Larry Turner, Esq.

"Just Like Me" from JUST LIKE ME: STORIES AND SELF-PORTRAITS BY FOURTEEN ARTISTS by Harriet Rohmer. Copyright © 1997 by Carmen Lomas Garza; Michelle Wood; Hideo Yoshido; Daryl Wells; Tomie Arai; Rodolfo Morales; Elly Simmons. Overall book project copyright © 1997 by Harriet Rohmer. All rights reserved.

"Out of the Dust" from OUT OF THE DUST by Karen Hesse. Copyright © 1997 by Karen Hesse. Published by Scholastic Press, a division of Scholastic Inc. Used by permission.

"Number the Stars" from NUMBER THE STARS by Lois Lowry. Text copyright © 1989 by Lois Lowry. Reprinted by permission of Houghton Mifflin Co. All rights reserved.

Unit 2 *It's a Mystery* Unit Opener: Untitled illustration #7 from "The West Wing" by Edward Gorey published in AMPHIGORY: FIFTEEN BOOKS by Edward Gorey. Published by Perigree Books/G.P. Putnam's Sons, a division of Penguin Putnam Inc. Reprinted by permission of Donadio & Ashworth, Inc.

"The Redheaded League" from THE REDHEADED LEAGUE, adapted from a story by Sir Arthur Conan Doyle. Published by Scholastic Inc.

"The Mysteries of Harris Burdick" from THE MYSTERIES OF HARRIS BURDICK by Chris Van Allsburg. Copyright © 1984 by Chris Van Allsburg. Reprinted by permission of Houghton Mifflin Co. All rights reserved.

"The Case of the Secret Message" from THE CASE OF THE SECRET MESSAGE by Sid Fleischman. Copyright © 1981 by Children's Television Workshop. Reprinted by arrangement with Random House, Inc.

"The Secrets of Vesuvius" from THE SECRETS OF VESUVIUS by Sara C. Bisel with Jane Bisel and Shelley Tanaka. Text copyright © 1990 by Sara C. Bisel and family and The Madison Press Ltd. Design and compilation copyright © 1990 by The Madison Press Ltd. Reprinted by permission of The Madison Press Ltd.

"Mystery of the Cliff Dwellers" by Joan Banks, with photos by Scott S. Warren, from *National Geographic WORLD*, February 1998. Copyright © 1988 by the National Geographic Society. Used by permission.

"Sky Pioneer" from SKY PIONEER: A PHOTOBIOGRAPHY OF AMELIA EARHART by Corinne Szabo. Copyright © 1997 by the National Geographic Society. All rights reserved. Published by Scholastic Inc.

"On the Flight Deck" from FLYING MACHINE by Andrew Nahum. Copyright © 1990 by Dorling Kindersley Limited London. Reprinted by permission of Dorling Kindersley Ltd.

Photography Credits

Pp. 2–3, 76–77, 188–189, 208–209, 212–213, 216ml, 488, 508, 528mr, 593[both], 596mr, 597br: © Corbis-Bettmann; p. 11br: © Culver Pictures; p. 14bl, 15tr, 37mr, 38br, 39tl, bl, 37mr: Karen Furth for Scholastic Inc.; pp. 14–15, 17bc, 36–37, 38bl, 39mr, 59br, 113br: Jack Vartoogian for Scholastic Inc.; p. 36ml: © Jack Vartoogian; p. 17tc: © Chase Swift/Westlight/Corbis; pp. 36tr, 435tc, 520tc: Ana Nance for Scholastic Inc.; p. 36bl: © Tria Giovan/Retna; pp. 42, 43, 44, 45, 46, 47, 48, 49, 54, 55 [baseball]: Bob Lorenz for Scholastic Inc.; pp. 42–43, 49mr: © Comstock; pp. 42–43: © Ken Levine/AllSport; p. 44, 46bl, tl, 47tl, br, 48–4954ml: © Focus on Sports; p. 45mr: © Brian Masck/AllSport; p. 45br: © Walter Looss, Jr./Sport Illustrated; p. 54br: © Ken Levine/AllSport; p. 55br: © Brian Masck/AllSport; p.57tl: Courtesy Achilles Track Club; p. 58bl, 112br, 113ml, 194bc, 198br, 211br, 532bl, 679: AP/Wide World; p.58bc, 110bl, 112tc, 166bc, p. 220bl, 221bl, 284bc, 333c, 335mr, 336bl, tr, 337bl, 370bc, 371bc, p. 427ml, 428bc, 429br, 430tr, 529br, 530mr, 603bl, 663bl: Stanley Bach for Scholastic Inc.; p.59bl, 191mr, 210tc, 419c: © Corbis-Bettmann/UPI; p. 71mr, pp. 434bl, ml, 435br, 491br, 520–521, 522bl, 531br:

Andrew M. Levine for Scholastic Inc.; p. 76ml: Library of Congress #704408; p. 78ml: © Jeff Baker/FPG Int'l; pp. 78–79: © Superstock; p. 104, 105br, 105c: Courtesy of the U.S. Memorial Holocaust Museum; p. 108bl: © Kennan Ward/Bruce Coleman; p. 109c, 111bl, br: © C.S. Perkins/Magnum Photos; p. 109bc: © Wolfgang Bayer; p. 110tr: © John Chellman/Animals Animals; pp. 116–117, 116c, tl, bl, 117br, 158ml, bl, tl, 159mr, 160bl, tr, 161bl, 167br, 223br: Bill Barley for Scholastic Inc.; p. 117tc: © Laurence Dutton/Tony Stone Images; p. 164bl, c, 165bl, 166bc, 220mr: John Lei for Scholastic Inc.; pp. 171bc, 175tl, 177tc, 181ml, br: © 0. Louis Mazzatenta/National Geographic Society; p. 172br, 179bl: © Cheryl Nuss/National Geographic Society; p. 173c: © Jonathan Blair/National Geographic Society; p. 190br, 213mr: National Air & Space Museum/Smithsonian Institution; p. 191mr, 210tc: © Corbis/UPI-Bettmann; p. 191tl: National Geographic Society Image Collection; p. 192ml, 195ml: George Palmer Putnam/National Geographic; pp. 190br, 192–193, 196bl, 197br, 201tr, 202br, 203bc, 204tr, 204ml, bc, 205tr, bl, 213bl: © Purdue Research Foundation, reprinted with permission. All rights reserved.;

p. 195mr, 199tc, 214–215, 217bl: Seaver Center for Western History/LA County Museum of Natural History; p. 198ml, 212tr: The Schlesinger Library/Radcliffe College; p. 200bc: Albert L. Bresnick; p. 207c: National Archives; p. 210, 216–217: © Corbis/Larry Lee; pp. 214–215: Peter Chadwick/DK Publishing; pp. 218–219bc: © Cosimo Condina/Tony Stone Images; pp. 218–219tc: © Charles Henneghien/Bruce Coleman; p. 219br: © Kathleen Campbell/Tony Stone Images; p. 219c: © Bruce Stoddard/FPG Int'l; pp. 220–221tr: © Bob Torrez/Tony Stone Images; p. 222mr: © David Hiser/Tony Stone Images; pp. 226–227, 226tl, bl, 227br, 285br, 302–303, 302ml, bl, 304tr, bl, 305mr, bc, 337br: Steve Leonard for Scholastic Inc.; p. 227tc: © Rhoda Sidney/PhotoEdit; pp. 252, 254: © Fred J. Maroon; pp. 253, 255: Earth Satellite Corporation; p. 282br: © Wes Thompson/Stock Market; p. 282bl: © Ed Wheeler/Stock Market; p. 301: Preamble by Mike Wilkins/National Museum of American Art/Art Resource; pp. 302tr, 303mr, c: John Bessler for Scholastic Inc.; pp. 308–327 [backgrounds]: Cecilia Zieba-Diaz; p. 328mr: © CTU Foster/Allsport; p. 328bl: © Jamie Squire/Allsport; p. 329: Courtesy Michael Stewart; pp. 332bl, tr: © Don Sparks/Image Bank;

Illustration Credits